DEVELOPING GUIDEL
FOR INSTRUMENTATI𝞢N
AND CONTROL

Implementing Standards and
Verifying Work Performed

DEVELOPING GUIDELINES FOR INSTRUMENTATION AND CONTROL

Implementing Standards and Verifying Work Performed

N. E. "Bill" Battikha

The International Society for Measurement and Control

ISA
The International Society for Measurement and Control
67 Alexander Drive
PO Box 12277
Research Triangle Park, North Carolina 27709

Library of Congress Cataloging-in Publication Data

Battikha, N. E.
        Developing guidelines for instrumentation and control:
    implementing standards and verifying work performed / by N.E. "Bill" Battikha.
        p.   cm.
        Includes bibiographical references and index.
        ISBN 1-55617-525-6
        1. Process control–Standards. 2. Engineering instruments.
    I. Title
    TS156.8.B38   1994
      629.8--dc20
                                                                94-29633
                                                                        CIP

Contents

CHAPTER 1

Introduction

PURPOSE

This book's primary purpose is to provide guidelines for developing standards for plants and/or corporate control engineering functions. The book is directed towards engineering and maintenance personnel in plants, consulting firms, and central engineering offices. The book describes how to develop a corporate standard and discusses the points that are typically included in a corporate standard. The reader and developer of such corporate standards will need to convert these points and checklists into the statements or clauses of a standard, after its content has been agreed upon. For example, Chapter 7 covers the checklist for the installation of instruments and control systems, while Appendix I shows an example of a final installation specification as it may have been developed from the checklist of Chapter 7.

The process of preparing corporate standards is time-consuming and sometimes frustrating, but generally it is a rewarding experience for the "champion" who prepared it and coordinated its activities. This book, a guide based on life experiences, is intended to help standards writers minimize and, hopefully, eliminate costly mistakes and frustrations. Engineers without experience in standards development tend to find the activity a formidable task; therefore, it tends to be avoided. The condition in which no standards exist in a corporation generally leads to expensive errors. At best, standards will avoid "reinventing the wheel" (doing the same type of work again and again).

Another purpose of this book is to act as a checklist for work done, which covers two functions: the work done by outside consultants and the work done directly by the plant. Work done by consultants usually results from the current trend to contract detail engineering (and sometimes front-end engineering) to outside consulting firms. Such consulting firms most often have an existing set of standards. In such cases it is more economical to follow these set standards than try to enforce the corporation's standard onto the consulting firm. However, the customer must check these submitted standards to ensure that on the whole they do comply with the philosophy and minimum requirements of the corporation. This book allows the performance of such a check against what the contractor suggests.

Work done by the plant directly (or by a central engineering function) also needs checking. This book and the checklists covering the different topics may help perform a critique's function. The user should be able to "stand back" and assess the quality of the work performed by himself or herself or by others. The checklists and thoughts that are presented in the chapters to follow provide a base from which a self-assessment can be performed.

This book presents an A to Z approach and is a how-to guide that is specific to the instrumentation and control industry. Its range is from the philosophy and front-end engineering to the standards and recommended practices that cover post-installation activities. The book will cross-reference, throughout its content, existing Instrument Society of America (ISA) standards, at the same time considering international aspects. Appendix B contains a complete list of ISA's standards and recommended practices.

This book is not designed to teach the technology of instrumentation and control. The user of this book is expected to be very knowledgeable in this field and to use this book mainly as a guide for the production of a corporate standard. The book is only a guide, with suggested opinions from the writer as to what the content of such a standard should generally be. However, in the final analysis, a typical corporate standard must be customized to reflect the requirements of:

1. the authorities having jurisdiction and
2. the needs of its users.

The final standard should be prepared and finalized to meet these requirements; otherwise, it sits on a shelf collecting dust—a failure to its purpose.

PURPOSE OF CORPORATE STANDARDS FOR INSTRUMENTATION AND CONTROL

Corporate standards establish guidelines for the engineering, installation, and maintenance of instruments and control systems within corporations. Such standards also guide their users to the appropriate available standards and, more particularly, to the codes and regulations in effect at the site. Compliance with the codes and regulations in plants is essential for legal and liability reasons.

Corporate standards also provide uniformity in the performance of technical work. This ensures a more efficient use of manpower and resources as well as higher quality in the production of technical data. Especially in today's trend toward reduced engineering and maintenance staff, corporate standards are an excellent vehicle for explaining to outside consultants and suppliers the way a corporation does things and how it wants the activities to be performed from design to maintenance.

Engineering standards provide the guidelines and a framework to ensure quality and consistency in control engineering activities for the generation of front-end engineering, detail engineering, equipment installation, and some of the key maintenance activities. To be of ongoing real value, such corporate standards should not be static; they should be reviewed continuously and upgraded as necessary. All users of a corporate standard should be encouraged to participate in the development of corporate standards.

The main activities typically covered by such a standard are engineering and design, installation, and maintenance. They are the framework around which this book (and eventually the finished standard) is structured.

Such a standard, in most cases, will not duplicate existing guidelines or standards available in industry and with which the plant would comply (for example, ISO 9000, ISA, etc.). Reference to such existing standards should be sufficient. Appendix A has a list of standard-writing bodies; Appendix B contains a list of the standards and recommended practices, with descriptions, that are published by the Instrument Society of America (ISA).

Many organizations would prefer to have such standards on paper (for example, in a ring binder); others would prefer electronic media; and in many cases, a combination of the two is used.

This chapter examines how to:

1. proceed with the preparation of a preliminary document that will become the future corporate standard;
2. issue it for comments internally within the organization;
3. receive the comments back;
4. obtain consensus on its final content (that is not an easy step); and
5. issue the final standard for use.

These generally required steps in the preparation of corporate standards are shown in their usual sequential order. Finally, the last step described is the procedures required to maintain the standard in good working order and available for its users (i.e., storage/update/retrieval/etc.).

PREPARING THE PRELIMINARY STANDARD

After a champion (coordinator) is selected, the first thing that comes to his or her mind is "Where do I start?" A good starting point could be the collection of existing standards that have been prepared over the years by different people in the organization. In large organizations it is quite common for the same subject to be addressed by different people, which results in different documents that address the same topic with obviously different requirements. The bottoms of desk drawers and old files sometimes yield old standards and specifications that may not be related to each other but may prove useful at this preliminary stage.

One's colleagues in industry may have standards that they might be willing to share. This step would prevent wasting many days reinventing the wheel. Their approach may be different, but they could provide a good starting point.

Another great source of technical information is major suppliers and vendors. When they know what is planned for the proposed standard, they are generally willing to share relevant material and technical information.

External consultants or someone with experience in preparing such standards should be consulted or, even better, could be used to develop the required corporate standard. However, this is not a commonly available resource, but if someone with this expertise could be found, much time could be saved. This experienced person would provide the requirements with a minimum disturbance to the activities of existing personnel.

One word of advice: Do not rewrite (in a different format) existing standards if they meet your requirements. It should be kept in mind that existing copyrighted standards must not be duplicated; they can be used as cross-references in an in-house corporate standard. Typical examples would be instrumentation symbols and identification, which are described in ANSI/ISA-S5.1, and the format and content of loop diagrams, which are described in ANSI/ISA-S5.4.

With all this data assembled, the coordinator now must streamline it. This generally requires rewriting the acquired selected pieces of information into "the preliminary standard." A word of advice at this point: A mishmash of documents that have not been streamlined should never be distributed. They will frustrate the readers, who are the future commentators and users. As a result, the documents may not be read and no comments good or bad may be received—a waste of time.

ISSUING THE PRELIMINARY STANDARD FOR COMMENTS

With the preliminary standard assembled and streamlined, it is now time to send it out for comments. The first step is to check in advance, either by phone or by mail (the latter is preferred), to discover who is willing to participate and spend the time necessary for insightful commenting. A response within a specific time should be requested. The advantage of a written request is that it tests the ability of the future commentators to fill out a simple form before getting into the real work of a standard review; it takes less effort to say "yes" over the phone. An example of a request letter and its reply form are shown in Figures 1-1 and 1-2. The first part (the

```
6 June 92




To: See Distribution List
From: Bill Battikha
Subject: Set of New Corporate Standards for
         Instrumentation and Control

    A need to develop our own set of standards has emerged.
These standards will provide us with guidelines for the
engineering, installation, and maintenance of instrumenta-
tion and control systems.
    Your contribution is essential in achieving such a
goal; it is a team effort. If you are willing to partici-
pate by commenting on the preliminary version (and future
versions), please complete the attached form and return it
to my attention by month end.
    If you have any questions or would like to discuss this
further, I can be reached by phone at extension 2930.

Regards,
Bill Battikha
Senior Control Engineer
```

Figure 1-1. Request Letter

```
RE: New Corporate Standards for Instrumentation and
    Control


To: Bill Battikha
    67 Alexander Drive
    RTP, NC 27709
    Phone number: 555-2930
    Fax number: 555-2958




[] Yes, I would like to participate in the preparation of
   the new standard.




From:



Full mailing address:




Phone number:



Fax number:
```

Figure 1-2. Reply Form

request letter) explains to the recipients the purpose of the activity. The second part (the reply form) presents a format for the recipients to answer with their willingness to participate in the activity of standard preparation. Note that the response to the request for comments will be a good indication of the interest in the eventual use of such a document.

Such a letter should be sent to any person involved in control and instrumentation who might have an interest in commenting, from managers to designers to maintenance personnel. In addition, other personnel may also be involved, such as those in electrical engineering, project management, and so on. It is sometimes a good idea to send a copy of the index of the preliminary standard with this letter; this gives an indication of the work involved and may whet the appetites of undecided potential contributors.

Once the answers have been received, it is time to send out the preliminary standard. A letter must be prepared to be distributed to all who answered affirmatively. The preliminary standard and a tentative overall schedule should accompany the letter, which should include a specific time for the commentator's response.

It is important to have everybody's name on the distribution list. This is a TEAM effort — not just the coordinator's. It is everybody's standard — not just the coordinator's. This point is highlighted because coordinators who take on such a task (and deliver at the end) tend to be drivers and leaders and may in the process forget the effort of "the team."

The date set as a specific answering time should not be too far down the road, since, generally, the work of commenting by the team will be done close to the deadline anyway. The time allowed for comments is in direct relation to the size of the issued preliminary standard. As a rule of thumb, if it appears that, for example, a week of work is needed for comments, four should be allowed. This gives time to adjust for work loads, other deadlines, vacations, etc.

RECEIPT AND HANDLING OF COMMENTS

While the preliminary standard is out for comments, phone calls asking questions, or for clarifications, or for making suggestions will probably come in. The coordinator should be available and should not schedule vacation time during this period. Around the set target date (the deadline), comments will start coming in. However, the coordinator should be ready for the following:

1. Quite a few will be late (from experience, about 30%).
2. Some others (another 20%), in spite of all the good intentions to participate, will not have the time or will not get around to doing the review and probably will never do it.

Roughly 50% of the comments will be received near the deadline date, and when the deadline is reached, the coordinator should expect to get on the phone to chase the missing ones. The time allowed for the remaining comments to be received should be about half the originally planned time to receive the majority of comments. Still, in spite of good follow-up efforts, not all participants will comment (that 20%). Even so, at this point the coordinator should proceed to the next phase.

Note that it is better to receive the comments written right on the preliminary standards that were sent out rather than on a separate, typed letter. This not only facilitates the checking and incorporation of all comments, it is also faster for the commentators.

Now that the majority of comments have been received, they should be reviewed one at a time. Any comments the coordinator agrees with should be entered on a master preliminary standard with the initials of the person who generated the comment next to the entry. This method of identification facilitates retrieval at the discussion stage. On the other hand, any comments the coordinator does not agree with (or does not understand) should be discussed with the person who generated them. An agreement may be reached and the comment added to the master preliminary standard, or it may be classified as "unresolved" for further action.

After all received comments have been reviewed, two documents exist: a master preliminary standard marked up with agreed upon comments and a list of unresolved points. This latter list will be used later on in a meeting to be set for resolving them as a team effort.

At this point, a letter should be issued to all participants (the team) to convene a discussion on ONLY the unresolved points. Note that the other points are not to be reopened at the meeting unless a key point is in question; if the agreed upon points are reopened, the discussions can take weeks instead of hours. It is expected, specially if travelling is involved, that only a small number of the team will attend this meeting. The notice of the meeting should list the unresolved questions (basically, the agenda of the meeting). It is a good idea to cross-reference the unresolved questions to the part of the standard to which they belong. This allows efficient use of everyone's time. The people who cannot attend should be encouraged to comment on these unresolved questions by mail so that at the meeting their written opinions can be presented to the team present and discussed.

At the meeting, the coordinator should start by thanking all participants for their attendance, then turn to the list of unresolved points. In a typical format the coordinator:

1. presents the first unresolved question and compares it to what the preliminary standard said;
2. allows a 20-minute open discussion on the question;
3. uses the last five minutes to summarize the discussion and present the common agreement;
4. obtains consensus approval; and
5. moves to the next point.

As can be seen, 30 minutes is average for each unresolved point. Therefore, it is easy to estimate how long such a meeting will take. For this meeting to be effective, the coordinator should keep the following points in mind:

1. Stick to the point in question, and listen attentively.
2. Maintain control at all times, and keep the meeting on track.
3. Stick to the schedule (as much as possible). It is common that some participants have the tendency to talk endlessly and may later on accuse the coordinator of bulldozing the meeting as he or she is trying to maintain them on track. Don't worry, that's normal.
4. Make sure everybody is participating.
5. The coordinator's ideas should be kept to a minimum; while acting as a mediator, he or she may ask questions if not happy with a statement or discussions.

At the end of the meeting, the coordinator should thank the attendees and confirm that the agreed upon points will be incorporated into the standards. Shortly after (within a week or so), minutes of the meeting, stating the points discussed and the solutions reached, should be issued to all the attendees as well as to the other members of the team who could not attend the meeting. A couple of weeks should then be allowed for any comments or objections.

In some cases, additional comments regarding the agreements reached at the meeting may be received. If these cannot be resolved over the phone, the coordinator may need a second set of meetings or, in some rare cases, a third.

FINALIZING THE STANDARD

At this stage, there is a marked-up master specification and all concerns are finalized. All the points discussed have been incorporated, and it is time to issue the standard as a "final draft" to all participants.

The letter accompanying the updated document, marked "To Be Issued As Final," should clearly state that this is the document as it will be issued for use unless someone has a *major* objection. The key word is major. Since it is quite normal that every time the document is reviewed someone will want to change something, which could result in an endless cycle. The letter should mention that such a standard is a live document and is expected to be updated from time to time. Therefore, if anyone has comments, and this will certainly occur as the standard is being used, these comments should be sent to the coordinator. After a certain period of time, depending on the number and importance of comments, a revised standard will be reissued. After two to four weeks, if no major comments are received, the document is ready for printing.

From experience, the number of copies to be printed should be:

1. the total of all participants,
2. all other potential users within the organization (those who will need to have the final standard but did not participate in its creation), and
3. an additional 20 to 30% spare documents (there will always be someone who will ask for an additional copy at some point in time).

In some cases, depending on the company's culture and its way of doing things, it might be beneficial to issue with the final draft a copy of the master set (that is, the one that incorporated all the comments received and finalized and in which each comment has the initials of the person who wrote it). This approach will unfortunately increase the amount of paper generated, and that paper will eventually be discarded (or recycled). However, it facilitates the review process for all participants since all changes to the original document that was issued for comments are highlighted.

ISSUING THE STANDARD FOR USE

Now that the standard is printed, it is time to issue it for use. This is done by distributing it with a note thanking all participants and underlining the team effort (it is OUR standard — it is not "imposed"). The note should emphasize that this is a live document that is expected to be updated and should ask for continuous feedback for improvements. In a few years, the standard should be reissued for comments, showing where improvements have been suggested, and the cycle should be repeated.

In some corporations, additional steps will occur at this point (for example, approvals from management, document classification and filing, and conformance to the corporate format).

STANDARD MAINTENANCE

The standard is now issued and in use. However, such standards must be maintained and updated to meet the changing requirements of its users and their increased experience on how to do things better, and also to keep up with the changes in technology. As an example, a standard issued only few years ago may specify that all electronic signals to be used should be 4–20 mA; however, with today's communication networks between smart transmitters and distributed control systems, such a requirement hinders the application of advanced technologies.

As a general rule and to maintain the value and functionality of in-house standards, they must be updated at intervals that vary from two to five years. Some of the ISO 9000 guidelines state that:

1. the latest issue of these standards must be available at all pertinent locations;
2. these standards must be reviewed and approved for adequacy by authorized personnel prior to issue and according to a procedure; such personnel must have access to background information upon which they may base their decisions, and
3. obsolete standards must be quickly removed from all users.

When additions or revisions are incorporated, is it the responsibility of a central function to distribute all updates to the existing holders? Or is it the responsibility of the user to check on a regular basis whether any updates exist? The first option, required by some document control standards, is more accurate in its performance but requires tracking of who has what — a sometimes difficult condition in today's fast changing and downsizing organizations. On the other hand, the second option creates a question in the minds of its users whether they have the latest version. The final decision should be based on company culture, plant needs, and communication capabilities.

If standards are not maintained, they eventually are ignored by users, who then start developing their own guidelines. This becomes the first sign of the demise of the corporate standards that took so much effort and coordination to produce. Within a period of time, the original standards become a hinderance rather than documents that help their users produce quality products.

Therefore, every few years the corporate standard should go through its cycle. A cycle involves preparing a preliminary standard, issuing it for comments, resolving these comments, meeting to agree on the unresolved questions, and then publishing the agreed upon points to all attendees.

A summary of the different steps involved in creating a corporate standard is shown in Figure 1-3.

1. PREPARE PRELIMINARY STANDARD.

   Collect existing data.

   Streamline all data and refer to existing ISA and other

   standards.

   Assemble into a preliminary standard.

2. ISSUE THE PRELIMINARY STANDARD FOR COMMENTS.

   Identify commentators (the team).

   Issue preliminary standard to the team and set the
   deadline for comments.

3. RECEIPT AND THE HANDLING OF COMMENTS.

   When the deadline is reached, follow up on the missing
   answers.

   Set new deadline for missing answers.

   Review all comments.

   Either agree with the comments received and, therefore,
   incorporate, or create a list of unresolved points.

   Set a meeting to discuss unresolved points.

   Issue minutes of meeting to the team.

4. FINALIZE THE STANDARD.

   Incorporate all agreed upon comments and allow a period
   for final review.

   Finalize the document.

   Print the document.

   Distribute finalized standard as needed.

Figure 1-3. Summarized Sequence of Events
for the Preparation of Corporate Standards

CHAPTER 2

Main Components

INTRODUCTION

A typical corporate standard for instrumentation and control (I&C) consists of many parts, each with a specific function. The detail, extent, and breakdown of each part is guided by the business requirements, the way a specific industry does business, and the corporate culture. The breakdown given here is only a guide; it does not have to be followed to the letter, but it provides in its format a common way of "doing things."

Depending on the culture and needs of the corporation for which such a corporate standard is being created, the size and content of such a standard varies greatly. Some standards end up as a 50-page document that gives general guidelines, while others may be a handful of thick ring binders.

In general, a standard starts with a statement of the overall philosophy, which lays the groundwork for the body of the standard. This is followed by three main parts (see Figure 2-1):

1. Engineering, which is divided into two parts — front-end and detailed design
2. Installation
3. Maintenance

In this chapter, the purpose of each of these sections and the interrelationship between them will be described. However, before this chapter considers these components, the following basic requirements must be considered by the preparer of the corporate standard:

```
1. Philosophy

2. Engineering, front-end and detail

3. Installation

4. Maintenance
```

Figure 2-1. Components of an Engineering Standard

1. Allocate a numbering system to the components of the standards to facilitate cross-referencing.
2. Agree on, or design from scratch, a format that each of the standards will follow.
3. Incorporate (by cross-referencing) the existing ISA standards and recommended practices and other relevant standards where they will apply to the corporate standard.
4. Understand ahead of time the approval procedures (if they exist) required by the corporation for standard generation and implementation.

Standard Numbering

It is good practice to number standards, which facilitates cross referencing. Such a numbering system in many cases follows an existing corporate guideline. In the absence of such a guideline, the following may be used:

- Philosophies and general guidelines, series 100.
- Front-end engineering, series 200.
- Detail engineering, series 300.
- Installation, series 400.
- Maintenance, series 500.

In turn, each of these major components may be broken down into smaller sections. For example, Maintenance (series 500) may have Calibration, series 510; Alarm and Trip System Testing, series 520; and Maintenance of Electrical Equipment in Hazardous Locations, series 530.

In turn, further breakdown may be required. For example, series 520 may be divided into Process Alarm and Trip Systems, series 521; Safety Alarm and Trip Systems, series 522; and so on.

Standards are most often developed by their experienced users, based on proven experience and performance. Standards should be sufficiently flexible to allow creativity and functionality yet should ensure conformance to local regulations and specific corporate needs and reduce errors. The question of balancing "lowest possible cost" with "functionality" is sometimes covered by corporate standards, but in most cases this is left to the discretion of the users.

Corporate standards may be developed and issued with two systems of measurement units. For instance, SI and US customary units may be shown at the same time, e.g., 110 kPa (16 psi).

Format

Corporate standards may have a fixed format that is used across all disciplines. Obviously, the standard for instrumentation and control would comply. In the absence of such a format, one needs to be developed. A fixed corporate format (as an example, see Figure 2-2) may display the following information on its front sheet:

1. Name and location of the company
2. Name of the group the standard is for
3. Name of the standard
4. The standard number
5. The page number (e.g., P. 1 of 6)

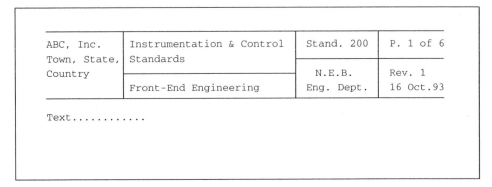

Figure 2-2. Sample Format for a Corporate Standard.

6. The revision number and date
7. The name (and sometimes the initials) of the preparer and custodian of the standard

The final standard should be distributed to all users and to new employees. In most cases, and for legal reasons, these standards are the property of the corporation and should not be sent outside the corporation without management approval. If such a standard is loaned to an outside organization, such as consultants, a confidentiality agreement may have to be signed by the outside user, and upon completion of the project the standard is returned to the corporation. The decision to make such standards available outside the organization should be carefully weighed. Doing so may increase paperwork and bureaucracy, and even with a signed agreement, confidentiality is difficult to maintain.

Existing Standards

One of the first steps in the preparation of a corporate standard is to look at what other standards-writing organizations have already written on the subject. The Instrument Society of America (ISA) has produced a multivolume collection of all the standards and recommended practices written and maintained by ISA: *Standards and Recommended Practices for Instrumentation and Control* (see Appendix B). It is an essential set of documents for practitioners in the field of instrumentation and control. In that same set of documents, an alphabetical index located at its end helps the reader identify, by subject area, the standards related to a particular subject, not only those produced by ISA but also those from other organizations such as IEEE, ASA, IEC, ISO, etc. Within the text, each standard is briefly described.

Approval Procedures

Once the corporate standards are finalized, all comments are incorporated, and all its participants have agreed upon its content, these documents must be certified or approved. Such approval may vary from an informal OK, to a stamped statement such as "Issued for Use," to a formal procedure.

The following is an example of one kind of formal procedure:

1. The coordinator prepares the final document, including getting the comments and finalizing with all the participants.

2. The coordinator signs the standards.
3. The coordinator obtains approval of the draft, as agreed between the participants, from the control engineering supervisor.
4. The coordinator submits the approved draft to engineering management and obtains their approval.
5. The supervisor signs.

In addition, some corporations have an engineering standards committee that has authority over all standards and corporate guidelines. This committee would review all standards, assign responsibilities, and give final approval of all published standards.

PHILOSOPHY

A statement of philosophy is ordinarily the first part of a standard (see Chapter 3). Its content is the purpose and extent of the parts to follow in the standard. It is generally developed by engineering personnel but is, in reality, a statement of purpose from management (generally engineering management, sometimes plant management).

Such a philosophy needs to be defined at the start of preparing corporate standards. Without it, the extent and scope of such a standard is undefined; therefore, the standard may vary depending on personal preferences.

The extent and ramifications of such a philosophy have a direct relationship to the cost of its implementation and to the degree of quality to be achieved at all levels. If, for example, the philosophy has a statement that reads "All design, installation, and maintenance work must be checked upon completion by a supervisor to ensure a low probability of error," that statement may add an extra 10 to 20% to design, installation, and maintenance costs, which appears high. On the other hand, it may save much larger correction costs further down the line.

The section of the standard that covers the philosophy is generally comprised of a purpose and an overview. This is followed by sections that relate to activities from engineering to maintenance with a philosophy on the performance of each.

ENGINEERING

Engineering is the first phase of technical activities and basically provides services to the production of a product (or products). Such services vary from the typical design work to many other activities:

1. Guidance on the application of codes and regulations
2. Supervising the work of others
3. Estimating
4. Planning
5. Scheduling
6. Advising and relationship with other disciplines
7. Training of personnel
8. Plant inspections
9. Assistance to maintenance
10. Procurement of contracting resources

These activities are generally not covered in a standard, but they may be part of a separate management or project control standard.

The purpose of engineering in general is to provide safe, cost- effective, and quality technical services to the end user. On the lighter side, a bumper sticker recently seen on the road read, "Engineering makes your dreams come true."

Control engineering, as described in this book, will be broken down into two distinct activities: front-end engineering and detailed design. Each of these activities has its specific functions. Sometimes there is the temptation to skip the front-end part and jump directly into the detailed design. However, at the detailed design phase this approach creates delays, errors, and the need for corrections that eventually take more time than was supposed to have been saved by skipping the front-end part.

Front-end Engineering

This phase of the engineering (described in Chapter 4) defines the key aspects of the instrumentation and control (I&C) scope of a project. This phase covers the preparation of the engineering data required for the start of detailed design. It follows the preparation of process (or piping) and instrument diagrams (P&IDs) and the completion of reliability studies and hazard analysis activities. In some cases the preparation of front-end engineering is performed along with the development and finalization of P&IDs, reliability studies, and hazard study analyses. Whichever approach is used, the final set of documents that form front-end engineering must meet and complement the P&IDs.

The corporate standard may require that all front-end engineering be prepared by instrumentation and control engineering personnel and be approved by process engineering and project management. Its content is dependent on the project requirements (see Chapter 4). Front-end engineering must be based on the plant policies and on the statutory requirements in effect at the site.

The documents that are generally prepared by I&C personnel under this phase are a combination of a description of the instrumentation and control system to be implemented and the process data information. These instrumentation and control documents form the basis upon which the detailed design can be started. They are essential, especially if the detailed design is done by a separate organization such as an outside engineering firm.

In general, a corporate standard would require that the information available at the completion of the front-end engineering phase are:

1. a drawing that describes the overall system (the P&ID),
2. a description of the control system with a section that identifies the expected reliabilities and hazards (the control system definition),
3. a description of the discrete logic (the logic diagrams), and
4. the process data to start specifying all instruments and equipment in contact with the process (the process data sheets).

Many corporate standards clearly state that no detail design can be started without the completion of front-end engineering. The two main reasons behind these requirements are:

1. to get a common agreement as to what the I&C system is providing and
2. to minimize costly design revisions and equipment changes later on when the detail design has started (or is even completed).

Detailed Engineering

This phase of the engineering (described in Chapters 5 and 6) includes preparation of all the detailed design documentation necessary to support the issue of bid requests for material and installation, of construction bids, of commissioning and start-up, and of maintaining the plant.

In today's economic climate, the detailed engineering phase is frequently contracted out, sometimes with other functional design activities such as electrical, piping, and mechanical. Corporate standards may clearly state that detailed engineering must be based on the information generated at the front-end engineering phase and meet the engineering standards and all statutory requirements in effect at the site. In all cases, the project manager should discuss the bid request with the control engineer to ensure that the selected contractor is capable of meeting the control engineering design requirements.

The corporate standard should ensure, when the design is done by outside contractors, that the plant (or corporation) will have the copyright to all designs, documents, drawings, software, and products provided by all outside contactors and suppliers.

The documents that are generally prepared under the detailed design phase include, depending on the project requirements, some or all of the following:

1. List of drawings and documents
2. Instrument index
3. Instrument specification sheets, including calculations (for control valves, orifice plates, relief valves, etc.)
4. Loop diagrams
5. Electrical control schematics
6. Manuals for programmable electronic systems (including PLCs and PCs)
7. Control panel specifications (including overall layout)
8. Control room requirements
9. Alarm and trip system testing
10. Operating and maintenance instruction manuals (including manufacturer's drawings/documentation and complex analytical system documentation)
11. Recommended spare parts list

INSTALLATION

This phase (described in Chapter 7) marks the transition point between the engineering and maintenance groups. Following the completion of the engineering data required for a safe, quality installation, a contractor is selected to do the installation work. A document is prepared to clearly describe the requirements of the plant and a description of the job to be done. This document, known as the installation specification, is then used by the contractor to estimate the cost of the installation.

A typical corporate standard would include an installation specification that generally consists of many parts, each covering a section of the installation. As an example, an installation specification may describe:

1. the scope of work,
2. the way instruments are to be mounted and installed,
3. the connections between the process and the instruments,
4. the wiring requirements,

5. the tubing requirements for instrument air, and
6. the checkout procedures.

Following the selection of a contractor, the installation work starts, based on the installation specification and on all the documentation provided by the engineering phase. The standard may require that the contractor, following the completed installation, goes through a checkout procedure with a representative of the plant. This ensures that the instruments and the control systems are installed according to the requirements.

Upon completion of the checkout phase, the installation is accepted by the plant (or its representative), and the installation as such is completed. The next stage is the commissioning and start-up, at which point maintenance takes over.

MAINTENANCE (POST-INSTALLATION)

Now that the instruments and control systems are installed and operating, the responsibility reverts to maintenance for assuring that the operation of these systems meets the design intent.

Corporate standards for maintenance activities (described in Chapter 8) may be a very large subject in itself. This book will concentrate on only two key topics: the maintenance of alarm and trip systems (ATSs) and the maintenance of instruments in hazardous areas in which fire and explosions may occur. The philosophies behind these two could easily be expanded to cover other maintenance activities that are related more to particular industries and to specific plant needs.

The preparation of maintenance standards must, more than any other, be a joint effort of different disciplines. Maintenance must at all times be kept in the designer's mind when instruments and control systems are being specified and designed. Items that are not accessible, poorly designed, or difficult to calibrate will not be well maintained, will eventually deteriorate, may affect the process performance, and may end up in the garbage — a waste of time and money and a poor record for the design effort.

CHAPTER 3

Philosophy

OVERVIEW

The philosophy of a standard is typically the first document in a set of corporate standards. It provides the basic recommendations for applying instrument and control systems to meet the needs of the corporation. This philosophy, sometimes referred to as a master plan, is in most cases generated by instrumentation and control engineering personnel to be approved by management. The importance of having this document approved by management is to avoid future conflicts with other disciplines as to the scope of authority and responsibility that the standard and the control team will encompass.

A standard's philosophy generally underlines general principles that cover the implementation of engineering, installation, and maintenance requirements. It also covers concerns the management has either from past experience or as the result of discussions. It also identifies good practices and legislative requirements in effect at the site. A standard's philosophy does not contain detailed requirements; it should be brief (from as small as a paragraph to as long as two to three pages). Its content depends on the company culture and on the way things are done and accepted within the organization.

Philosophies may, in many cases, use national or international standards as a basic guide. In this book both ISA's *Standards and Recommended Practices for Instrumentation and Control* (see Appendix B) and ISO 9000 are used. However, it is worth noting at this point that ISO 9000 is nondisciplinary and does not look at the specific needs of control technology. Philosophies for modern corporate standards generally incorporate some key ISO 9000 requirements. However, it is imperative to emphasize that the content of this book is mainly a memory jogger (or a guide) and should not be taken "as is," since statutory, technical, and corporate needs vary from one site to the other.

Sometimes control system philosophies describe how standards should be implemented and by whom. Such a philosophy may indicate responsibilities at different levels, such as those of the manager of control systems, the senior engineer, the instrument service specialist, etc. (A typical list of job titles and descriptions is shown in Appendix C.) Again, the need to go into such details depends on company requirements and culture.

COMPONENTS

A typical philosophy for a corporate control engineering standard may need to consider the following points:

1. Purpose of the instrumentation and control (I&C) function
2. Overview
3. Front-end engineering
4. Detailed engineering
5. Installation
6. Maintenance

The following questions act as a checklist of items for the person preparing the philosophy of a corporate standard to consider. It is a starting point for a document that will reflect in its detail the culture and overall needs of a corporation.

Purpose

This part of the philosophy covers the purpose of the I&C function, its reason for existence, and its philosophy of operation.

Is the purpose of the I&C function to provide high quality and cost-effective services in the instrumentation and control technology for design, installation, operation, and maintenance? Are both these requirements of importance, or is cost the only matter of importance?

Should the I&C function remain abreast of technological advances and legislative activities? Or should the function update its know-how only when the need arises?

Is a statement included to define the purpose of this engineering discipline? Is there a need to define its purpose?

Is there a clear procedure to describe the process of converting the customer needs and requirements to specifications and, finally, into instrumentation and control systems? Is such a procedure required, or should the function rely only on the knowledge and expertise of its members? If the procedure is not required, would the corporation accept different ways of implementing the required work (since different people may do the same job differently)?

Overview

This part of the philosophy of the corporate standard covers the general guidelines to be followed in instrumentation and control, the requirements to meet preset quality standards, and the guidelines for document control and management.

☐ GENERAL:

Are all design activities and responsibilities described in the standard? Would this description be overkill? Should the function rely instead on common practices understood by the users (design and maintenance personnel)?

Are these corporate engineering standards to be supplied to design contractors to enable them to conform to the plant's requirements and to ensure consistency between different projects and different consultants? Or is it to be treated as for-internal-use-only documents? If they are to be sent outside the corporation, should secrecy agreements be signed? Would this approach create legal problems?

Is the group expected to generate acceptable profits? Or is the group basically a nonprofit organization created to support production?

Is work assigned to qualified people? Should their qualifications be confirmed and compared to preset requirements?

Are there means to evaluate and monitor contractors (review of previous performance, supplier surveys, etc.)?

Is there a procedure to review customer complaints? How are these complaints handled?

Are there specific steps to be taken in design? In approval procedures? Are such steps defined? Eventually, would the implementation of such steps be a reality or do they exist only on paper?

Are there provisions to handle last-minute design changes? Is there a definition of what consists a last-minute change?

Is each function to be performed described with a clearly identified responsibility? Is there a need to identify such responsibilities?

Is there a need for the use of schedules to show progress vs. original timing? If not, how is performance of the I&C function measured?

Is there a need to monitor costs? Are costs monitored on a milestone basis? If not, how are costs monitored?

Are these corporate standards to be periodically checked for validity and effectiveness? How frequently should they be checked?

□ **QUALITY:**

Are safety and quality the main reasons behind the production of this standard? Are there other reasons (such as costs or levels of technology)?

Will the assigned control supervisor review all documents and designs done within the company or by the outside contractor? Is this to be done during and at the completion of the front-end engineering and the detail design phase? If no design review is done, how is quality maintained?

Is the training of personnel identified and provided? Is such training supplied periodically or only as required?

Should statistical methods be used to monitor quality? Are statistical techniques used to monitor performance of design, installation, start-up, and maintenance? If not, are monitoring tools required? Are quality audits planned and performed?

Are audit results communicated to management? Are deficiencies corrected? Is there an audit schedule?

Are auditors trained to audit? If not, how is the audit carried out? Are training needs identified and provided to fill these needs?

Would some tasks (for example, design check) require specific qualifications, training, experience (e.g., an engineer with 10 years experience in a specific field)?

Are all design activities identified and traceable through all their stages? If not, how is this controlled?

How is nonconforming design handled, controlled, and disposed of? Are causes of nonconformance investigated and preventive action taken against recurrence? Are trends in errors monitored?

Is there a quality policy? Is this quality policy defined, documented, and implemented?

☐ **DOCUMENTS:**

Is all design data retrievable from a central location and at all other required locations? If not, how is this done? Is it acceptable?

Should all instrumentation symbols and identification conform to a single format? Is such a format the latest issue of ANSI/ISA-S5.1? In addition, should there be any exceptions (for example, the letter M may be used for moisture measurement and the letter G shall be used for gaging).

Are all project drawings to be generated on computer-aided design (CAD) equipment and to conform to ISA symbology and to the plant's engineering standards? Is the same symbology used throughout? Is the same CAD software used for all documents? If not, are translating capabilities required between different software?

Should the generation of all drawings on CAD be coordinated with the plant to ensure compatibility of software types and revisions? Are any deviations from these requirements first approved by the plant and by the assigned control engineer?

Does the plant have a system in place for identification, collection, indexing, filing, storage, maintenance, retrieval, and disposition of pertinent engineering records?

Is the nature of all modifications identified on the documents? Does this include the date of the modification and the name of the person(s) who made each modification?

Are all documents reviewed and approved for adequacy by authorized personnel prior to issue and according to a procedure? Do such personnel have access to background information upon which they may base their decisions?

Are the pertinent issues of appropriate documents available at all locations? Are obsolete documents promptly removed from all points of issue?

Is there a general policy on the management of drawings and documents?

Are all plant drawings and documents updated as revisions are implemented? Are they continuously maintained to an as-built condition?

Are these documents the reference data for plant personnel? Is the storage of documents such that these documents are accessible when technical data is required?

As reference data, are these documents accessible to all who require them? Is the changing of data on these documents closely controlled?

Is one person, appointed by management, responsible for the condition and maintenance of plant documents and drawings? Is this responsibility clearly identified?

Are the procedures for document and drawing revisions closely and carefully implemented? Are changes to design and documents controlled according to set procedures? Should exceptions to these rules first get management approval?

Front-End Engineering

This part of the corporate philosophy covers the purpose of the front-engineering portion of the standard. In this section, the standard may clearly indicate that no detailed design is to be started until the front-end engineering is completed and approved.

Does the front-end engineering identify the need and requirements of the project? Is it the base of any detail design?

Are the documents identified as front-end engineering required as inputs to all detail design? Are these documents reviewed for accuracy with the final user (the customer) before the start of detail design?

Do all safety-related trips and alarms have a high degree of reliability? Does every production site meet set targets of reliability and safety performance for such critical trips?

Are good project definition and a clear understanding of the project requirements considered essential to ensure that a quality design package will be produced? How are changes to these requirements handled?

In order to facilitate filing and cross-referencing of all documentation, do all the front-end engineering documents have some minimum information? For example, is the following available on each document?

- Name of plant (or process)
- Document title
- Project number
- Revision status
- Number of pages (pages to be numbered)
- Author's name
- Date of issue
- Name of person revising the document
- Date of revision[!S]

Detailed Design Engineering

This section of the philosophy identifies the generation of all detail design and its relationship with front-end engineering, installation, and maintenance.

Should any activities that cost more than a certain preset amount be first justified and then approved by management prior to the start of detailed design? What is that limited amount? Are there any exceptions to the rule?

Is the final detail design verified and checked prior to installation? If not, how is the final design in compliance with the original needs?

Should design corrections include problem identification and actions taken to prevent a repeat of the problem? Or is the correction done on the spot, are no records kept, and does it basically rely on the experience of the person doing the design work?

Are there procedures for design generation, design checking, and design changes? Is there a need for such procedures?

Should design generation,checking, and changes be signed by an appointed control engineer? Should the engineer have a minimum of experience and know-how?

Is design verification done by personnel other than the person doing the design? If not, how is impartiality maintained?

Should the installed control equipment on all sites be in compliance with the requirements of the electrical authority having jurisdiction in the said area? If not, should approval of the local authority be obtained?

Are specification sheets for orifice plates, restriction plates, control valves, and relief valves filed with (or attached to) their calculation sheets? If not, where are they filed? Are they accessible?

Do the minimum design requirements consist of a scope definition, process data sheets, specification sheets (and calculation sheets if needed), loop diagrams (and/or interlock schematics), and an update of the instrument index? What constitutes minimum design requirements? Is this fixed or it would vary from job to job? How is this decided and by whom?

Are all drawings produced on CAD? How are these electronic files controlled? Who is responsible for their maintenance?

To be able to facilitate the filing and cross-referencing of all documentation, do all documents that constitute the detailed design engineering have the following information?

- Name of plant (or process)
- Document title
- Project number
- Revision status
- Number of pages (pages to be numbered)
- Author's name
- Date of issue
- Name of person revising the document
- Date of revision

Are independent design reviews performed? Is the independence of these reviews maintained by ensuring that personnel not involved in the design are performing the review? Are these reviews based on project needs and on preliminary specifications? Are designs compared with input requirements? Is the design comparison performed at 50% and 100% of completion? On critical systems, is this comparison performed at 25%, 50%, 75%, and 100% of completion?

Do design reviews include problem identification and corrective action to prevent recurrence?

Does the standard ensure that the design is checked and conforms with the electrical code in effect at site, ISA standards, corporate standards, etc.? Is nonconforming design kept away from conforming design? Is it marked as such? Should the personnel performing the check be skilled, know the standards, and record the results of the check?

Are suppliers and contractors evaluated for their ability to provide the requirements? How is this evaluation done? Who does the evaluation? How frequent is this evaluation reviewed?

Are audits performed and planned? Are their results communicated? Are deficiencies corrected? Are records of audits maintained?

Installation

This section of the philosophy applies to the installation of instrumentation and control equipment. It tends to be short, since these requirements are shown directly in the installation specification.

Should the standard ensure that all equipment and installation comply with all code, statutory, and plant requirements in effect at the site? How is this requirement ensured? Is it the responsibility of the installing personnel to ensure and meet compliance?

Should the specifications and drawings prevail wherever the specifications or drawings call for quality and/or requirements that are superior to those required by the applicable codes and statutory requirements?

Maintenance

This part of the philosophy is very much dependent upon the corporate culture and the way management perceives the maintenance function. It is very common that separate manuals on maintenance philosophies and guidelines are generated for all disciplines, thus including the I&C function. However, the following is included as a starting point from the I&C point of view.

Is sufficient control maintained over all measurement systems used in the development, manufacture, installation, and servicing of products to provide confidence in decisions or actions based on measurement data? Does this definition of measurement systems include related computer hardware and software?

Are all design changes after implementation controlled? Does this control consist of:

1. requests in writing;
2. changes evaluated only by a knowledgeable team that consists of at least a process engineer, a control engineer, and an operator; and

3. permanent changes documented in all related documentation (e.g., operating manuals, test procedures)?

Is technology transfer to operators done through training and manuals? If not, how is it done?

With the completion of this section, the ground is set for the development of the standard.

CHAPTER 4

Front-End Engineering

INTRODUCTION

This phase is the first step in engineering design. It defines the instrumentation and control requirements, states the major aspects of the control scope of a project, and covers the preparation of the engineering data required for the start of detail design. This phase follows (and sometimes parallels) the preparation of preliminary P&IDs and process hazard analysis for the process under control.

The process hazard analysis is an essential part of the design activities. It can be performed using at least one of the following methodologies:

1. What-if
2. Checklist
3. What-if/Checklist
4. Hazard and Operability Study (Hazop)
5. Failure Mode and Effects Analysis (FMEA)
6. Fault Tree Analysis

The subject of process hazard analysis is generally outside the scope of an I&C corporate standard. Additional information on each of these methods can be found in OSHA's Part 1910, Appendix D, or in other pertinent publications.

The preparation of a standard for front-end engineering will vary according to the requirements of a corporation. The following is a general guide to its potential content. The person who is developing the preliminary standard to be issued for comments may want to achieve common agreement on its content, extent, and size before starting the development. It is imperative to underline the fact that the content of this chapter is only a memory jogger and should not be taken "as is," since statutory, technical, and corporate needs vary from one site to the other.

Once the standard is issued and comes into use, the activities of front-end engineering are generally carried out by the user (or by the appointed representative) based on:

1. the project requirements,
2. the engineering standards, and
3. the statutory requirements in effect at the site.

In general, the four documents that are prepared under this phase and must be ready before the start of detailed design are:

1. the process and instrumentation diagram (P&ID),
2. the control system definition,
3. the logic diagrams, and
4. the process data sheets.

These documents must be updated when changes are made during the course of the project, and changes do occur. Once approved and agreed upon, no changes to these documents should be implemented without prior approval from the project manager and the assigned control engineer (or control supervisor, depending on company policy).

When the content of these documents becomes finalized, they must be marked as such. Following installation, commissioning, and successful start-up, all front-end engineering documentation should be updated to an "as-built" form and must be maintained as changes occur throughout the life of a plant's control system.

PROCESS AND INSTRUMENTATION DIAGRAM (P&ID)

The P&ID is a very important document because it is the basis of the detailed design and operating documents. P&IDs are also used for communication within the engineering team, the operators, and maintenance. It is generally created by a team that consists of at least a process engineer and a control engineer. P&IDs normally show all items of plant equipment, process pipelines, valves, in-line devices, and the instrumentation required to operate the plant.

P&IDs are usually approved by the process plant engineer. This approval includes all revisions (dated and numbered). The control engineering corporate standards do not normally cover the preparation of P&IDs but may refer to it since control engineering personnel may be involved in the preparation of a P&ID standard. The following description of the typical P&ID is included here to present a preliminary guideline for the content of such a document.

P&IDs are usually developed from material balance sheets and the plant control requirements. A typical material balance sheet is shown in Figure 4-1. To facilitate future engineering work, P&IDs are cross-referenced to the material balance sheets.

P&IDs normally identify the following:

1. Plant equipment, including electric motors, and sometimes max/normal/min levels in vessels and height of seals
2. All pipelines, valves, relief valves, vents, drains, and in-line devices such as check valves, filters, and reducers (sloping lines and tracing/insulation should also be indicated)
3. Controls and instrumentation, including signal transmission method and control valve actions on air/electrical failure (FO, FC, FL)
4. The set pressure for all relief valves, rupture disks, pressure regulators, and temperature regulators

The equipment layout on a P&ID usually follows a sequence from left to right of the drawing. This clarifies the process sequence when viewing diagrams joined together in strip displays. P&ID information should be spread over many sheets to avoid congestion.

For clarity, diagrams for the supply and distribution of utilities and services such as instrument air, steam, and cooling water are normally drawn separately from the

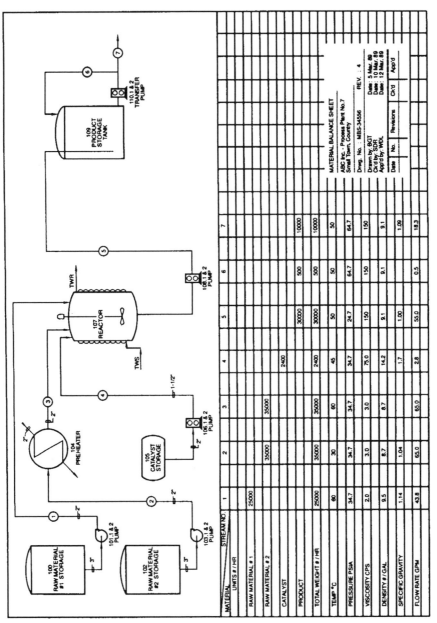

Figure 4-1 Typical Material Balance Sheet

process diagrams. It is usual to prepare one diagram for each service and to mark the cut point on each utility line where it becomes part of the process drawing.

Any plant item should be shown only once. If, for clarity, an item needs to be shown on another P&ID, it would be shown in dotted lines.

From an instrumentation and control point of view, P&ID symbology should be based on corporate standards; if there are none, they could then be based on ANSI/ISA-S5.1, Instrumentation Symbols and Identification.

ANSI/ISA-S5.1 acknowledges that the level of detail to be applied to a document is at the discretion of the user. Generally, on a P&ID there should be sufficient detail to convey the functional intent of the loop and to understand the means of measurement and control of the process. The full complement of instruments in a loop is, in most cases, shown on other documents such as loop diagrams.

As a rule, control functions that must be shown on the P&IDs as separate elements are (1) all in-line instruments, (2) all hardwired interlocks/alarms, and (3) all connections to the control system. Functions that need not be shown on the P&IDs as separate elements are (1) I-to-P/P-to-I converters if they are part of the final control element, (2) intrinsic safety barriers, and (3) any elements that are not required to convey the functional intent of a loop.

To save precious P&ID drawing space, interlock diagrams, logic diagrams, or PLC programs are normally used to describe the detail logic of the interlocks instead of showing them on the P&ID. The preparation of logic diagrams is described in ANSI/ISA-S5.2, Binary Logic Diagrams for Process Operations. A typical P&ID is shown in Figure 4-2.

Good engineering practice should ensure that for all P&IDs:

1. engineering and symbology is based on existing plant standards and good engineering practice,
2. changes are followed by a study to ensure safety, and
3. procedures exist regarding the handling of revisions.

CONTROL SYSTEM DEFINITION

The corporate standard should include a section on the purpose and content of a document called the control system definition. The purpose of this document is to ensure that all key aspects of the engineering for instrumentation and control are clearly and formally documented before detailed design starts and before the instrumentation and control equipment is purchased. The control system definition should be available for review by all concerned. This document also provides a clear basis for the detailed design phase of a project, especially when undertaken by firms outside the organization such as engineering companies. Another major advantage of such a document is a more accurate cost-estimating process.

The control system definition generally covers the following considerations:

1. A general description of the process
2. A description of the potential control system
3. The safety requirements for the particular application
4. Other miscellaneous requirements such as electrical area classification and reliability requirements

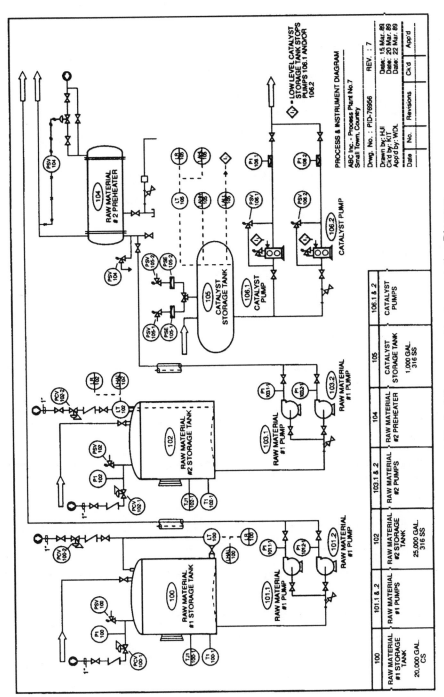

Figure 4-2 Typical Process and Instrumentation Diagram

The following points are shown in a questionnaire format to remind the writer of the control system definition of the different topics that need consideration. At the end, the answers to these questions may become the core of knowledge necessary for the required document.

Process Description

Is the existing process continuous, batch, manufacturing, or a combination?

What are management's requirements for data logging, production reports, efficiency reports, or links to other management information systems?

How many operators are needed? How many are in the control room? Are they full-time or part-time?

What is the required response time by the operator(s)?

Does the control room(s) fulfill the needs of the process and the operators?

What are operation's requirements:

- For start-up and shutdowns?
- For automatic versus manual operation?
- For response to alarms and trips?
- For the location and functionality of operator interface equipment?

Control System Description

Is the control system centralized or distributed? Does this philosophy meet the need of the process and operators?

Is the control system capable of accommodating future improvements? Is it flexible? Does it need special requirements for future expansions/ modifications?

If the control system is microprocessor-based, how is the memory protected? Are the displays functional?

Is the operator consulted in system selection?

Is the configuration/programming an in-house function or is it contracted?

Is there a need for control system redundancy?

Does the control system have the capability to handle all the incoming data and outgoing controlled outputs?

Is the scan rate of the control system acceptable?

Is the control system well understood by the different users?

Are all the required plant control functions being performed in the control system?

Are the alarm and trip systems performing their functions? Within the required response time?

Can the operator sort out alarm and trip priorities as they start actuating in series (ricochet effect)?

Are the alarm and trip functions protected from uncontrolled modifications?

Are there any special instrumentation needs (such as analyzers, testing of alarms/trips)?

Is the effect of malfunctions and/or shutdowns of the control system and its components (e.g., inputs, outputs, power supply) acceptable?

Are alarms required to indicate malfunctions/failures of the control system?

Which annunciator sequence is required? (ISA-S18.1 establishes uniform annunciator terminology, the sequence of designations, and sequence presentation and to assist in the preparation of annunciator specifications and documentation.)

Are special safety features required? If yes, how are the emergency circuits to be designed? Is there a need for a master safety relay? Should the system incorporate watchdogs (internal/external)?

What is the required reliability and quality of the power supply and of the instrument air supply? Is any backup required?

What will be the type of communication between the control center and the plant (no walkie-talkies are allowed)?

Will computers and networks be installed and operated under acceptable environmental conditions (temperature, humidity, vibration, static)?

What is the level of training of the staff (supervision, operations, maintenance)? Is additional training required? At what stage of the project is training to be performed?

It is worth noting at this point that the use of programmable electronic systems (PESs) provide tremendous capabilities of control but require certain precautions to minimize specific risks, such as system failure, environmental effects detrimental to the system, and uncontrolled hardware/software modifications. All these risks can be minimized and in many cases almost eliminated with a well-designed, properly installed, and well managed application.

Safety Considerations

What are the main process hazards?

What is the required operator speed of response in case of alarm/trip actuation?

What is the required reliability of the control system?

Should the control circuitry fail in a fail-safe mode? If not, has this condition been checked and deemed acceptable?

What are the requirements for fire protection? What are the requirements for fire detection and fire fighting? In case of fire, are the means of escape identified?

In case of injury, what facilities are available? What are the means of communication? Is the control room considered an emergency center? If yes, is it equipped for such a function?

Other Considerations

What are the area classifications for the different plant locations? Should the standard ensure that all installed equipment conform to such requirements?

What are the environmental limitations of the control system (dust, humidity, corrosive atmosphere)?

What are the control system maintenance requirements?

Is the control system capable of sustaining the production of quality products? Are there any returned products? Are there any customer complaints?

Are there specific environmental regulations to be met by the control system and its associated instrumentation?

What is the required reliability for critical measurements? What is the required testing frequency? Is there a need for duplicated or triplicated control systems to handle critical loops?

LOGIC DIAGRAMS

Logic diagrams, another set of front-end engineering documents, need to be addressed by the person preparing the corporate standard. These logic diagrams define discrete (ON/OFF) controls, which cover all time-based and state-based logic used in process control. This includes programmable logic controller sequences and hard-wired trip systems.

There is a definite need for the logic controls to be well described since they allow the performance of hazard analysis studies and the clear transfer of information between engineering disciplines as well as between engineering, maintenance, and operations. If the logic is very simple, a written description in the control system definition or a description on the P&IDs is generally adequate. However, and this is the majority of cases, intricate logic is used. In this case, logic diagrams may be produced in conformance with ISA-S5.2, a standard intended to facilitate the understanding of the operation of binary systems and improve communications among the users of such data. The standard provides symbols for binary operating functions. In addition, this symbology can be applied to any class of hardware whether it be programmable, electronic, mechanical, hydraulic, manual, or other.

An example of a completed logic diagram is shown in Figure 4-3.

PROCESS DATA SHEET (PDS)

Process data sheets (see Figure 4-4) are yet another part of front-end engineering. The person who prepares the corporate standard must develop a section on them. PDSs contain the process data related to a particular instrument. They form the base upon which the process information is relayed from the process engineer to the instrument engineer. Specification sheets are then prepared and instruments selected.

Generally, PDSs are generated by the control engineer following the preparation of P&IDs and the definition of the control equipment. The process data (pressure, temperature, etc.) is then completed by the process engineer.

It is of prime importance to have these PDSs completed before the preparation of instrument specification sheets. Verbal communications and assumptions on the part of the person completing the instrument specification sheets are the source of trouble and expensive errors.

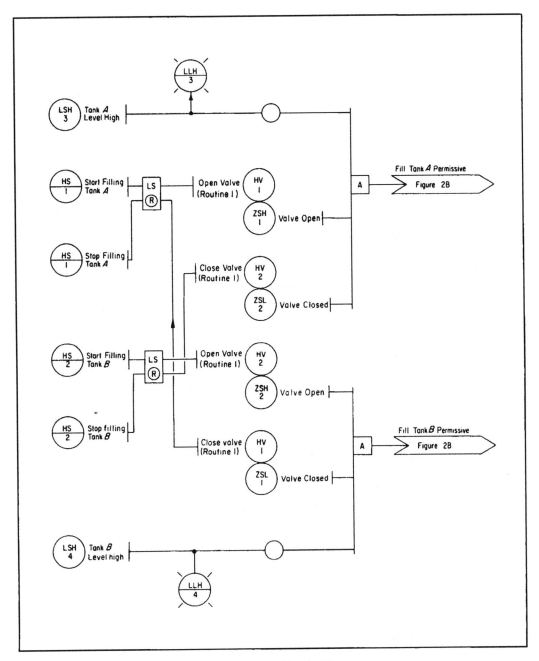

Figure 4-3. Typical Logic Diagram

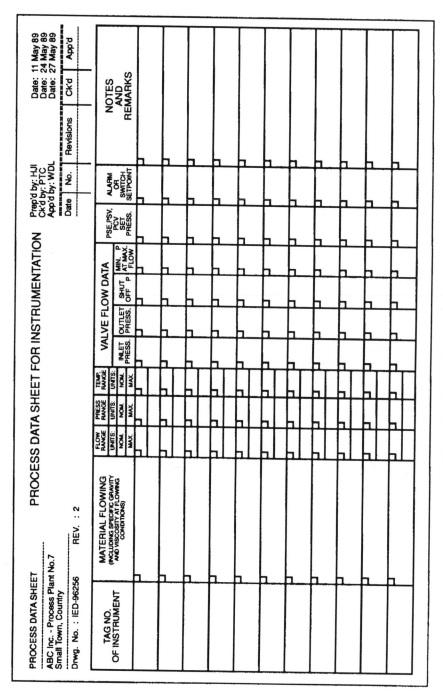

Figure 4-4 Typical Process Data Sheet

CHAPTER 5

Detailed Engineering — Documentation

OVERVIEW

The section of the corporate standard covering detailed engineering is generally the largest since it covers so many activities. In this book, detailed engineering is covered by both Chapters 5 and 6. This chapter covers the preparation of all the detailed design documentation necessary to support bid requests, construction, commissioning and maintenance of the plant; Chapter 6 covers the specification of instruments and control equipment.

The person who prepares the preliminary corporate standard to be issued for comments to all participants has the task of deciding what should be included and the required level of detail. The answer is dependent upon the needs of a corporation, but a general approach is shown in this chapter and may be used as a starting point. It is imperative to underline the fact that the content of this chapter is only a memory jogger and should not be taken "as is," since the statutory, technical, and corporate needs vary from one site to the other.

In the 1990s business environment, corporate and plant engineering staff are at a minimum level, and the detail engineering phase is frequently given to an engineering contractor or to an equipment supplier. In most cases in which an engineering contractor is doing the detail work, the instrumentation and control engineering portion is contracted out as part of a larger engineering package that would include other disciplines such as electrical, mechanical, civil, etc. Detail engineering must be based on all statutory requirements in effect at the site, the front-end engineering, the project requirements, and the engineering standards.

In cases in which the detailed engineering is given to an engineering contractor, a definition of the scope of that contractor is required to avoid misunderstandings and future additional costs. Appendix D is a format that may be used for such conditions. In other cases, such as when the detailed engineering is done by the supplier of packaged equipment, Appendix E may be used as a guide.

To conform to ISO 9000, the plant must have in place a system for identification, collection, indexing, filing, storage, maintenance, retrieval, and disposition of pertinent engineering records. Such requirements may have to be covered by the corporate standards. In some cases, these requirements are covered under a separate document, or they may be part of the philosophy section of the corporate standard.

Document Quality

The detailed engineering, along with all other documentation, must maintain a certain level of quality. As a starting point, it must be ensured that each document carries the required reference information. The following is a typical example of such information:

1. Drawing number
2. Drawing title
3. Type of drawing
4. Date originated
5. Latest revision
6. Date of revision
7. Approved revision

In addition, it is strongly recommended, where practical, that the nature of any changes be identified if the document is revised.

As a general rule and by using some of the ISO 9000 guidelines:

1. the latest issues of appropriate documents must be available at all pertinent locations;
2. documents must be reviewed and approved for adequacy by authorized personnel prior to issue and according to a procedure, and such personnel must have access to background information upon which they may base their decisions; and
3. obsolete documents must be quickly removed from all users.

Types of Documentation

The detail design documentation covered under detailed engineering includes drawings and documents as required to meet the needs of the legislative requirements in effect at the site and the plant. The engineering records covered in this unit represent essential technical data and may be considered as minimum technical information for the field of instrumentation and control. It is up to the plant's technical management to decide whether any additional documents are required. As an example, typical documentation may include the following:

1. Instrument Index
2. Loop Diagrams
3. Interlock Diagrams
4. Instrument Specification Sheets, including calculations (for control valves, orifice plates, relief valves, etc.)
5. Manuals for programmable electronic systems (DCS, PLC, PC, etc.)
6. Control Panel Specifications (including overall layout)
7. Control Room Requirements
8. Operating Instructions

Alarm and trip system testing is, in most cases, also required. It is described in detail in Chapter 8.

Two additional documents, generally not prepared by the control and instrumentation discipline but of prime importance to the detailed design phase, are piping drawings and location and conduit layout drawings.

Piping Drawings

In many cases, such drawings, produced by the piping engineering group, would show all field instruments (complete with elevations and tag numbers) and the equipment or process line upon which they are mounted or to which they are connected. Since the piping isometrics (which must be prepared by the piping group anyway) would have all the details required, this approach has two main advantages. First, fewer drawings are prepared and, therefore, cost is reduced. Second, having only one drawing instead of separate instrumentation location and installation drawings avoids errors that occur when two drawings show the same information and one of them is later revised (and the other one is "forgotten").

The needs for instrument (instrument air, power, and wiring) are shown on the instrument loop diagrams and need not be repeated on the piping drawing. Special requirements, such as specific orientation, clearances, or supports, can be shown on the piping drawing. However, corporate culture may still require separate location and installation drawings for instruments.

An item of major consideration in piping drawings is the correct indication of control valves. It is quite common for instrument personnel to supply dimensions to piping personnel. One main source of information is the valve vendor, or, in the absence of such data, ISA has published a series of standards that provide standard valve dimensions. These standards are listed in the ISA-S75 series (see Appendix B).

As piping drawings are being prepared with the instruments shown on them, the following points may have to be considered by the person preparing the corporate standard:

1. Does the corporate standard ensure that the designer keeps in mind that plant personnel need access to the instruments? Therefore, are all instruments, including vessel or piping connections for sampling or for sensing elements, located so they are accessible from structural platforms or grade?
2. Is access from permanent ladders normally restricted to minor types of instruments, such as pressure gages, dial thermometers, or thermocouples, where location cannot be changed to permit access from a platform or grade?

Location and Conduit Layout Drawings

These drawings, generally produced by electrical engineering, show all field run conduits and cables with details on the identification and number of wires. This information is generally available from the loop diagrams. These drawings also show the location, elevation, and size of cable trays, junction boxes, and control/interlock panels. A recent trend has been the use of computer-based relational database managers to table the conduits and wires instead of generating drawings. The main advantages of such an approach are its simplicity, ease of updating, and low preparation cost.

Specific Applications of ISA Standards

ISA has published a series of seven standards specifically for the nuclear industry (see Appendix B, the S67 series). In addition, ISA has produced two standards for fossil power plants (see Appendix B, S77.41 and S77.42).

Other standards-writing bodies also produce industry-specific standards, since many of such organizations are technology-oriented in scope (e.g., American Welding Society).

Tagging

For all the users of instruments and control systems to be able to locate instruments in the plant, they must be identified. Therefore, one of the first requirements of a corporate standard is to ensure that every instrument has a label bearing its tag number. Items to be considered by the person preparing the corporate standard follows.

Do the instrument tag numbers either conform to a company standard or to ISA-S5.1?

Whatever the choice, company standard or ISA, is it uniform throughout the plant?

Does a typical instrument tag number consists of two parts: a letter combination followed by a dedicated loop number? (Typical letter combinations are shown in Figure 5-1.)

Are the labels for field and back-of-panel-mounted instruments embossed stainless steel tags? If not, is there a possibility that a corrosive atmosphere (or rough handling) will damage the labels?

Are they attached with stainless steel wire? Are they riveted? Are they screwed to allow removal? Is removal of such labels tightly controlled? How is it controlled?

Are the labels for control room front-of-panel-mounted equipment Lamacoid™ nameplates? What colors are used for nameplates? Are these colors in compliance with the plant operating norms? Are they acceptable to the operators for day-to-day use? Are they fixed by suitable adhesives or rivets?

INSTRUMENT INDEX

This document is an index of all items of instrumentation on a specific project or for a particular plant. Its main purpose is to act as a cross-reference and as a listing document.

The generation of such a list could be simple and manually generated and maintained, or could be generated and maintained on personal computers using database managers or even a word processing file. This computerized approach facilitates the updates of the instrument index.

The instrument index is normally in tabular form. To function as an index, this document needs to cross-reference, for each item of instrumentation, all documents and drawings that are related to this particular item. A corporate standard would generally indicate the content of a typical instrument index. Typically, the following are representative of the items to be listed on an instrument index:

1. Tag Number—This a unique instrument identification (e.g., TT-238), and its allocation, in most cases, is based on ANSI/ISA-S5.1, Instrumentation Symbols and Identification. A label bearing the instrument tag number should be provided for every instrument, and these labels must match the listing in the instrument index. The labels for field instruments are generally embossed stainless steel tags and attached with stainless steel wire, while the labels for control room equipment are usually black lettering on white background Lamacoid™ fixed by suitable adhesives.

First-Letters	Initiating or Measured Variable	Controllers — Recording	Controllers — Indicating	Controllers — Blind	Self-Actuated Control Valves	Readout — Recording	Readout — Indicating	Switches & Alarm Devices* — High**	Switches & Alarm — Low	Switches & Alarm — Comb	Transmitters — Recording	Transmitters — Indicating	Transmitters — Blind	Solenoids, Relays, Computing Devices	Primary Element	Test Point	Well or Probe	Viewing Device, Glass	Safety Device	Final Element
A	Analysis	ARC	AIC	AC		AR	AI	ASH	ASL	ASHL	ART	AIT	AT	AY	AE	AP	AW			AV
B	Burner Combustion	BRC	BIC	BC		BR	BI	BSH	BSL	BSHL	BRT	BIT	BT	BY	BE		BW	BG		BZ
C	User's Choice																			
D	User's Choice																			
E	Voltage	ERC	EIC	EC		ER	EI	ESH	ESL	ESHL	ERT	EIT	ET	EY	EE					EZ
F	Flow Rate	FRC	FIC	FC	FCV, FICV	FR	FI	FSH	FSL	FSHL	FRT	FIT	FT	FY	FE	FP		FG		FV
FQ	Flow Quanity	FQRC	FQIC	FQC		FQR	FQI	FQSH	FQSL			FQIT	FQT	FQY	FQE					FQV
FF	Flow Ratio	FFRC	FFIC	FFC		FFR	FFI	FFSH	FFSL						FE					FFV
G	User's Choice																			
H	Hand		HIC	HC						HS										HV
I	Current	IRC	JIC	IC		IR	II	ISH	ISL	ISHL	IRT	IIT	IT	IY	IE					IZ
J	Power	JRC	JIC	JC		JR	JI	JSH	JSL	JSHL	JRT	JIT	JT	JY	JE					JV
K	Time	KRC	KIC	KC	KCV	KR	KI	KSH	KSL	KSHL	KRT	KIT	KT	KY	KE					KV
L	Level	LRC	LIC	LC	LCV	LR	LI	LSH	LSL	LSHL	LRT	LIT	LT	LY	LE		LW	LG		LV
M	User's Choice																			
N	User's Choice																			
O	User's Choice																			
P	Pressure Vacuum	PRC	PIC	PC	PCV	PR	PI	PSH	PSL	PSHL	PRT	PIT	PT	PY	PE	PP			PSV, PSE	PV
PD	Pressure, Differential	PDRC	PDIC	PDC	PDCV	PDR	PDI	PDSH	PDSL		PDRT	PDIT	PDT	PDY	PE	PP				PDV
Q	Quanity Differential	QRC	QIC	QC		QR	QI	QSH	QSL	QSHL	QRT	QIT	QT	QY	QE					QZ
R	Radiation	RRC	RIC	RC		RR	RI	RSH	RSL	RSHL	RRT	RIT	RT	RY	RE		RW			RZ
S	Speed Frequency	SRC	SIC	SC	SCV	SR	SI	SSH	SSL	SSHL	SRT	SIT	ST	SY	SE					SV
T	Temperature	TRC	TIC	TC	TCV	TR	TI	TSH	TSL	TSHL	TRT	TIT	TT	TY	TE	TP	TW		TSE	TV
TD	Temperature Differential	TDRC	TDIC	TDC	TDCV	TDR	TDI	TDSH	TDSL	TDSL	TDRT	TDIT	TDT	TDY	TE	TP	TW			TDV
U	Multivariable					UR	UI							UY						UV
V	Vibration Machinery Analysis	VRC	VIC			VR	VI	VSH	VSL	VSHL	VRT	VIT	VT	VY	VE					VZ
W	Weight Force	WRC	WIC	WC	WCV	WR	WI	WSH	WSL	WSHL	WRT	WIT	WT	WY	WE					WZ
WD	Weight Force Differential	WDRC	WDIC	WDC	WDCV	WDR	WDI	WDSH	WDSL	WDSL	WDRT	WDIT	WDT	WDY	WE					WDZ
X	Unclassified																			
Y	Event State Presence	YRC	YIC	YC		YR	YI	YSH	YSL				YT	YY	YE					YZ
Z	Position Dimension	ZRC	ZIC	ZC	ZCV	ZR	ZI	ZSH	ZSL	ZSHL	ZRT	ZIT	ZT	ZY	ZE					ZV
ZD	Gauging Deviation	ZDRC	ZDIC	ZDC	ZDCV	ZDR	ZDI	ZDSH	ZDSL		ZDRT	ZDIT	ZDT	ZDY	ZDE					ZDV

Note: This table is not all inclusive.

*A, alarm, the annunciating device, may be used in the same fashion as S, switch, the actuating device.

**The letters H and L may be omitted in the undefined case.

Other Possible Combinations:

FO	(Restriction Orifice)
FRK, HIK	(Control Stations)
FX	(Accessories)
TJR	(Scanning Recorder)
LLH	(Pilot Light)

PFR	(Ratio)
KQI	(Running Time Indicator)
QQI	(Indicating Counter)
WKIC	(Rate-of-Weight-Loss Controller)
HMS	(Hand Momentary Switch)

Figure 5-1 Typical Letter Combinations

2. Description — The function/purpose of the instrument is described here (e.g., cooling tower inlet temperature).
3. P&ID — The process (or piping) and instrument diagram (P&ID) on which tag numbers are shown must be referenced.
4. Line/Equip. — The number of the line or equipment onto which the instrument is mounted is identified. This facilitates the search for an instrument on a particular P&ID as well as simplifies the search for piping, mechanical, and vessel drawings.
5. Spec. Sheet — The specification sheet number for a particular device is listed.
6. Manufacturer's Drawings — Vendor-supplied drawings and manuals are cross-referenced here to facilitate future retrieval. In many cases, these drawings and manuals have numbers similar to plant-produced documents to conform to an established numbering system.
7. Loop Drawing — The wiring or tubing of the instrument is shown and referenced on this drawing.
8. Interlock Diagram — The interlock diagram in which an instrument is present is identified here.
9. Location Drawings — The location of the instrument on a line (or vessel) is referenced for future use at installation time or later on during maintenance. This drawing could be a piping drawing as discussed earlier on in this chapter.
10. Notes — Any notes or remarks related to instruments are listed (e.g., "Instr. supplied with cooling tower").

Some additional data that can be found on an instrument index are:

1. equipment supplier and model number,
2. other drawings that relate to a specific instrument (e.g., installation details),
3. the measuring range,
4. purchase order number, etc.

A typical Instrument Index format is shown in Figure 5-2.

For the coordinator and producers of the corporate standards, a final check on the subject of the instrument index should be able to answer the following questions.

Is the instrument index prepared in a form suitable to the plant's needs (for example, in an electronic database)?

Does the instrument index contain all the necessary information for the retrieval of other related documents (spec. sheets, loop diagrams, etc.)?

LOOP DIAGRAMS

A corporate standard must include a statement of corporate needs and policies with regard to loop diagrams. In general, a loop diagram should be prepared for each instrument loop on the project that contains more than a single instrument. Normally, the only instruments not requiring loop diagrams are interlock systems (which are shown on the interlock diagrams) and local devices such as gages, regulators, and relief valves (for these devices, an entry in the instrument index should be sufficient).

The loop diagrams show the detailed arrangement for instrumentation components in all loops. All devices, pneumatic and electronic, that carry the same loop number

| INSTRUMENT INDEX | | | | | | | Date | No. | Revisions | By |

INSTRUMENT INDEX
======================
ABC Inc. - Process Plant No.7
Small Town, Country

Drwg. No. : MBS-34556 Sht. 1 of 10

By: BGT   Date: 5 Mar. 89

TAG	Descrptn.	P&ID	Line/ Equip.	Spec. Sheet	Mfg. Dwg.	Loop Dwg.	Interlock Diagr.	Locat. Dwg.	Notes

Figure 5-2. Typical Instrument Index

are generally shown on the same loop diagram. This diagram will show, as a minimum, the interconnection of the devices, their locations, their power sources, and their control actions.

The content and format of the loop diagram should conform to the plant standards (or, if they do not exist, it may conform to ANSI/ISA-S5.4, Instrument Loop Diagrams). Figures 5-3 and 5-4 are reprints from this standard, which was published to provide the guidelines for the preparation of loop diagrams. Such a standard assists in understanding loop diagrams and establishes the minimum required information as well as identifies optional information that may be shown on the loop diagram. A corporation may decide to show more (or less) detail than is recommended by ANSI/ISA-S5.4.

It should be mentioned at this point that some organizations use computer-based database managers instead of loop drawings to keep track of the instrument loops. This practice is more suited to modern distributed control systems than to analog instrumentation.

The following questions will assist the person preparing the corporate standard in providing a section on loop diagram preparation and tailoring it to the needs of the corporation.

Are the electrical and pneumatic details of a single loop not to be separated?
Are drawings, where possible, made without the use of intersheet connections?

Should each instrument loop be grounded at one point only? Is this point preferably in the control room?

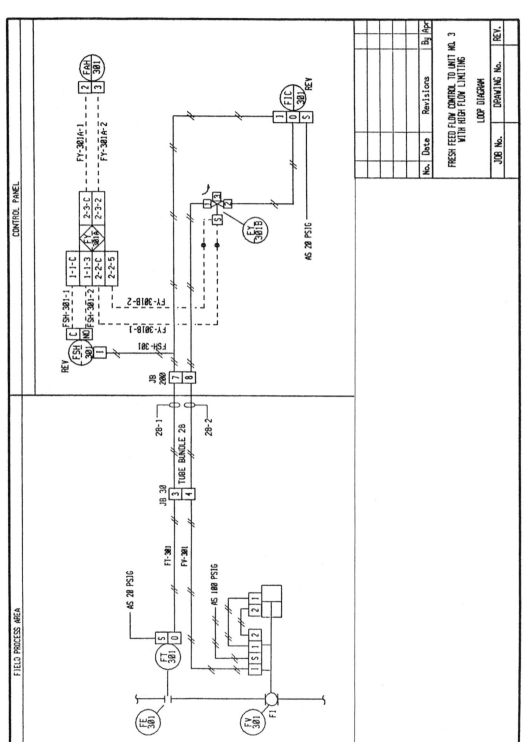

Figure 5-3 Typical Loop Diagram, Pneumatic Control

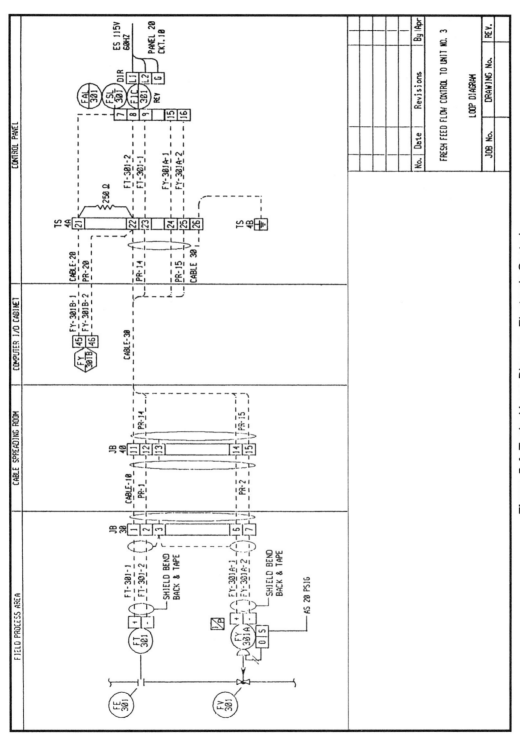

Figure 5-4 Typical Loop Diagram, Electronic Control

Should each ground be connected to its respective reference point by no more than one wire (single-point grounding)?

Should the corporate standard stipulate that under no circumstances should two or more systems share a common single ground wire, either equipment ground or control common?

Are all cable shields to be continuous (connected across junction boxes, etc.)? Typically, three terminals will be required for analog signals and two terminals for discrete signals.

Is care taken to adequately insulate the shield over its entire length to maintain the one point connection?

Are the loop diagrams prepared in accordance with good engineering practice? Are the wiring and tubing numbering systems on these diagrams correct?

A corporate standard would generally recommend that loop diagrams be the source of wire numbers for analog devices (i.e., controllers, indicators, or recorders) and for discrete devices that are not shown on any interlock diagram. The same rules apply for creating wire numbers on loop diagrams as for interlock diagrams, the only difference being that since there are no rung numbers, loop numbers are used. Each wire in the plant should have a unique number. The wire number should be composed of a loop number followed by a dash and a sequential number starting with 1. If discrete devices shown on the loop diagram are also shown on an interlock diagram, the wires connected to them should have numbers generated on the interlock diagram.

It should be mentioned at this point that loop diagrams were originally developed based on the concept of physical connections between individual devices, each performing a specific function. Modern control systems tend to have, typically, a measurement, a final control element, and a computer-based control system that performs most of the functions. The representation on the loop diagram would not show the functionality of the control function. On the other hand, to show all this functionality on the P&ID may, in some cases, overload the P&ID. Some corporations have adapted SAMA (Scientific Apparatus Makers Association) symbology to represent the control function. It should be noted that SAMA no longer writes nor supports its published standards. Copies of SAMA standards, to be used for historical purposes only, are available from ISA.

The functionality of control functions performed in software should be shown on dedicated drawings. The final decision as to where the functionality of the software should be shown (i.e., on the P&ID or on a SAMA symbology drawing – depends on the complexity of the loop and the corporate culture). If SAMA drawings are used, they could be part of the control system definition document (see Chapter 4).

INTERLOCK DIAGRAM

The Interlock Diagram (also known as Electrical Control Schematic) is the next item to be considered when preparing corporate standards. This diagram shows the detailed wiring arrangement for discrete (on/off) control (see Figure 5-5). Generally, the only control circuits that do not require an interlock diagram are analog loops, which are shown on loop diagrams. With the introduction and extensive use of programmable electronic systems to perform logic functions, the use of the interlock diagram is not

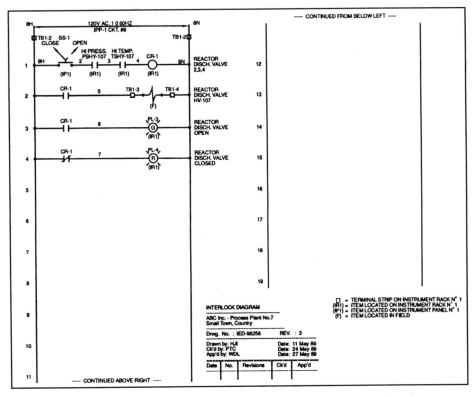

Figure 5-5. Typical Interlock Diagram

as extensive as it was few years ago. However, some applications still require such drawings.

A good quality interlock diagram will always be in agreement with the corresponding logic diagram. Logic diagrams are explained in Chapter 4, under "Front-End Engineering."

All devices on these diagrams will generally have a tag number, location, and service description. In addition, all rungs on these diagrams are numbered. Each rung on a project should have a unique number, and each wire in a plant should have a unique number. These diagrams are the source of wire numbers for discrete control.

The numbering of rungs on interlock diagrams should be sequential. The numbers start from the top of the diagram and increase, going down the ladder and continuing through all the diagrams created for the project. There should never be more than one rung with the same number on the same project. The wire number begins with the rung number followed by a dash and a sequential number on the rung, starting with 1. The wire number does not change after going through a terminal block (unless it is a fused terminal block). It changes only after the switching device or load, i.e., fuse, switch or coil.

A final check of the interlock diagrams should be able to answer the following:

1. Are the interlock diagrams in accordance with good engineering practice?
2. Do they confirm the information shown on the P&IDs?
3. Are the logic diagrams in agreement with the interlock diagrams?
4. Is the wire numbering system correct?

INSTRUMENT SPECIFICATION SHEETS

The purpose of specification sheets is to:

1. list the pertinent details for use by engineers and vendors, as well as by installation and maintenance personnel;
2. provide a record for the functionality and description of a particular instrument; and
3. provide uniformity in content, form, and terminology, which, in turn, saves time for users of such data.

Their importance necessitates the need to have them as part of a corporate standard. Again, the needs of a corporation must be considered when this portion of the standard's preliminary draft is being prepared. More information concerning the specification of instruments, when completing the instrument specification sheets, is mentioned in Chapter 6.

It is of great importance to ensure that the specification sheets include compliance with the electrical code, which should be stipulated in the standard. All electrical equipment furnished for a project must comply with the requirements of the latest edition of the electrical code in effect at the site. This equipment must be approved (UL, FM, or CSA) or, as a minimum, have the approval of the electric power authority in the region in which the equipment is installed. Nonapproved equipment should not be installed; otherwise, liability, legal, and insurance problems may arise.

Electrical instruments and control systems in hazardous locations must obviously conform to the electrical code in effect at the site. In addition, ISA has published a series of standards and recommended practices that cover this subject: S12.1, S12.4, RP12.6, S12.10, S12.11, S12.12, and S12.13 (see Appendix B). In addition, the choice of all components must take into account the nature of the materials present, e.g., in the manufacture of azide, copper or lead azide can be inadvertently formed from the installation material; also PVC is vulnerable to attack by certain organic chemicals.

Intrinsic safety (IS), through the use of barriers, is the preferred method of protection in hazardous environments in many corporations and is, therefore, clearly stated in the corporate standard. Safety obtained by explosion-proof boxes or purging could be lost as a result of carelessness, corrosion, or damage to the equipment. Where IS barriers are used, the following questions may help in the preparation of a corporate philosophy.

Are IS loops grounded separately from other equipment?

Should the resistance to ground be less than 1 ohm? If not, does the resistance conform to the vendor's recommendations?

In addition to the IS barriers, is the power supply line also grounded? The requirement for a completely separate grounding is to eliminate the possibility that a fault in power circuits or the effects from lightning could raise the potential of the barrier's ground above an unsafe level.

Does the application of IS barriers closely follow the vendor's recommendations? Should an independent check be performed following any installation, modification, or maintenance IS activity?

For the preparation of instrument specification sheets, existing forms, with instructions, can be found in ISA-S20. The purpose of these forms is to:

1. assist in the preparation of a complete specification by listing and providing space for all principal descriptive options;
2. promote uniform terminology;
3. facilitate quoting, purchasing, receiving, accounting, and ordering procedures through a uniform display of information;
4. provide a useful permanent record and means of checking the installation; and
5. improve efficiency from the initial concept to the final installation.

Figure 5-6 shows a typical completed instrument specification sheet using one such ISA standard form. Some corporations develop their own set of specification sheet forms to meet their more specific needs (see Appendix J).

©ISA S20

Specification Forms for Process Measurement and Control Instruments, Primary Elements and Control Valves

ABC Inc.—Process Plant No. 7 Small Town, Country	DIFFERENTIAL PRESSURE INSTRUMENTS	SHEET 1 OF 1
	NO | BY | DATE | REVISION	SPEC. NO. 710.01 — REV. 1
		CONTRACT — DATE 4/88
		REQ. 3451 · P.O. N6321
		BY ED — CHK'D ED — APPR. JHB

	1	Tag No. LT-102	Service LEVEL RAW MATERIAL #2 STORAGE
GENERAL	2	Function	Record ☐ Indicate ☐ Control ☐ Blind ☐ Trans ☒ Integ ☐ Other
	3	Case	MFR STD ☒ Nom Size ____ Color: MFR STD ☐ Other
	4	Mounting	Flush ☐ Surface ☐ Yoke ☒ Other
	5	Enclosure Class	General Purpose ☐ Weather proof ☒ Explosion proof ☐ Class For use in Intrinsically Safe System ☐ Other
	6	Power Supply	117V 60 Hz ☐ Other ac ____ dc ☒ 24 Volts
	7	Chart	12 in. Circ. ☐ Other ____ Range ____ No.
	8	Chart Drive	24 hr Other ____ Elec. ☐ Spring ☐ Other
	9	Scale	Type ____ Range: 1 ____ 2 ____ 3
XMTR	10	Transmitter Output	4-20 mA ☒ 10-50 mA ☐ 21-103 kPa (3-15 psig) ☐ Other For Receiver, See Spec Sheet
CONTROLLER	11	Control Modes	P=Prop (Gain), I=Integral (Auto Reset), D=Derivative (Rate) Sub: s=Slow, f=Fast If ☐ Df ☐ P ☐ PI ☐ PD ☐ PID ☐ I_s ☐ D_s ☐ Other
	12	Action	On Meas. Increase Output: Increases ☐ Decreases ☐
	13	Auto-Man Switch	None ☐ MFR STD ☐ Other
	14	Set Point Adj.	Manual ☐ External ☐ Remote ☐ Other
	15	Manual Reg.	None ☐ MFR STD ☐ Other
	16	Output	4-20 mA ☐ 10-50 mA ☐ 21-103 kPa (3-15 psig) ☐ Other
UNIT	17	Service	Flow ☐ Level ☒ Diff. Pressure ☒ Other
	18	Element Type	Diaphragm ☒ Bellows ☐ Mercury ☐ Other
	19	Material	Body 316 SS Element 316 SS
	20	Rating	Overrange ____ Body Rating ____ psig
	21	Diff. Range	Fixed ☐ Adj. Range 20-200" W.C. Set At 140" W.C.
	22		Elevation 0 Suppression 0
	23	Process Data	Fluid CHEMICAL Max Temp. 60°C Max. Press. AMB.
	24	Process Conn.	½ in. NPT ☒ Other
	25	Alarm Switches	Quantity ____ Form ____ Rating
	26	Function	Meas. Var. ☐ Deviation ☐ Contacts To ____ on Inc. Meas.
	27	Options	Pressure Element ☐ Range ____ Material Temp. Element ☐ Range ____ Type Filt Reg. ☐ Sup. Gage ☐ Output Gage ☐ ____ Charts Valve Manifold Cond. Pots ☐ Adj. Damp ☐ Integral Sq. Rt. Ext. ☐ Integrator Other
	28	MFR & Model No.	AJAX 13495-OPT

Notes:

ISA Form S20.20a

Figure 5-6. Typical Spec. Sheet

A corporate standard may need to specifically state that a process data sheet must exist for every item of instrumentation that is in contact with the process. More information on process data sheets is available in Chapter 4.

MANUALS FOR PROGRAMMABLE ELECTRONIC SYSTEMS (PESs)

The primary purpose of a PES manual is to serve as a reference for the ongoing support and maintenance of the PES system after final commissioning and start-up have taken place.

This part of a corporate standard should provide a framework and checklist from which the manual (or manuals) for programmable electronic systems (PESs), such as DCSs, PLCs and PCs, can be produced. The exact manual layout will depend on the plant needs, the level of training, the corporate culture, and the system selected. The information contained in such manuals would span the hardware and software from the input/output modules through the operator interface and/or supervisory computer.

Typically, the above scope may be broken down into the following sections, with each showing its contents:

1. Overview and General Information
   - Manual(s) layout description and index
   - Brief description of the PES
   - PES design philosophy (such as failure modes, etc.)
   - PES modification history
2. System Start-up Procedure
   - Overview, in which critical process and personal safety information must be highlighted
   - Specific start-up instructions
   - List of control set points and parameters
3. PES Communications
   - Data communication overview (include block diagram)
   - Network information
   - Cabling and connection information (pinouts, jumpering, shielding requirements, dip switch settings)
   - List of available reference manuals
4. Input/Output, including PLCs and Stand-alone Controllers
   - Overview
   - Input/output cross-reference list
   - Program structure overview
   - Annotated program file listings
   - Device memory allocation listing
   - Program backup procedure
   - General information; software versions, dip switch setting, jumper configurations, electrostatic damage prevention, etc.
   - List of available reference manuals
5. Operator Interface
   - Overview
   - System screen layout and listing
   - Operator keyboard functional description complete with function key index, if applicable
   - Full database listing including link structure, if any

- Annotated program block listing
- I/O scanner(s) configuration and listings
- Backup procedure
- Host computer general information (operating system/version, directory structure, hardware components description, dip switch settings, jumper configurations, electrostatic damage prevention, etc.)
- List of available reference manuals

6. Reference documents
   - Index
   - Equipment manufacturer's product data sheets for all PES components
7. Miscellaneous
   - Index
   - List of support persons, including manufacturer's "Hot Line" support
   - System backup disk(s).

The writing style of this manual should be clear and concise. Descriptive sections should avoid excessive technical jargon, and vendor-specific acronyms should have their meaning spelled out on first occurrence (e.g., RAM = random access memory). In addition, the group that will be responsible for PES support and maintenance at the plant should be consulted as to the number of manual sets required.

The manual(s) should be updated to incorporate any system modifications that take place. In addition, a modification history that documents the nature of the modification and the date and person responsible for the change should be maintained in the manual's overview section. The corporate standard may be specific and state that all modifications must comply with:

1. the legislation in effect at the site (this is particularly applicable to critical loops), and
2. good engineering practice. Such practice may have to ensure that all hardware/software changes must consider the following before implementation:
   - Is there a safety implication?
   - Is a change really necessary?
   - What are all the effects on the system and the environment?
   - What else needs to be done to match the change?
   - What will the change cost to supply and implement?
   - What is the priority and importance of this change?

All system modifications may be recorded on existing change forms supplied with the corporate standard. Typical blank forms with an explanation of their use are shown in Appendix F.

PLC Program Documentation

An important part of any documentation package is the PLC program (where PLCs are used). With the proliferation of PLCs, the corporate standard should specify the format in which the program (generally ladder logic) is described. Without such a description, the review and editing, specially on large programs, becomes an impossible task.

The corporate standard in many cases would specify certain requirements to ensure program legibility. PLC program documentation may, for example, conform to the following requirements:

1. The programming should be developed on an IBM™-compatible PC and be written in format as requested by the plant.
2. The CRT should display a minimum of 8 programming lines.
3. The individual I/O description at the rung should show:
    - on the first line, the tag number (e.g., LSH-123);
    - on the second line, a description (e.g., TANK 17); and
    - on the third line, any notes (e.g., instrument location or PLC I/O address, etc.);
    - in addition, all outputs/inputs should be cross-referenced to the rung(s) to which they connect.
4. Each rung and each section of the program (containing many rungs) should be clearly explained; up to 16 lines can be used for each rung; the ability to display or not display the rung descriptions should be available.
5. The PLC program may be simulated on the PC prior to commissioning, and the software used should have the ability to compare two programs and flag the differences.
6. The software used must comply with the existing plant software.

The preparer of a corporate standard may consider it more practical to include a sample PLC program instead of a description. However, he or she should keep in mind that different documentation packages may not have exactly the same approach and format capabilities.

CONTROL PANELS SPECIFICATIONS

The corporate standard should address control panel specifications. It is common to have such a specification available in a word processor format to allow customizing the requirements for each application.

The subject of control panels as presented here is broken down into design, construction, assembly, testing, and shipping of control panels. Specifically, it will address the following:

1. General Requirements
2. Documentation
3. Custom Panels
4. Standard Panels
5. Nameplates
6. Graphic Displays
7. Electrical Considerations
8. Purging
9. Pneumatics
10. Certification
11. Inspection and Testing
12. Shipping

Each section is presented as a questionnaire designed to help the producer of a corporate standard identify the various topics that should be covered. An example of a completed functional specification for a control panel may be seen in Appendix H.

One of the first rules to be followed in control panel building is to ensure that all electrically operated instruments, or the electrical components incorporated in an instrument, must comply with the requirements of the current edition of the electrical code in effect at the site and should be approved and bear the approval label (UL, CSA, etc.). In addition, ISA standards and recommended practices for instrumentation, which provide a valuable source of information and guidelines, are identified throughout this section. Another key item to consider is that when the panel is in a hazardous area, an appropriate enclosure must be specified to conform with the electrical code requirements in effect at the site.

General Requirements

Is it expected that the manufacturer will furnish the panels completed fabricated and finished, with all components mounted, piped, wired, and tested? Should all this work be in accordance with the requirements of the owner identified in an attached specification?

Should the standard state that all instruments and equipment not specified as being supplied to the panel manufacturer are the responsibility of the panel manufacturer and should be in accordance with all the requirements of the owner?

Is it a requirement that the work of furnishing the control panel be carried out by certified and trained tradesmen? Should these tradesmen have adequate supervision and the equipment necessary to complete the work?

Should the panel manufacturer be required to produce evidence of tradesmen's certification and training?

Is the panel manufacturer responsible for the correct installation and assembly of all items or equipment, and for carefully reading and rigidly adhering to the manufacturer's instructions? Should any damage resulting from failure to observe the manufacturer's instructions be the panel manufacturer's responsibility?

Unless otherwise specifically called for on the drawings or specifications, should the standard ensure that uniformity of manufacture is maintained for any particular item throughout the panel?

Should all instruments be installed and connected in such a way that the instrument can be maintained and removed for servicing without having to break fittings, cut wires, or pull hot wires? Should the standard ensure that the panel manufacturer provides necessary unions and tubing connections to all instruments to allow removal?

Should the front-of-panel instrument location and distribution follow the process flow path from left to right?

Is a clock required? Is it to be mounted on the panel?

ISA has produced a series of recommended practices that deal with control panels. ISA-RP60.3, Human Engineering for Control Centers, presents design concepts that are compatible with the physical and mental capabilities of the control center operator while recognizing the operator's limitations.

Documentation

Will the owner (or his or her appointed representative, such as a consulting firm) supply the panel fabricator with all documentation required for complete and correct fabrication and assembly of the panels?

Such documentation normally includes:

1. Instrument Index,
2. Loop Diagrams,
3. Electrical Control Schematics,
4. Instrument Specifications,
5. Front-of-Panel General Layout,
6. Nameplate Drawing (where applicable), and
7. Certified Vendor Drawings (where applicable).

Does the Front-of-Panel General Layout show the physical size of the control panel and approximate positions of front-of-panel instruments, lights, switches, push buttons, and displays? Does this drawing give approximate locations of tube and cable entries and pneumatic/electric supplies? Should exact cutout dimensions be the responsibility of the panel manufacturer?

Are there instances in which some or all of the above documentation is to be generated by the panel fabricator? Is this requirement clearly stated as such to avoid additional costs at the end?

Is the panel manufacturer expected to furnish the following drawings for approval by the owner(prior to commencement of construction)?

1. Steel Fabrication Drawings (for custom panels)
2. Detailed Front-of-Panel Layout
3. Detailed Back-of-Panel Layout
4. Wiring Diagram and Terminal Layout
5. Tubing, Air Header, and Bulkhead Layout

How many sets of drawings are required (for example, either one reproducible set or three copies)?

After panel completion and checkout, how many drawings will the manufacturer furnish of the above drawings in an "as-built" condition? Should the standard require that, in addition, a set of "as-built" drawings be placed in the drawing pocket prior to shipment?

Should the standard include a recommendation that all drawings be generated on CAD systems? Should these drawings conform to the owner's standards? Should this be coordinated with the plant to ensure compatibility of software revisions? If that is the case, would a copy of all the files be transferred on the owner's system, simplifying future modifications?

ISA-RP60.4, Documentation for Control Centers, covers the type, content, and extent of documentation required as record data and information particular to a control center facility.

Custom Panels

☐ MATERIALS:

Should the panel be constructed of steel and be of welded construction? Such a requirement is sometimes not acceptable because of the process and its environment. Other materials, such as stainless steel and fiberglass, are sometimes used. This should be defined at the front-end engineering stage.

Where steel is used, is the control panel face to be of a minimum thickness (e.g., 3/16 in.)? Are the top, sides, and other sections of the panel of a minimum thickness (e.g., 14 gage)?

Are bottom mounting channels required? Should they be of a specific size? Example: 4″ × 2″ × 1/4″ steel with slots for 1/2 in. anchors at least every 12 inches.

Are interior angles required for reinforcement? For example, 1-1/2″ × 1-1/2″ × 1/4″ steel.

☐ FABRICATION:

Should the standard require that the panels be of rigid construction, free standing, and without any external bracing or support?

Where required, are all sheet or plate areas suitably reinforced with welded channel or angle stiffeners to prevent deformation or buckling?

Are removable panels provided to allow safe cutting of holes for cable entry?

Are all holes in a panel smooth and regular and made by punching, sawing, or drilling and filing?

Where a door is specified, is it formed and braced to form a rigid unit? Are hinges to be of the continuous type? Depending on the environment in which the panel is located, should doors be completely gasketed, fastened with at least a two-point latch and comply with the panel rating? Should the panel fabricator install a permanent drawing pocket at a convenient location inside a rear of panel door?

Where a hinged console is specified, should the hinged section form a rigid unit? Is a safe support at each end of the console provided in order to keep the console section open for maintenance? Should the hinged section, like the door, be completely gasketed?

Where a removable cover is specified, should it have two circular flush handles with latch? Should this cover be formed and braced to form a rigid unit and be completely gasketed?

☐ FINISH:

Are all surfaces ground smooth and sanded free of rust, scale, and extraneous marks? Is there a requirement that all surfaces be vapor degreased or washed completely and thoroughly with solvent?

☐ **PAINTING INSTRUCTIONS:**

For inside surfaces, should two coats of glossy white be applied, including brackets and supports?

For outside surfaces, should spot putty be applied where required and then sanded to a smooth finish? Is this then followed by applying two spray coats of enamel of a specified color? For example, the color may be beige for control room panels and ASA 61 grey for field panels.

In addition, should one spray coat of grey primer surfacer be applied to all inside and outside surfaces of the panel prior to painting?

Standard Panels

To take advantage of lower costs and better deliveries than for custom panels, do standard panels meet most of the requirements?

In the case of free-standing interlock/terminal panels that contain wall- or surface-mounting devices, should the standard ensure that the panel manufacturer uses panel enclosures that comply with:

1. the codes and regulations in effect at the site,
2. the area classification,
3. the environmental requirements, and
4. the plant requirements?

Has special consideration been given to the use of doors with acrylic panels to allow viewing of the panel content without opening doors?

Nameplates

Are all instruments located at the front of the panel with nameplates indicating the tag number?

Are all annunciators windows engraved as required?

Should the panel fabricator supply and mount, for all panel instruments, an engraved 3-ply laminated plastic nameplate (say, white on black core)? Are the edges bevelled? Is the minimum size of characters acceptable (e.g., 3/16 in. high)?

Should the standard specify that nameplates for all panel devices are to be attached with adhesives only in clean room environments? And they are to be mechanically attached with rivets or screws in all other areas?

The purpose of ISA-RP60.6, Nameplates, Labels, and Tags for Control Centers, is to assist the designer in choosing and specifying the method of identifying items that are mounted on a control panel.

Graphic Displays

Is a graphic display required?

Is the graphic display a true representation of the process?

Note: ISA-S5.5 establishes a system of such graphic symbols. Such a standard complements, whenever possible, ISA standards S5.1 and S5.3, RP60.5, and ANSI/ISA-S51.1 (see Appendix B).

Electrical

Is the wiring arranged so that all wires coming into the panel go to individual terminals?

Are these wires marked as shown on the drawings?

For internal wiring, should the standard request that not more than two wires go to one terminal point?

Should all wires be identified at each end with a permanent marker indicating the wire number as shown on the drawings?

Should the standard ensure that no wire splicing is permitted in cable ducts or anywhere in panel except on identified terminal blocks?

Are terminal strips in compliance with the plant's requirements?

How many spare terminals are required? For example: At least 25% or 10 spare terminal points, whichever is greater, should be provided on each strip unless otherwise specified.

Is a grounding lug provided to accept a ground wire? Should it be mounted in close proximity to the power distribution panel?

Are all terminals suitably protected so as to make accidental touching of live parts unlikely? Is an exception allowed in locations where access to the live parts is through an enclosure not normally open except for electrical maintenance?

Where 24-V DC power supplies are required to power instrument loops, is the panel manufacturer required to supply and install a dual power supply system? Is that system protected by diodes in case one of the two should fail? Is each power supply unit sufficient to power all loops in the panel and have at least 25% spare capacity? Does each of the two power supplies have an output contact to alarm in case of failure?

Should all 120-V AC wiring be run in cable ducts separate from low voltage wiring? Should thermocouple, 24-V DC, and 120-V AC wiring be run in three separate cable ducts?

Should the panel fabricator be required to furnish and install multiple circuit power distribution panels, as required, with circuit breakers?

Should the circuit breakers be of a type approved by the plant?

Should at least two tool receptacles (with ground fault protection) and two overhead lights, with switches, be provided for each 8 feet (2.5 m) of panel length?

Should the power for panel-mounted instruments and for back-of-panel instruments be normally provided, by 3-prong grounded plug and flexible cord, to conveniently located receptacles? Should all other wiring be hard wired to terminals unless otherwise specified on drawings?

Should each instrument loop have its own power supply disconnect switch to enable servicing without affecting other loops? Should the disconnect include its own overload protection device (e.g., 0.5-A fuse)?

Where a conduit, raceway, cable, or other conductor system crosses a boundary between hazardous areas of different classification or between a hazardous area and a nonhazardous area, should vents or seals or both be provided to ensure that no flammable atmospheres or substances can be transmitted through the conduit or cable across such a boundary?

Should the standard clearly recommend that areas of high fire risk be avoided when locating panels?

To ensure that the safety of equipment used in hazardous areas is not jeopardized, should the panel manufacturer have the responsibility to ensure that:

1. only certified equipment is installed in hazardous areas, and
2. the code requirements in the control panel are strictly followed?

Should the standard recommend that for intrinsically safe applications:

1. all cables carrying intrinsically safe (IS) circuits are not run alongside other cables;
2. no intrinsically safe circuit cable is terminated in the same enclosure or terminal block housing as the nonintrinsically safe wiring;
3. field wiring terminals for intrinsically safe circuits in control room areas, panels, etc., are segregated from other nonintrinsically safe field wiring terminals and located in separate enclosures;
4. unused intrinsically safe circuit cables (even if only temporarily) are disconnected and removed from equipment at both ends;
5. at the control panel, IS cables are bonded together and to ground;
6. spare cores in a multicore cable are connected to IS ground in the control panel only, which is normally the safe area, and elsewhere are fully insulated; and
7. all intrinsically safe cables, wiring, and other equipment is positively identified?

Will the selection, sizing, and color coding of the wires be left to the code requirements in effect at the site and also to the preferences of the maintenance personnel at the plant? Should the standard, instead, be more specific and define additional requirements? For example:

On 120-V AC power and discrete control signal wiring:

1. all power wiring should be #12 gauge;
2. all discrete control signal wiring should be #14 gauge;
3. all such wiring should be stranded copper, cross-linked polyethylene-insulated, 600-V minimum insulation, 90°C. minimum temperature rating;
4. the phase or hot conductor (L1 or H) is black;
5. the neutral conductor (L2 or N) is white; and
6. the grounded conductor (G or GND) is green.

Purging

Where purging is required for pneumatic or electrical panels for either control room or field mounting, is the purging done with clean, dry, oil-free instrument air?

Does the standard ensure that purging conforms to the pressure-sensing and interlocking requirements of the electrical code in effect at the site and ISA-S12.4 (see Appendix B)?

Does the air purge ensure that there are at least three changes of air per hour in the enclosure? Is the purge meter visible? Is it adjustable from the front of the closed panel?

Pneumatics

Do all of the external connections terminate at a bulkhead plate?

Is each bulkhead termination permanently identified according to the instrument loop diagrams?

Are both ends of tubing identified by permanent markers according to the instrument loop diagrams?

Is it required that a minimum number of bulkhead connections, complete with their bulkhead union fittings, be provided on the bulkhead plate (say, at least 20% or 6 spare bulkhead connections, whichever is greater)?

For panels that require purging, should one bulkhead termination be provided for connection of the purge meter?

Should all tubing be identified by a stainless steel tag at all instrument terminations and at all fittings? Should the tag bear the tubing identification shown on the documentation? In the absence of this identification number, should the tag bear the identification number of the instrument to which it connects and the function (i.e., input, output, air supply, etc.)?

Should the standard recommend that all tubing be installed in a neat and orderly manner, free from kinks and flats?

Should all tubing be run with adequate support? Should all valves have rigid support?

Should all tubing be arranged to provide easy removal and maintenance of instruments and accessories?

Should the standard define the color coding requirements? For example,

Air supply to instrument — red

Transmitted measurement — orange

Controller output to valve — yellow

All other signals — natural

Note: In the absence of plant standards, ISA-RP60.9 may be used.

For the requirements of the air supply system inside the panel, is a 2-in. instrument air supply header required? Should it have 1/4-in. takeoffs equipped with shutoff valves for each instrument and a 1/4-in. drain valve at its lowest point?

Is there a requirement for a number of spare extra takeoffs with shutoff valves to be installed (e.g., at least 20%)?

Should the panel manufacturer supply and install a duplex air filter regulator complete with 2-in. input pressure gage and two 2-in. output pressure gages in each panel? Should these units have an output of 20 psig (or 140 kPag) and be capable of handling inputs over the range of 40 to 100 psig (275 to 700 kPag)?

Should the capacity of each filter regulator be at least 25% greater than required by the instruments installed in the panel?

Should a pressure relief valve, capable of handling the combined maximum capacity of the two filter regulators, be installed? Should it be located on the downstream side of the filter regulators, before the takeoff points? What should the relief valve be set at (e.g., at 25 psig or 175 kPag)?

For field panels where pneumatic instruments are employed, should the panel fabricator supply and install an identical air supply system to the control room panel whenever three or more air users are installed in or on the panel?

Should the panel fabricator ensure that all lines installed are clean, both internally and externally? And that all joints are free from leaks by performing pressure tests in accordance with ISA-RP 7.1 (see Appendix B)?

Should Teflon™ tape be the only jointing material used on the pipe threads of fittings, valves, etc., in the panels? Should Teflon™ (tape or paste) or any pipe sealant not be used in tube fittings to avoid plugging pneumatic components?

Additional information on this subject may be obtained from ISA-RP60.9, Piping Guide for Control Centers.

Certification

Should the panel manufacturer normally obtain from the appropriate authorities all necessary inspections for the approval of the wiring and equipment supplied and installed?

Should the panel manufacturer bear the cost of all such inspections and approvals?

Should all deficiencies noted by such inspections be corrected by the panel fabricator at no cost to the owner?

After all approvals have been obtained, and if so required, should the panel fabricator affix to the panel his or her shop-approved label (for example, UL in the US and CSA in Canada), as well as union labels covering electrical and pipefitting, along with any other labels deemed necessary?

Should such labels be affixed prior to panel checkout by the owner?

Inspection and Testing

Should it be noted in the standard that the owner's representative may visit the shop of the panel manufacturer at any time during the panel fabrication in order to check progress and/or inspect the panel and its internal components?

Upon completion of all assembly work, should the panel fabricator thoroughly check the panel mechanically and functionally prior to the arrival of the owner's representative? Should the standard ensure that high voltage testing equipment must not be used?

Should the panel fabricator, as a minimum, perform the following checks?

1. The physical appearance and mechanical construction of the panel, inside and outside
2. All nameplates for correct location, spelling, wording, and size of letters
3. Any signs of physical damage or negligence
4. All electrical power circuits for correct operation
5. All air supply lines for correct operation
6. Leaks in pneumatic lines
7. All electrical and pneumatic circuits for correct functional operation, loop by loop
8. All alarm circuits for correct operation

Should the panel fabricator correct any errors and omissions at no cost to the owner?

Would modifications and/or changes to the panel at the request of the owner's representative be charged or credited, as the case may be, for the amount of labor and/or material involved only?

Shipping

To avoid damage during shipping, should all tray-mounted and plug-in instruments be removed, reboxed, and shipped separately in tagged boxes?

Will the panel fabricator ship the panel by air-ride truck, suitably protected for shipping?

Should any and all damages to the panel, complete with instruments and/or instruments shipped separately, caused by inadequate protection for shipping be made good by the panel fabricator at no cost to the owner?

Note: ISA-RP60.11, Crating, Shipping, and Handling for Control Centers, provides a guide to the general methods available for protection against physical damage, vibration, pilferage, and climate. It also describes procedures and problems involved in handling, shipping, and storage.

CONTROL ROOM REQUIREMENTS

Control room design, in general, must meet two basic requirements:

1. The codes and regulations in effect at the site
2. Good engineering practice

A set of corporate standards should provide the guidelines to achieve these two requirements.

First and foremost, all control room equipment must meet the electrical code in effect at the site and bear the approval label of the local electrical authority (e.g., UL, CSA, etc.).

Control rooms form the nerve center of a plant. They are generally air conditioned and pressurized with clean air. Temperature and humidity are controlled to preset conditions (see ANSI/ISA-S71.01, Environmental Conditions for Process Measurement and Control Systems: Temperature and Humidity). When designing control rooms, the designer must ensure that their design and use conforms to good engineering practice and to company standards (in the absence of such standards, a good source of information is ISA's RP60 series of recommended practices for control centers).

ISA has published seven recommended practices that are related to control rooms (also referred to as control centers). See Appendix B for titles in the RP60 Series.

A checklist has been developed to help the producer of a corporate standard identify and address the points that are related to the specification of control room needs from an I&C point of view. Obviously, this list will have to be modified and adapted to reflect the need and culture of each corporation. This checklist, as shown in this section, has been categorized as follows:

1. Design
2. Security
3. Fire Protection
4. Air Conditioning
5. Electrical/electronic
6. Communication

Design

Is easy (and safe) access available to bring the control room equipment into place?

Are the control room doors are of the self-closing type?

Is a clock required?

Is there a minimum of 3 ft (1 m) clearance between the back of any panel and the nearest obstruction?

Is there a need for a minimum of two sockets in a control room? Should socket outlets with ground fault protection be provided behind all panels for portable electrical tools?

Has the design ensured that the process lines do not enter the control center except for instrument air (this is a safety requirement)?

Is the air conditioning unit outside (to avoid noise)?

Is the cabling (high voltage vs. low voltage) routed for the avoidance of electrical noise?

Is the control room located, whenever possible, away from sources of vibration? Is it completely protected from heavy rain, external fire-fighting water, etc.? Is the control room required to be earthquake-proof?

Has the area classification been taken into account when locating the control room?

Where required and where economically justifiable, has the control room been provided with a false floor for passage of cables and/or tubing? In that case, are smoke detectors installed underneath the false floor? Are floor panel materials flame-resistant and anti-static?

Security

Is the control room a high security area where restricted entrance is required? How is this restriction to be maintained?

Would only approved personnel be allowed in the control room? Is the use of badges or magnetic cards essential?

Is access to software part of the security system?

Should duplicate software copies be stored in a separate location? What is the accessability to these storage areas?

Fire Protection

What are the fire hazards? Can the fire hazards be eliminated?

Does the standard ensure that the fire protection system in the control center conform to the requirements of the local codes and regulations as well as the requirements of the insurance companies?

Does the fire protection also protect the operator in the control room (i.e., the fluid used in the fire protection should not harm personnel)?

Would all HVAC functions and nonessential power services shut off in the event of fire?

Does the design ensure the availability of fire-fighting equipment? Are hand-operated extinguishers of dry CO_2 provided at the entrance to the control room? Is the use of automatic fire-extinguishing systems a requirement?

Have other disciplines looked at noncontrol items such as exits, emergency lighting, etc.?

Has the fire hazard been reduced by ensuring that power is cut off as soon as a fire is detected (fires could start from electrical faults)? Has the designed ensured that power supplies can be manually or automatically isolated? Are sensors required?

Should the standard recommend the availability of handy fire-fighting equipment? Is there an appropriate response plan in case of emergency?

Is the control room (including the floor) constructed of noncombustible material to avoid damage from outside fires? Typically, one-hour fire resistance is acceptable unless the applicable regulations require a stricter fire resistance (this includes doors, roof, etc.). Does the furniture consist of metal chairs and cabinets? Is the upholstery made of fire-retardant materials?

Is a separate area for high-risk devices (such as printers) required for control rooms for critical applications? Is paper storage kept at a minimum in the control room?

Should the standard state that basements are not recommended (since they may accumulate water from fire fighting or from rain)?

Where water may accumulate under the floor, is a water detector required?

Is there a need to ensure that the ventilation system is separate for the control room?

Should the storage of records (or tapes) be in fire-proof safes? Should the safes be in the control room or in a remote area?

Is a sign posted to advise all personnel that smoking is not allowed in the control room? Are appliances (such as coffee makers) allowed in a specific area of the control room?

Is the fire detection system designed by qualified fire protection specialists?

Air Conditioning

Is the air conditioning (a/c) unit sized to maintain temperature and humidity within the requirements of the control systems (for example, around 75°F or 24°C and 50% RH)?

Has the design ensured that the a/c unit will supply clean air in the control center? Clean air includes air filtration (filtering out particles of five microns and larger) as well as the removal of any dangerous gases that could seep into the control center.

Did the designer keep in mind that power failure will stop the a/c unit and start a heat buildup? Has consideration been given to having more than one a/c unit do the job in case a unit fails?

Should the a/c stop in case of fire? Should there be a manually operated switch (protected from accidental triggering) clearly identified and located near the door to shut down the a/c and computer power in case of emergency?

Where is the a/c air intake located? Are there potential hazards? Is the ventilation system of control rooms drawn from a safe and clean source?

Is the a/c capable of forcing air from the control room openings at a preset velocity (e.g., 60 ft/min, 20 m/min) with all doors and windows open? The pressure and velocity requirements need not be met simultaneously.

Do the a/c requirements meet the environment to which it is subjected? For example, the control room may be air conditioned with at least 15 changes per hour and be pressurized with clean air to 0.1 to 0.25 in. W.C. (or 3 to 6 mm W.C.). However, as a general rule, temperature and humidity conditions should conform to ISA-S71.01 (see Appendix B).

Should the standard clearly state that pressurized rooms located in hazardous locations must conform to the code and statutory requirements in effect at the site (such as NFPA 496) and should be clearly marked with:

1. a notice worded "WARNING–PRESSURIZED ROOM";
2. a warning at both the control switch for the source of pressurization and at the relevant points of isolation indicating the time T in minutes for which purging is to operate before the electrical supply can be switched on or restored; and
3. a warning at all entrances to the pressurized room against the introduction of any flammable materials?

Electrical/Electronic Considerations

Is all cabling adequately sealed to prevent water entry?

When both electrical power services and control signal cabling are distributed using subfloor cable trays, does the design ensure that the tray for electrical power distribution and the tray for control and communication signals are kept at a minimum of 3 ft (1 m) apart? And cross at right angles only, in order to minimize the potential of electrical noise generation?

Has the designer ensured the correct implementation of electrical peripheral functions such as grounding, lighting, and the prevention of electronic interference?

Are all power and chassis grounds and cable shields connected to the grounding electrode?

Has the standard considered the lighting requirements (for instance, lighting for CRT areas is less than for printers and disk drives, and for maintenance purposes, high lighting is needed)?

For example:

The lighting of control rooms may be provided by variable ballast, glare-reducing, fluorescent fixtures mounted above parabolic egg-crate-type ceiling panels. There should be at least two independently controlled circuits: one for general room lighting and the second for panel lighting. These should be from 60 to 75 ft candles and 100 to 120 ft candles, respectively. In addition, video displays, being light emitters, require about 45 ft candles and will be provided on a separate circuit.

Are dimmers used to control different sections of the control center? Does the standard note that the lighting circuit, when dimmers are used, should be separate from the power circuit to the control system to avoid electrical noise?

If lighting is not supplied from the UPS, is emergency light provided in the control room?

To prevent electronic interference, are microcomputers and networks far from high-power electrical equipment?

Should data processing equipment such as personal computers and PLCs be connected to a dedicated isolation transformer? If not, have the effects of noise and reduced voltage levels, as well as the recommendations of the equipment supplier, been considered before a final decision is made?

Communication

Does the standard clearly state that walkie-talkies are not to be used in control rooms that contain electronic equipment, such as PLCs and computers? Has a sign to that effect been installed on the door?

To avoid the effect of electrical noise generated by walkie-talkies, is an FM transceiver, with a roof-top mounted antenna, supplied for communication with field operators who are using walkie-talkies? Are they operating on a unique assigned frequency to avoid interference from other nearby units? Is a movable microphone with long cords (or telephone handsets) provided on each console?

OPERATING INSTRUCTIONS

The operating instructions contain the description of the operation of the plant. This document is multidisciplinary, and it should be decided at the philosophy stage of a corporate standard where the responsibility should reside. Generally, it is under process engineering, but, for the purpose of a control engineering corporate standard, the control portion of it should be addressed.

The involvement of control engineering in this document consists basically of a verification that the contents of the document and the existing functions of the control system match. It is a good idea for control engineering personnel to discuss with the operators their point of view on the operating instructions.

The following questions will help the control engineer ensure quality operating instructions that cover the I&C portion.

Are all monitoring and control instructions documented? Are they clear? Are they complete?

Are operating instructions compatible with other documents, such as P&IDs, loop diagrams, and interlock diagrams?

Will the operating instructions be available to the operator? Will the operators review these instructions?

CHAPTER 6

Detailed Engineering—Specification of Instruments and Controls

GENERAL CONSIDERATIONS

Part of the instrumentation and control (I&C) designer's function is to understand the process and to implement the required control system with the proper instruments. Therefore, it is necessary to provide guidelines in the corporate standards for achieving this. The specification of instrumentation and control equipment, as covered in this chapter, represents the more common types of equipment, which should give sufficient guidelines for the preparer of the corporate standard for items not covered in this book.

The correct selection of instruments and controls should typically consider the process and plant requirements, good engineering practice, and compliance with all code, statutory, and plant requirements in effect at the site.

This chapter will look at the specification of I&C equipment. The guidelines used will help the preparer of a corporate standard in assembling a preliminary document on the subject.

The chapter is divided into five main segments. Such a breakdown gives a reasonable starting point for a preliminary standard.

1. General Considerations
   Terminology
   Hazardous areas
   Air supply
   Electrical power supply
2. Field Instrumentation
   Transmitters
   Pressure measurement
   Temperature measurement
   Flow measurement
   Level measurement
   Weight measurement
   Analyzers
   Control valves
   Pressure relief devices
3. Control Room Instrumentation
   Controllers
   Recorders
   Annunciators

4. Alarm and Trip Systems
   Design
   Reliability
   Documentation
   Testing and maintenance
5. Programmable Electronic Systems
   Implementation
   System selection
   Design considerations
   Testing and maintenance

It should be mentioned at this point that two ISA standards, ISA-S71.01 and ISA-S71.04, cover the environmental conditions for process measurement and control systems for temperature, humidity, and airborne contaminants (see Appendix B).

In many cases, corporations require that a given instrument be of a specific make. The selection is based on plant experience and the desire to minimize the variety of equipment, thereby reducing the inventory of spare parts, the training required, and the time taken for maintenance. Throughout this chapter, recommendations are included, which are shown to indicate the format of a corporate standard. They are not to be used as a guide in design or as a training tool in understanding and selecting I&C equipment.

As a starting point, it should be mentioned in any corporate standard that the plant's instrument numbering system should conform to a common plant standard or, in its absence, to ISA-S5.1.

Another item of importance is the definition of which measuring units to use. There will be cases in which two units may be used simultaneously (which may create "translation"problems). Many industries are moving towards the SI units of measurement. Whichever system is used, it may be a good idea to add a section in the standard that lists these units. The following table may be an example of such units. In some cases, a conversion table that shows SI units and other units may also be incorporated.

Terminology

It is important to ensure that the terminology used in describing function of instrumentation is uniform. ISA-S51.1, Process Instrumentation Terminology, includes definitions for many specialized terms used in the industrial process industries, such as accuracy, dead band, drift, hysteresis, linearity, repeatability, and reproducibility. This standard assures that vendors and users speak the same language when referring to product specifications.

Table 6-1. Suggested Units of Measurement Definition

Description	Units of Measurement
Pressure	Pa
Flow	L/min
Temperature	deg. C
Volume	L
Sound	dB
Mass	kg

Hazardous Areas

Electrical instruments and systems located in hazardous environments must conform to the electrical codes and statutory requirements in effect at the site.

In the US and Canada, hazardous environments are classified according to Classes, Groups, and Divisions. Three Classes define the kinds of hazardous materials that could be present: Class I for flammable gases and vapors, Class II for combustible dusts, and Class III for flyings (particles that are more a fire hazard than an explosion hazard). Seven Groups (A, B, C, D, E, F, and G) list materials of similar hazard. For further details and a list of materials, refer to the applicable electrical code. Finally, two Divisions define the probability that the hazard is present: Division 1 for hazards that are expected to be present under normal operating conditions and Division 2 for hazards that are expected to be present only in the event of failure in the plant. Information on the subject may be found in ISA standards S12.1, S12.4, RP12.6, S12.10, S12.11, S12.12, and S12.13 (see Appendix B).

In Europe, the classification is different, but there are similarities. There are no Classes, and the existing area classification deals only with risks due to flammable gases and vapors. There are no specific area classifications for dusts and flyings (as in North America). There are two Groups and three Zones (formerly called Divisions). Group I is reserved for mining use only, and Group II is used for all other industrial applications. Group II is then subgrouped into three categories (IIA, IIB, and IIC) according to gas type. Finally, Zone 0 is for continuous hazard locations, Zone 1 is for intermittent hazard locations, and Zone 2 is for hazards that occur only under abnormal conditions. Zones 0 and 1 are similar to the North American Division 1, while Zone 2 is similar to Division 2.

It is the function of the designer to ensure that the equipment installed and the wiring method used conform to the recommendations of the electrical code in effect at the site and with the area classification shown on the plant engineering records. A corporate standard may be specific as to what must be used under the different classifications. As an example of such a recommendation, Table 6-2 gives a good indication of the possible solutions. A similar table may be used in a corporate standard.

Air Supply

Instrument air is required in most plants; it is generally used to drive control valves. In most designs, on instrument air failure, control valves would normally go to their fail-safe positions (probably shutting the plant down). Designs that do not follow this philosophy need to be carefully assessed to ensure that no hazardous conditions may exist.

The importance of instrument air necessitates that, in most cases, a section in the corporate standard define some minimum requirements. The quality of instrument air is essential to the correct operation of such devices. Dirty air will plug the sensitive pneumatic systems, and moisture can freeze. As a guide, instrument air should conform to ISA-S7.3. Also, ISA-S71.02 provides users and manufacturers with the means to specify the pneumatic parameters of an air supply system to which a specified measurement may be connected. In addition, most instrument air systems must conform to certain other quality requirements, such as those found in ISA standards S7.3, S7.4, and RP7.7 (see Appendix B).

Typically, an instrument air supply system consists of air generation, air drying, and air distribution. The air to these systems is provided usually from an air com-

Table 6-2. Wiring Methods and Types of Protection

Location	Wiring Methods	Type of Apparatus
	CLASS I LOCATIONS	
DIVISION 1	• Threaded rigid or steel intermediate metal conduit or mineral insulated cable (Type MI) with approved fittings. • All boxes, fittings and joints must be threaded and explosion-proof. • Approved flexible fittings where necessary for motors etc. NOTE: Wiring or intrinsically safe systems need meet requirements for ordinary (nonhazardous) locations only. • All conduit 2 in. or larger and conduit or cable entering enclosures containing arcing, sparking, or ignition cable hot surfaces must be sealed within 18 in. of the enclosure. Cables not capable of transmitting gases and vapors need not be sealed. • All conduit leaving the Division 1 location must be sealed.	• Explosion-proof • Pumped or pressurized for Division 1 • Intrinsically Safe apparatus
DIVISION 2	• Threaded rigid or steel intermediate metal conduit, mineral insulated cable, metallic or non metallic sheathed cable (Type MC, SNM defined in NEC) or enclosed gasketted busways. • Type TC tray cable or PLTC tray cable. • Boxes and fittings explosion proof only if they contain ignition capable arcs or hot surfaces. NOTE: Wiring in circuits which under normal conditions do not release enough energy to cause ignition of the gases or vapors which may be present need meet only requirements for ordinary locations. • Seals: For explosion-proof enclosures same as Division 1, and in all conduit or cable runs leaving Division 2 and entering nonhazardous locations.	• Explosion proof if apparatus contains ignition capable arcs or hot surfaces. • General purpose apparatus if there are no ignition capable arcs or hot surfaces exposed to atmosphere. • Purged or pressurized for Division 2.
	CLASS II LOCATIONS	

DIVISION 1	• Rigid or intermediate metal conduit or mineral insulated cable (Type MI) with approved fittings.
	• Fittings and boxes shall have threaded bosses for connection of conduit or cable fittings and shall have no openings through which dust may enter. If taps, joints, or terminal connections are made in box, it must be approved for Class II locations (dust-ignition proof).
		• Dust-ignition-proof (heavy dust-tight construction), purged, or intrinsically safe.
		• Maximum Surface Temperature.
		• (See **Note 1**).
		  Group E—200°C
		  Group F—150/200°C
		  Group G—120/165°C

DIVISION 2	• Rigid or intermediate metal conduit, electrical metallic tubing • Mineral insulated cable • Sheathed cable, types MC, ALS, CS, or SNM • Dust-tight wire ways	• Dust-tight (can be gasketted sheet metal; Type tests less onerous than for dust ignition proof). • General purpose if incapable of causing ignition by arcs or hot surfaces. (Temperature 120°C) • Maximum surface temperature same as for Division 1
	CLASS III LOCATIONS	
DIVISION 1	• Rigid or intermediate metal conduit, Type MI, MC cables. • Boxes and fittings must be tight to prevent escape of sparks or burning material.	• Tight covers, no holes • Rotating machinery must be totally enclosed. • Surface temperature limits 120°/165°C (See **Note 1**) Intrinsically Safe apparatus
DIVISION 2	• Essentially same as Division 1	• Essentially same as Division 1

Note 1. Lower temperature applies to apparatus subject to overload (motors, transformers) in normal operating condition. Higher temperature applies under abnormal conditions, or to apparatus not subject to overload.

pressor followed by an aftercooler and a prefilter. At this point the air generated is defined as "plant air." This part of the supply system is generally not the responsibility of the instrument designer, and its scope is therefore not covered under a typical I&C corporate standard. One concern of the instrument designer is oil. The designer may want to recommend a nonlubricated compressor.

Air drying basically treats the plant air to "instrument air" quality. This is normally done with an air dryer. The three most common types of air dryers are adsorbent, absorbent, and refrigerated. The decision to have to include in the corporate standard a definition of the specific type to use is debatable. On one hand, having the same type across all plants within the corporation facilitates maintenance and reduces the learning curve. On the other hand, no two applications are identical, and needs vary from plant to plant. This part of the supply system may be covered either by mechanical engineering or by the I&C function. It depends on the engineering structure within the corporation and on the experience and knowledge of its engineering personnel. A summarized comparison between these three is shown in Table 6-3. As a rule of thumb, the pressure drop across the entire drying and cleaning system should typically not be more than 10 psig (70 kPag).

Air supply distribution systems generally consist of air headers, normally at pressures of 90 to 100 psig (620 to 690 kPag). This part of the supply system generally

Table 6-3. Common Air Dryer Types

1.
Type: Absorbent (deliquescent desiccant)
Principle: Uses a hygroscopic desiccant that is consumed and generally requires a prefilter and an after-filter.
Advantages:
- Low initial cost
- Simple to use
- Has no moving parts
Limitations:
- Limited dew point suppression
- Desiccant must be replaced periodically
- Requires high maintenance since the desiccant is generally manually drained daily

2.
Type: Adsorbent (regenerative desiccant)
Principle: Uses a regenerative type of hygroscopic desiccant and generally requires alternate flow paths (beds), one in use while the other is being purged of its water; also requires a prefilter and an after-filter.
Advantages:
- Low dew points
Limitations:
- High initial cost
- High operating cost
- Periodic servicing of desiccant towers

3.
Type: Refrigerated
Principle: Uses mechanical refrigerated cooling
Advantages:
- Constant dew point
- Low maintenance
- Low operating cost
- Not damaged by oil vapors
Limitations:
- Limited dew points

falls under the responsibility of the piping designer, and its scope is not covered under an I&C corporate standard.

The following questions may assist the developer of a corporate standard in preparing a section on the subject of instrument air.

Is the compressor sized to handle 150% of the total estimated instrument air requirements? If not, what criteria are used for calculating its required capacity?

Could the compressor contaminate the air with oil? (Note: This type of compressor should not be used; permanent contamination may occur and instrument problems will develop.)

Is the instrument air used for instruments only? Are other users, such as pneumatic tools, cleaning, etc., using plant air?

Is the instrument air system independent of the plant air system?

Is clean, dry, oil-free instrument air supplied at a minimum pressure of 90 psig (620 kPag), with a dew point of 20°F (10°C) below the ambient winter design temperature at atmospheric pressure?

Is the instrument air dryer designed for automatic regeneration? Does it have a prefilter and an after-filter?

Does each instrument air system also include an air receiver that protects against loss of air compression and is independent of any noninstrument air users? If not, has the effect of immediate air loss been assessed and deemed acceptable?

Is the receiver for each system sized to provide acceptable hold capacity in the event of loss of instrument air supply? Is it sufficient (e.g., minimum five (5) minutes capacity)?

Is an alarm provided to indicate when the air pressure in the system has fallen — for example, when the air pressure in the system falls to 70 psig (500 kPag)?

Are header take-off points mounted at the top of air headers to feed the branches? If not, has the possibility of plugged air lines been identified?

Are shutoff valves located at the branches to allow individual isolation of the instrument air supply? Are these shutoff valves easily accessible to maintenance?

Should the designer specify an air set that consists of a filter/regulator located at each instrument using instrument air? Should these air sets be supplied with the instrument? If supplied with the instrument and since not all instruments are from the same supplier, is there a problem in having different types or styles at the plant?

Is instrument air piping routed within 25 ft of each device that requires instrument air supply? At which point does instrument air tubing connect piping with the instruments?

Is the instrument air supply sized to meet the requirements of all instrument air users? Does this include future requirements?

How are air supply requirements estimated? Note: The corporate standard may require that an accurate calculation of instrument air requirements be performed, which tends to be a time-consuming activity. Or, the corporate standard may provide a rule of thumb, which includes typical leaks and instrument purges, to be used for calculating air supply requirements. For example:

$55(s)ft^3/h$ $(1.5(s)m^3/h)$ for each instrument user

$180(s)ft^3/h$ $(5(s)m^3/h)$ for each piston operated on-off valve

Is there a need to provide some basic rules to ensure instrument air reliability? If so, has scheduled testing been determined? What is the frequency of such testing?

Note: For both pneumatic and electric supplies, ISA-S71.02 establishes uniform classifications of power to be supplied to process measurement and control equipment. This standard provides a means of specifying the pneumatic and electrical parameters of a power system.

Electrical Power Supply

Electrical power supply services are required for all modern control systems and are covered in the content of a typical corporate standard. These power supply services must conform to the requirements of all regulatory bodies having jurisdiction at the site and should be approved as such. If this is not possible, approval of the local electrical authority must be obtained. Such needs are generally highlighted in the corporate standard.

Overview

A few general questions may provide a starting point in defining the content of the preliminary document.

Is the power supply to individual equipment capable of isolation by means of individual circuit breakers or fuses? Should these devices be clearly identified and labelled?

Are supplies to instruments controlled and protected in groups according to the class of service? As an example, the following two classifications may be observed: critical (for items that affect safety, health, and the environment) and noncritical (for other items such as production and quality). Other classifications may be preferred (see Figure 6-1).

Are ground circuits provided and connected to ground through grounding electrodes? Should the standard always ask the users to refer to control equipment vendor recommendations and experience?

Is lightning protection provided where required, with lightning rods located at the high points of the plant structure?

Should each loop be individually fused at the terminal block (to allow isolation for servicing of any loop without disruption of the remainder)?

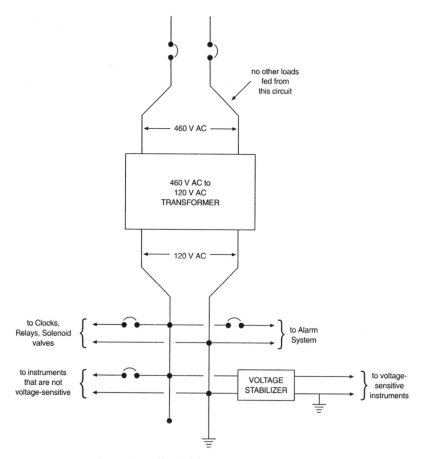

Figure 6-1. Typical Instrument Power Supply

Should only quick-disconnect, fused terminal blocks be required? If not, what protects the loop? How is an individual loop isolated?

Where smart transmitters are not used, should two-wire transmitters be specified wherever possible? Where would the loop power supply be located? In the control room or in the interface area?

Effects of Power Loss

Where the process being controlled would be affected by a power loss on the control system and system outage cannot be tolerated, an uninterruptible power supply (UPS) should be considered. If there is no UPS on the control system, the preparer of the standard (and eventually the designer) needs to consider the following points.

What happens to the process and to the control system on sudden power restart following a power loss? Are there any unwanted effects?

Would the control system outputs trigger unwanted and sometimes dangerous signals?

Does the program restart in orderly fashion?

What happens to the memory? What happens to the programs? Does the integrity of the software remain?

What is the effect of the time delay between the processor first coming into action to control outputs and by a memory update?

Are any safety aspects to be considered? What is the effect on the process under control?

Is there a need for two separate sources of electrical power? Should such separation or redundancy consider routing, reliability, circuit protection, etc.?

Should the time needed to switch from one feeder to the other be considered? Would this time affect the UPS retention time?

Quality of Power Supply

In most industrial applications, it is particularly important that quality and integrity of the power supply be maintained at a very high level for process computers and their ancillary hardware. Such importance should be reflected in the corporate standard. The standard may specifically state that power protection can be achieved through the use of such devices as an on-line UPS, an isolating transformer, or a surge suppressor. The questions that follow should assist in the generation of a corporate standard on this subject.

Should a properly sized and installed voltage stabilizer (such as a ferro-resonant isolating transformer) provide the suitable power conditioning for this application?

What insurances are required that the ferro-resonant transformer is not oversized? Is the sizing of transformers generally done in accordance with the recommendations of the control system vendor?

Does the electrical service specification generally meet or exceed that of the most sensitive device served?

Can problems be isolated through the isolation of instrument supply and signal circuits?

Is the system capable of reducing the effects of power system load changes and switching transients?

Is there a need to separate feeds and their functions? Some plants may find this an extreme and therefore not required, while others may find this separation (and its associated cost) justifiable. For example, should there be four separate feeds — one to clocks, relays, and solenoid valves; a second to instruments that are not voltage sensitive and to instruments with built-in voltage regulators; a third to alarm system and horns; and a fourth to a voltage stabilizer and then onto all instruments (see Figure 6-1)?

Should loop power supply voltage be specified? For both analog and digital circuits? Should it be specific (for example, 28-V DC ±0.5 volts with a maximum AC ripple of 0.1 V peak to peak)?

Uninterruptible Power Supply (UPS)

Where it is unacceptable that all control circuits simply fail safe in the event of a power supply failure, an uninterruptible battery-powered supply (UPS) is generally required to maintain all instruments and control equipment in operation. The corporate standard may then need to define the requirements of such a UPS. The following questions should help the person preparing such a standard to identify the main points to consider.

How much extra capacity should be provided in the UPS to safely shut down the plant? In some cases, especially where the requirement is for large time-retention capacity, it may prove more cost-effective to provide a combination of a UPS and a diesel-driven generator. However, due consideration should be given to the consequences should the diesel-driven generator fail to start.

What are the options on UPS failure? Is a bypass static switch transferring power supply to on-line power sufficient? Should this transfer be manual or automatic? Following this transfer, should consideration be given to the quality of raw on-line power (and, hence, the possible requirements for a ferroresonant transformer)?

Should all the active electronic components of the UPS be of the solid-state type?

Should the UPS be of the on-line type (i.e., the commercial AC source is converted to DC, the DC supplies the battery charger and power to the inverter, and the load is continuously supplied by the inverter)? Upon failure of the commercial AC power, the load is then supplied by the inverter which, without any switching obtains its power from the batteries.

Should the UPS installation require two separate service feeders (the UPS is serviced from one service feeder and the bypass AC, through the static transfer switch, is serviced from a separate service feeder)?

Should the standard ensure that the UPS be approved by a recognized electrical authority (such as UL, CSA, etc.)?

Should the AC to AC efficiency be specified before selecting a unit (e.g., 95%)?

Should all UPS components be protected from incoming surges, internal faults, and overloads?

What displays and controls should a UPS panel have as a minimum (for example: input AC voltmeter, output AC voltmeter, output AC ammeter, output AC frequency, manual bypass switch)?

What alarms should the UPS provide to maintenance (for example: dry contact opens on UPS failure, dry contact opens when AC is fed from automatic transfer switch or from the manual bypass during maintenance, etc.)?

Is maintenance access an important consideration? Should all wiring and maintenance be accessible from the front? What is the minimum access clearance at the front and at the back?

Are any special tools (or special training) to be supplied with the UPS?

Is there a limit on the noise generated (e.g., less than 60 dBA)?

Is the AC input always 120 V AC (or could it be 240 V AC)? Should this be a field-selectable choice?

What is the input voltage range (e.g., +10%, −15%)?

Is the rectifier of sufficient capacity to maintain the batteries charged and supply the full required load simultaneously? Can the batteries be recharged under full load at a certain percentage of full capacity (for example, 95%) within a preset time (e.g., 10 hrs)?

Is the DC output regulated within a predetermined and acceptable range (e.g., within a +/−1% with a max 2% RMS ripple)?

Are the batteries sealed and maintenance-free? If not, are any gases emitted by the batteries?

What is the required discharge time at rated load (e.g., 45 minutes)?

Is the automatic frequency regulation maintained within a preset range (e.g., ±0.1 Hz) under all load conditions?

What is the allowable steady-state voltage deviation (e.g., by more than ±3% with a 0 to 100% variation within 3 cycles)?

Is the static transfer switch:

1. solid state,
2. make before break type, and
3. completely removable with no interruption to the load?

Are all transfers bumpless?

What is the power factor (e.g., 0.8)?

How many sets of drawings and documents are required from vendors?

What are the UPS dimensions? What are the battery cabinet dimensions? What is the total weight? Can the UPS equipment be easily moved in place?

What are the temperature limits for the UPS components?

What location is required? Indoors? Is air conditioning required?

Electrical Supply Grounding

Grounding is an essential part of any modern control system. Unfortunately, in many cases, the correct implementation has been overlooked. The inclusion in the standard of a section to reflect the basic grounding requirements helps ensure quality installations and trouble-free operations.

The following questions will assist in the development of a corporate standard on this subject.

Is the grounding to be implemented following the vendor's recommendations? Should the vendor be required to check (or even approve) the final design to ensure correct implementation?

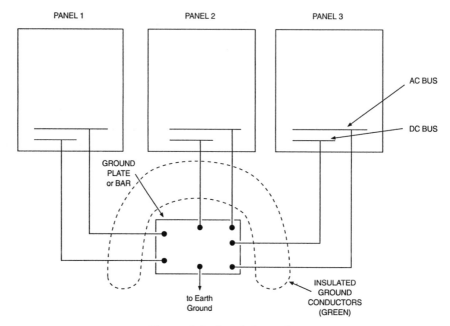

Figure 6-2. Panel Grounding

Is there a separate electrical power ground circuit? Does it provide a maximum impedance (e.g., 5 ohms) to ground?

Is the neutral of the instrument power supply system grounded via an insulated (green) grounding conductor to a location as close as possible to the grounding electrode?

Are the instrument circuit grounds tied to the same ground electrode that is used for power grounding (therefore ensuring that all instrument grounds are at the same potential)?

Should all spare conductors in a multiconductor cable be grounded so that they do not induce large voltage surges on signal circuits when nearby lightning strikes occur?

Is the grounding of cable shields for any system utilizing DC current usually terminated at a ground bus in the panelboard?

Should panelboards have one ground only for AC and DC? Or should separate AC and DC ground buses be implemented?

What is the typical size of a ground bus (e.g., 1/4-in. thick and 1 × 1-1/2 in. plate)? What is its contruction material (e.g., copper)? The corporate standard may rely on the information from the instrument vendor or may have its own preferences, with a typical sketch (see Figure 6-2).

FIELD INSTRUMENTATION

One of the larger parts of design activities is the selection of field instruments, such as transmitters, switches, and valves. A designer must keep many parameters in mind when such a selection is made. The corporate standard will cover concerns that are both general (and applicable to most industries) and specific to a particular industry or plant. The following general questions may help the producer of such a standard highlight the key parameters to be covered.

Should electrical approval be obtained from the authority having jurisdiction at the site? If not, does this affect the electrical code or insurance requirements?

Can the process connections for transmitters and switches be isolated through a shutoff valve? Are pulsation dampeners, siphons, and diaphragm seals used where needed? Are these requirements identified at the front-end engineering level, or are they left to the discretion of the designer at the detailed engineering stage?

Is the wiring or tubing in conformance with the information on the loop diagrams and in the installation specification? When should this conformance be checked—at the end of construction, just before start-up, or at preset milestones? Is this check done by the same person doing the work or should it be done by someone else?

Is the enclosure rating appropriate for the environment it is in? See Table 6-4 for US applications, Table 6-5 for Canadian applications, and Table 6-6 for European applications.

Table 6-4. NEMA Designations for US Applications

Type 1 : General Purpose—Indoor

Type 2 : Dripproof—Indoor

Type 3 : Dusttight, Raintight, and Sleet-or Ice-resistant—Outdoor

Type 3R : Rainproof and Sleet-or Ice-Resistant—Outdoor

Type 3S : Dusttight, Raintight, and Sleet-or Ice-proof—Outdoor

Type 4 : Watertight and Dusttight—Indoor and Outdoor

Type 4X : Watertight, Dusttight, and Corrosion-resistant—Indoor and Outdoor

Type 5 : Superseded by Type 12 for Control Apparatus

Type 6 : Submersible (occasional, temporary), Watertight, Dusttight and Sleet-or Ice-resistant—Indoor and Outdoor

Type 6P: Submersible, Watertight, Dusttight and Sleet-or Ice-resistant—Indoor and Outdoor

Type 7 : Class I, Division 1, Group A, B, C, or D—Indoor Hazardous Locations—Air-break Equipment

Type 8 : Class I, Division 1, Group A, B, C, or D—Indoor Hazardous Locations—Oil-immersed Equipment

Type 9 : Class II, Division 1, Group E, F, or G—Indoor Hazardous Locations—Air-break Equipment

Type 10 : MESA (formally Bureau of Mines)

Type 11 : Corrosion-resistant and Dripproof—Oil-immersed—Indoor

Type 12 : Industrial Use—Dusttight and Driptight—Indoor

Type 12K: Industrial Use—Dusttight and Driptight—Indoor (with knockouts)

Type 13 : Oiltight and Dusttight—Indoor

Table 6-5. CSA Enclosure Designations for Canadian Applications

CSA Enclosure 1 : General Purpose—Indoor

CSA Enclosure 2 : Dripproof—Indoor

CSA Enclosure 3 : Weatherproof—Outdoor

CSA Enclosure 4 : Watertight—Indoor or Outdoor

CSA Enclosure 5 : Dusttight (nonhazardous dusts)—Indoor

CSA Enclosure for Hazardous Locations Class I, Group A, B, C, or D
(see Note)

CSA Enclosure for Hazardous Locations Class II, Group E, F, and G
(see Note)

Note: If the Division is not marked on the nameplate, the equipment has been approved for both Divisions 1 and 2.

Table 6-6. Degrees of Protection of Enclosures for European Applications

The degree of protection for an enclosure is indicated by a symbol that
consists of the two-letter code IP (meaning International Protection)
and a two-digit number indicating the degree of protection (example, IP54).

1. The first number indicates the degree of protection against contact and ingress
   of solid foreign bodies:

   0 = No Protection

   1 = Protection from large object (>50 mm)

   2 = Protection from medium-sized objects (>12 mm)

   3 = Protection from small objects (>2.5 mm)

   4 = Protection from very small objects (>1 mm)

   5 = Protection from harmful deposits of dusts

   6 = Dustproof

2. The second number indicates the degree of protection against the ingress
   of water:

   0 = No protection

   1 = Protection from drops of condensed water

   2 = Protection from drops of water when the enclosure is tilted up to
       15 degrees from the vertical

   3 = Protection against spray water falling up to 60 degrees from the
       vertical (rainproof)

   4 = Protection against splashing from any direction

   5 = Protection against water jets from any direction

   6 = Protection against conditions on ships' decks (deck watertight)

   7 = Protection against immersion (under stated conditions of pressure and time)

   8 = Protection against indefinite immersion (under specified pressure)

Transmitters

Transmitters represent an important element of the inputs into any control system. Their proper selection, installation, and use are essential in ensuring reliable operation. A corporate standard may set guidelines for the minimum requirements in such applications. The developer of a corporate standard is generally faced with the formidable task of looking at all the different types of transmitters and deciding where to draw the line and how much detail is required. If maximum detail is chosen, such a standard will be a huge depository of technical data that is already available in numerous reference books. A better approach would be to select the minimum requirement and some basic guidelines, then refer to standards and handbooks already in existence.

As a starting point, the following ISA standards deal with this subject:

1. ISA-S50.1, Compatibility of Analog Signals for Electronic Industrial Process Instruments, applies to analog DC signals used in process control and monitoring systems to transmit information. Its purpose is to provide compatibility between the different components of a given system.
2. ISA-S37.1, Electrical Transducer Nomenclature and Terminology, establishes:
   - uniform nomenclature for transducers, and
   - uniform simplified terminology for transducer characteristics.
3. ISA-RP37.2, Guide for Specifications and Tests for Piezoelectric Acceleration Transducers for Aero-Space Testing, establishes primarily for the aerospace industry:
   - a uniform minimum general specifications for design and performance characteristics,
   - a uniform minimum acceptance and qualification test methods, including calibration,
   - a uniform presentation of minimum test data, and
   - a drawing symbol for use in schematics.
4. ISA-S37.5, Specifications and Tests for Strain Gage Linear Acceleration Transducers, establishes:
   - a uniform minimum general specifications for design and performance characteristics,
   - a uniform minimum acceptance and qualification test methods, including calibration,
   - a uniform presentation of minimum test data, and
   - a drawing symbol for use in schematics.
5. ISA has two standards for transducers that measure force and displacement: S37.8, Specifications and Tests for Strain Gage Force Transducers, and S37.12, Specifications and Tests for Potentiometric Displacement Transducers. Both these standards provide:
   - a uniform general specifications for design and performance characteristics,
   - a uniform acceptance and qualification test methods, including calibration techniques,
   - a uniform presentation of test data, and
   - a drawing symbol for use in electrical schematics.

The following questions may help the producer of a corporate standard set the guidelines required for transmitters in general. Additional information may be found in ISA-S20 (see Appendix B).

Should transmitters, whenever possible, be of the indicating type? Should the transmitter indicator be of a minimum size? If indication is not required, is control room indication sufficient for both the operators and for maintenance?

Should transmitter enclosures always be suitable for local conditions and area classification? Are exceptions allowed? Should such exceptions be first authorized? Note: Such exceptions must not contravene the electrical code in the effect at the site.

Is each transmitter, where feasible, provided with easily accessible span and zero adjustments? Should these adjustments be protected from tampering?

Where two-wire transmitters are used, should transmitters always employ a two-wire transmission system with a linear 4–20 mA output (some analyzers might be an exception)?

Should the output signal of the transmitter be electrically isolated from the case and ground?

For pneumatic transmitters, should nonindicating-type pneumatic transmitters have a 3-1/2 in. diameter (or other size) receiver gage on the output signal? If not, how is indication provided?

Should all pneumatic signals be 3–15 psig (20–100 kPag) and conform to ISA-S7.4?

What is the required accuracy? Does it meet the process requirements? Is the required accuracy achievable with pneumatic transmitters?

What is the effect of vibration and shock? Can these effects be assessed before equipment installation?

What is the effect of power supply variation? Is it acceptable? Does it meet the vendor's minimum requirements? Is there a need to supply clean power? What is defined as clean power?

Are the wetted parts in contact with the process compatible with the process fluid? Is this material compatibility the responsibility of the designer or the vendor?

Should the transmitter range be adjustable or fixed? If adjustable, should it be sealed?

Is zero elevation or suppression required? Where should the location of zero and span adjustments be? Outside the instrument? Under the cover? Should they be sealed?

Is lightning suppression required? How is this requirement assessed, especially in open areas?

How accessible is the transmitter when installed? How frequently does the instrument need to be accessed (for maintenance, testing, calibration, etc.)?

Is steam or electrical tracing required? Are the advantages and availability of steam vs. electrical heating assessed?

What service and support are available from the vendor? How long has the vendor been providing this service? Are there references from other users?

Should both the maximum process and maximum ambient temperatures be considered? Are these maximum temperatures transients, or do they maintain for extensive time periods?

Does the process temperature exceed the limits of the sensing element? Does the impulse piping protect the sensing element from extreme process temperatures?

Are the electronics protected from the process temperature? In the case of high process temperature, are remote electronics available?

Where ambient and process temperature vary widely, what is its effect on the accuracy of the measurement? Is temperature compensation required? Is there a need for a special transmitter housing?

On low ambient temperature, should winterizing be considered? Have the effects of winterizing failure been considered? Are such effects acceptable?

Are both the operating pressure range and the maximum pressure considered? Are they within the acceptable range of the transmitter? Is the overpressure rating of the selected transmitter at least 150% of the maximum rated operating pressure?

Is there a possibility that the process can develop a vacuum? If yes, can the transmitter handle vacuum? Up to what limit?

On differential pressure transmitters, is the transmitter capable of handling the static line pressure over long periods of time?

What is the effect of overpressure? How long will the transmitter need to withstand overpressure? (This is particularly important for differential pressure transmitters.)

Is the transmitter capable of handling the surrounding humidity? Is there a requirement for a 0–100% RH capability?

Is the transmitter capable of handling the corrosive environment both from the process side (e.g., acid fluids) as well as from the environment side (e.g., salt water on an offshore oil rig)?

Is damping required?

Where does the power come from? Is it available? Is it sufficient to power the transmitter? Is it reliable? Is it of a quality that is required by the transmitter?

The following sections of this chapter will look at the most common types of measurement and control equipment used in the industry. Here, again, questions are provided as a guide in the development of the corporate standard. It may be that some of these types of instruments and control equipment are not applicable to a particular industry (or may be rarely used); in such cases, the preparer of the corporate standard may decide to include only the relevant parts. The following types are not all-inclusive but do represent a good portion of the most common ones used in instrumentation and control equipment:

1. Pressure measurement
2. Temperature measurement
3. Flow measurement

4. Level measurement
5. Weight measurement
6. Analyzers
7. Control valves
8. Pressure relief devices

Pressure

Pressure is one of the most common measurements made in process control. It is also one of the simplest for which to select a specific type of device. One of the key items to watch for is the primary element (i.e., strain gage, Bourdon tube, spiral, etc.). Primary element materials should be selected to provide sufficient immunity to the process fluids and at the same time provide the required measured accuracy under the process conditions it will encounter.

The ISA has produced three standards for pressure transducers: ISA-S37.3, Specifications and Tests for Stain Gage Pressure Transducers; ISA-S37.6, Specifications and Tests for Potentiometric Pressure Transducers; and ISA-S37.10, Specifications and Tests for Piezoelectric Pressure and Sound-Pressure Transducers. These three standards provide uniform general specifications for design and performance characteristics, uniform acceptance and qualification test methods including calibration techniques, uniform presentation of test data, and a drawing symbol for use in electrical schematics.

Generally, all equipment used in pressure-retaining systems must comply with local statutory requirements. In most cases, pressure devices designed for a pressure greater than 15 psig (103.4 kPag) that contain lethal, toxic, or flammable substances may need to be registered, regardless of design temperature. Individual countries may have specific requirements. As an example, in Canada, all equipment used in pressure-retaining systems designed for a pressure greater than 15 psig (103.4 kPag) and a temperature equal or greater than 150°F (65°C) must be registered as fittings by the manufacturer in compliance with the Boiler and Pressure Vessels Act for the province of installation and CSA Standard B.51.

The following questions are designed to help the producer of a corporate standard identify the points to consider when creating the standard.

Are all pressure-measuring instruments isolated from the process by a piping valve? Is such a valve (and its associated piping/tubing) in compliance with the piping requirements for the process fluid in question?

If the fluid measured is toxic or corrosive, are a blowdown valve and blowdown line provided? In addition, where the process pressure is very high (e.g., greater than 2 MPa), is a separate blowdown valve provided?

Is there a need for pulsation dampeners? Are the materials of such dampeners in conformance with the fluid being measured?

Is there a need for siphons (e.g., on all vapors above 140°F or 60°C)? Are the syphons made of the right material?

Where diaphragm seals are used, do they require a flushing connection? Is there a minimum dimension for the flanged connections (e.g., not less than 1 in. flanged connection)? Do the rating and material of flanges comply with the pipe line or vessel specifications? Has it been confirmed that the seal fill fluid is compatible with the process fluid?

Should all pressure gages for field mounting be 4-1/2 in. diameter with blowout disc (because sudden pressure surges may exist)? Should these gages have a standard connection (e.g., 1/2 in. male NPT bottom) unless different requirements are dictated by pipe line or vessel specifications?

What is the acceptable error as a percentage of full-scale reading (e.g., not to exceed ±1%)? Is this error permissible within the process requirements?

When specifying a range for the gage, is the maximum working pressure to which a gage is subjected 75% of full-scale pressure range?

Is the gage subjected to severe mechanical vibration (e.g., compressors)? Is protection from such vibration required?

Does the process require special safety precautions (e.g., for liquid chlorine, toxic fluids, etc.)? Have these safety precautions been assessed?

Is the fluid clean or dirty? Are these conditions changing due to abnormal operating conditions? Is the fluid corrosive to the gage material in contact? Are there any solids in suspension that may solidify or clog?

If the application involves high process temperatures, is the dissipation of heat considered? If condensation may occur, is a pigtail syphon required?

Since in most cases the piping discipline supplies the isolation valve, has it been confirmed that the gage connection fits the supplied connection?

Is it preferred to have separate connections for each pressure impulse point (e.g., the failure of the pressure gage connection will not affect the pressure switch connection)? Is this requirement a must for critical and trip measurements? Does the connection comply with the piping specification?

Has it been assessed, based on the fluid being measured, whether the connection should be on the top or side of the process line? Would exceptions to such requirements be acceptable?

Has the need for test and drain valves been considered? Is access for maintenance available? Are the isolating valves accessible from the ground or a platform?

Is there a need to establish in the standard that all connections should be 1/2 in. NPT for process lines and 1/4 in. NPT for instrument air? Should a 3/4 in. process connection be used, which is then reduced to 1/2 in. at the instrument?

On oxygen service, has the equipment been degreased and ordered as such for this application? Have such gages been labelled "FOR OXYGEN SERVICE"? Has the material in touch with the process been carefully checked?

On liquid chlorine service, have precautions similar to those for oxygen been implemented?

Should differential pressure transmitters have a valve manifold (with blowdown valve or vent valve)? Should this manifold be of a material that meets at least the piping specification for the fluid in question?

If solids will accumulate in the impulse line, should tees and plug fittings (or ball valve) be installed instead of elbows to allow rodding of plugged lines?

Is the impulse piping as short as possible?

Are the instruments in gas applications self-draining (i.e., lines are slopped towards the process to avoid trapping condensables and liquids)?

Are instruments in liquid and condensable applications self-venting (i.e., lines are slopped towards the instrument to avoid trapping of gas)?

Does the standard ensure that the selected instrument is in conformance with the electrical classification of its location?

Is the accuracy of the instrument within the process requirements?

Temperature

Many types of devices are used for temperature measurement, the most common of which are:

1. thermocouples,
2. resistance elements (known as RTDs),
3. bimetallics, and
4. filled systems.

Thermistors and pyrometers are also used but not as frequently and will not be covered in this book. However, some general considerations for optical-type temperature measurements have been included.

Temperature measurements, in most cases, start with a temperature element. Many corporate standards may dictate a preference that temperature elements should be part of a field-mounted temperature transmitter assembly. The assembly would typically consist of a thermowell, a temperature element, and a temperature transmitter. Where a temperature transmitter assembly is not possible, the standard may then allow individual thermocouples or RTDs to be used. Corporate standards may also recommend that instruments used for control or alarm shall have upscale burnout unless otherwise specified.

In general, a corporate standard on temperature measurement may require that the following points be considered when specifying temperature measuring devices:

1. Temperature range
2. Accuracy and response time
3. Durability
4. Effects of existing electrical noise and vibration
5. Process condition (oxidizing, reducing, or corrosive atmospheres)
6. The number of elements to fit inside one well
7. Type of output signal required
8. Environmental requirements such as enclosures or hazardous areas

Thermowells

In industrial applications, temperature elements are in most cases used with thermowells. The exception to this general rule occurs with the internals of some equipment (e.g., compressors, turbines, etc.); surfaces; fast responses where thermowells will create too much of a delay; air space temperature measurements; and bearings.

The following questions may help the preparer of a corporate standard provide a section that covers the application of thermowells.

Are thermowells installed where good mixing is ensured such as pipe bends? If not, are the errors and delays in measurement acceptable?

In vessels where a vapor-liquid interface exists, are thermowells located in the liquid phase? If not, how is the accuracy of the measurement ensured?

In combining streams, are thermowells located at a minimum length downstream from the junction to ensure good mixing (e.g., ten pipe diameters)?

One of the main disadvantages of thermowells is the delay they create in measuring temperature changes. Should such a delay be limited? Should a certain time be allowed for a step change to be reached? For example: When a thermocouple assembly is subjected to a step change in temperature, its output shall reach 63% of the total temperature change in three seconds or less. It should be kept in mind that the effect of time delay could be significant; for example, typical temperature elements with a 1- to 10-second time delay may degrade to a 20- to 50-second delay.

Are thermowell construction and material carefully matched with the process requirements? Do these process requirements also include abnormal and emergency conditions?

Should the thermowells be required to comply with the pipe line or vessel specifications? If not, is the installation safe and reliable?

Should thermowells be furnished with a standard size connection for all vessels and alloy steel pipe lines (say, 1-1/2 in. flanged or 1 in. NPT threaded)? Should this connection be the same required for pipe line or vessel specifications?

Are the well's diameter, length, and material in compliance with the process and piping needs? Is there a need to standardize on the well material (e.g., 316 SS) with special applications requiring special materials? Has it been checked with the piping designer that the well dimensions fit the allocated space?

Should all wells in a plant have flanged connections (rather than screwed type)? Should such a requirement be standardized?

Has consideration been given to vibrations resulting from the effect of vortex shedding when in fluids with velocities greater than 6 ft/sec (2 m/sec)? Should tapered stems be used? Should a stress analysis be performed?

Should the temperature element tag number be stamped on the well? If not, is there a problem if two wells are interchanged?

If a temperature element is inserted in a process without a well, should (for safety reasons) a clear label be attached to the element to indicate that no well is present?

Has the optimum immersion length been considered? For example, if the well is installed perpendicular to the line, the tip of the well should be between 1/2 to 1/3 the pipe diameter; if the well is installed in an elbow (the recommended option), the tip should point towards the flow.

RTDs and Thermocouples

The selection of an RTD or thermocouple (T/C) may be governed by the corporate standard based on the application requirements. Many corporate standards include a table that shows the general features of RTDs vs. thermocouples to facilitate selection, to speed up the decision-making process, and to ensure quality in design. Two of the many differentiating factors between RTDs and thermocouples are the temperature range each may measure and the accuracy they provide. Table 6-7 shows how a corporate standard may decide to provide guidance for such applications based on temperature range alone.

Instead, the standard could recommend that under a certain temperature (e.g., 120°C) an RTD should be used, and above that temperature a T/C should be used.

The following questions may be used as a guide in preparing a section on RTDs and thermocouples.

Is a specific material to be used in RTD manufacturing (e.g., platinum)? Should the RTD have a standard resistance (e.g., 100 ohms at 32°F or 0°C, and a temperature coefficient of 0.00385 ohms/°C)? Should the RTD employ a three-wire or four-wire system of connection?

Since an RTD's accuracy and service life may be limited at high temperature, has care been taken to minimize the effect of mechanical stress, vibration, shock, or gas contamination?

Has the design considered the response of the RTD compared to the faster thermocouple? Is this acceptable to the process requirements?

Since the accuracy of RTDs and thermocouples varies with temperature, has the operating temperature accuracy been deemed acceptable?

If an RTD is supplied without an integral transmitter, is the unit a 2-, 3-, or 4-wire configuration? Did this decision consider the length of lead wires and its effect on measurement accuracy?

Should thermocouples be specified as a mineral-insulated type with a metallic sheath? Should the junction be welded and insulated?

Is there a minimum diameter for thermocouple wire (e.g., 0.5 mm with wire tails a minimum of 0.8 mm diameter)? For high temperature applications (e.g., over 900°F or 500°C), should a different wire gage be used (e.g., 14 AWG)?

Is the design of the T/Cs such that stray electrical signal pickup is not a problem?

Table 6-7. Element Temperature Ranges

Temperature Range °F (°C)	Element Type
Below 250 (120)	3 or 4-wire RTDs
From 250 (120) to 1200 (650)	Type J (Iron-Constantan)
From 1200 (650) to 2000 (1100)	Type K (Chromel-Alumel)
Above 2000 (1100)	Check with Engineering Dept.

Since the mV to temperature is not linear, has linearization been included in the control loop?

Is T/C burnout protection required?

Should the T/C be grounded (good temperature transfer but subject to stray electrical noise) or ungrounded?

Does the standard ensure that the color coding, accuracy, and symbol designation for thermocouples and extension wire be in accordance with the local authority having jurisdiction at the site (for example, the American National Standard for Temperature Measurement Thermocouples, MC96.1, as reaffirmed by ANSI in 1969)? (See Appendix B.)

To ensure measurement accuracy, will the measurement system be calibrated as a whole prior to installation?

Should the standard recommend that head-mounted transmitters be supplied for thermocouples and RTDs where the transmitter can withstand the environment? Otherwise, should a remote transmitter be recommended?

Bimetallics

Bimetallics are used generally in local temperature gages and in local temperature switches. The following questions are a guide in preparing a section on this subject in the corporate standard.

To facilitate reading, should local temperature indicators be all-angle bimetallic with a 5 in. minimum diameter dial? Should the capillary type be sometimes used where operating visibility is required?

Should temperature switches be capable of continuously withstanding a temperature exceeding its range by an allowable value (e.g., at least 5%)?

Should each temperature switch have a set repetition accuracy under normal operating conditions (e.g., of ±1% of the span or better)?

If vibration exists, should the thermometer be filled with a damping fluid? Is this fluid compatible with the process fluid (in case of leakage)?

Should the unit be back-connected, front-connected, or an all-angle type?

Filled Systems

Capillary tubing for filled systems is generally armored for industrial applications, has a maximum length of 24 feet (or 8 meters), and is continuously supported and protected against damage. A corporate standard may require that all filled-system temperature instruments be fully compensated for ambient temperature variations.

The following questions may help the preparer of the corporate standard start a section on this subject.

Since such systems may have response times varying from 2 to 60 seconds (and up to 90 seconds when fitted with a well), what are the process requirements? Is the instrument response time acceptable?

Has the effect of ambient temperature on the capillary system been considered? Is compensation required?

Is the bulb immersed sufficiently to ensure that the actual temperature is being measured? Is external insulation required?

Has the design allowed for the size of the sensing bulb and the measurement span (it is larger than RTDS and thermocouples)?

Since the system must be leak-free in order to maintain accuracy, are occasional checking and testing required?

What is the required distance between the bulb and the readout device? Is it under 200 feet? Should the standard limit the length of such capillaries (for example, to 30 ft)?

Is the capillary's material of construction compatible with the surrounding environment? Should the standard specifically state certain standard materials (e.g., to be of stainless steel with a flexible sheath)?

Has the design ensured that the capillary is well supported and protected through its entire length?

Does the plant have the facilities and capabilities to calibrate such systems?

In addition to the above types, noncontact optical pyrometers (such as infrared measurement devices) have their own applications. In these cases the following should be considered in the corporate standard.

Is a special housing required to protect from high surrounding temperatures (e.g., cast aluminum jackets to accommodate coolants) to meet production needs (e.g., water cleaning, sprays, etc.)? Is heat tracing during cold winters required?

Are focusing devices required, such as sighting telescopes, alignment tubes, and aiming flanges?

Are safety shutters required to safeguard the lenses?

Is a motorized base needed to direct the instrument's position?

Flow

A corporate standard in many cases provides guidance on the evaluation criteria for flowmeter selection. Of the typical pressure, temperature, flow, and level measurements, flow tends to be the most difficult and, therefore, the most subject to incorrect device selection. Such evaluation criteria in the standard helps greatly to reduce errors in selection. It should be mentioned at this stage that for environmental reasons, flowmeters that contain mercury should not be used.

If a corporate standard addresses the evaluation of flowmeters, it should consider requirements such as the application under which the flowmeter will operate, the hardware, the human factors, and the installation/maintenance.

The following text may help the producer of a corporate standard identify the points to be addressed. The evaluation may be in the form of a table or remain in text form. All the items and parameters listed will become requirements to be identified in the instrument specification sheet.

Note: Many of the points addressed for the evaluation of flow transmitters also apply to other types of process measurements (pressure, level, etc.).

Note: The values mentioned in the following text are based on generalized numbers and are not to be used at their face value. These numbers will increase and decrease with different vendors.

Application

- Line size

    This is one of the main items to consider since not all measuring devices cover all the line sizes. For example, the maximum size of most vortex meters is generally around 8 inches. The main question is whether the selected flow device can handle the line size (and required flow).

- Type of fluid

    This item may limit the type of device available. For example:
    1. On vortex meters and differential pressure devices, liquid, gas, and steam can be measured.
    2. On magnetic meters, severe service for conductive fluids can be measured, where orifice plates or vortex shedders are not suitable.
    3. On most turbine meters steam cannot be measured.

- Pressure and temperature of fluid

    These parameters are not only used to size the selected flow device but also to identify the type of measurement capable of withstanding the process conditions.

- Straight pipe run or straighteners

    This is a requirement that directly affects the piping and may sometimes (especially on existing installations) be a problem. For example, for pressure differential devices, typically a straight run of 20 upstream pipe diameters is required, with 5 pipe diameters for the downstream side. A pitot tube requires 40 and 10, respectively. For variable area flowmeters, none are required.

- Clean/dirty fluid

    Some measuring fluids may be plugged or erroded if dirty fluids are used. For example, differential pressure devices would normally not be used where dirty and/or corrosive fluids are used (flow nozzles may handle such conditions), but magnetic meters are well capable of accurately measuring dirty, viscous, corrosive, abrasive, and fibrous liquids.

- Pressure loss allowed

    Many flow-measuring devices drop some of the line pressure. In some cases this is not desirable, and the need to consider the amount of pressure drop is of great importance. For example, the pressure drop for differential pressure devices varies from low to moderate; in pitot tubes in particular, pressure drop is low when compared to other types, and elbow taps have no mentionable pressure loss; on mag meters there is no pressure loss.

- Other items to be considered in flowmeter selection:
    1. Specific fluid properties
    2. Type of required measurement (i.e., mass or volume)
    3. Criticality of data and, therefore, the instrument reliability

4. Wetted material requirements
5. Viscosity and density
6. Reversible flow capability since some may not
7. Ambient temperature and vibration to which the instrument will be exposed
8. Area classification where the meter will be located

Hardware Factors

- Accuracy
  This requirement is directly related to the needs of the process. On elbow taps the accuracy may reach 10%, while on vortex meters and on magnetic meters accuracies of ±0.5 to 2% are common. The question is, therefore, one of the required accuracy and which measuring device can meet this accuracy. It should be noted that this accuracy should be maintained within the minimum to maximum flow range (not just at the normal value).

- Turndown (rangeability)
  The range between minimum and maximum flows is essential in determining which flow techniques to use. For example, orifice plates have a 3 : 1 turndown; mass flowmeters can reach 100 : 1.

- Type of output
  Most modern systems are electronic. Older pneumatic systems may influence the type of measuring devices. On differential pressure devices, the transmitter output could be electronic or pneumatic; vortex meters and magnetic meters are electronic only.

Human Factors

- If a desired readout is required, is it digital or analog? The size of the digits must be determined, as well as whether they will be expressed in percent or in engineering units.
- The computer interface must be expressed (e.g., an RS-232 link or some other communication protocol).
- The capabilities of the in-house maintenance staff must be determined. There may be a need for training. Maintenance may be done by an outside contractor. It must be determined whether such an outside contractor can reach the site within an acceptable time.
- As part of the cost of ownership, the cost of high maintenance items that require specialized equipment and expertise must be considered.
- Plant preferences must be considered. Perhaps the plant has similar instruments; whether or not they are satisfactory should be determined.
- The extent of vendor support is very important, since it should be there when needed and should include technical support as well as spare parts.

Installation/Maintenance

- Since installation and maintenance require shutdown, it is necessary to determine (1) whether the device selected can be removed on line and (2) how essential it is to the ongoing process.
- Installation and start-up time for the device must be reasonable, and its operation must be well understood.

- The needs of required preventive maintenance must be determined as to frequency. The robustness of the instrument in comparison to its required performance must be considered.
- It should be determined whether the instrument fails in a mode that maintains safety and draws the operator's attention.
- The difficulty and frequency of calibration must be considered, as well as whether this should be done at the site or at the vendor's facilities.
- For required spare parts, it must be determined how many are needed, how frequently they will be needed, and whether the vendor can provide this service.
- The element and transmitter must be accessible from either grade or platform.

In addition to the previous evaluating criteria for flowmeter types, there are many types of flow measurement. The most common are:

1. differential pressure,
2. vortex shedding,
3. variable area,
4. magnetic, and
5. turbine.

In addition, other types that are frequently used are mass flowmeters, positive displacement flowmeters, sight flow indicators, target and ultrasonic flowmeters, etc. These will not be considered here, but the approach taken for the first types should give the preparer of the standard a good feel for the technique of incorporating these other measurement devices. The following questions look at the most common measuring devices and their particularities.

Differential Pressure Flowmeters (orifice plates, flow nozzles, venturis, elbows, and pitot tubes)

Is the differential pressure equipped with three valve manifolds? Is it integral to the transmitters? Has it been mounted by the instrument supplier? On toxic and hazardous fluids, should a five-valve manifold with drain or vent legs to a safe location be provided?

Is a square root extractor required?

Should the standard transmitter ranges be selected first and the orifices sized accordingly, rather than vice versa? For liquid service, should a standard 100-inch W.C. (2500 mm W.C.) maximum differential pressure be used unless the available pressure drop is less than 4 psi (28 kPa)? Should the standard limit the ratio between the differential pressure and the static absolute pressure?

In general, should orifice plates be used only for:

1. clean, nonerosive, noncrystallizing fluids,
2. permissible errors of over 2%, and
3. a required rangeability of not more than 3:1?

Should the orifice plates be sized only according to accepted industry standards? Should the minimum ratio of orifice diameter to pipe inside diameter be within a set range (e.g.,not be less than 0.3 and not exceed 0.7)?

Should orifice plate information, including tag number, be stamped on the upstream side of the extension handle? Would a loose tag wired to the handle acceptable?

Should flange taps be used on lines 8 in. and smaller? Should vena contracta taps be used on lines 10 in. and larger?

For thin wall pipe with backing flanges, should vena contracta taps be used in all sizes? Could pipe meter runs or integral orifices be specified for 1-1/2 in. or smaller pipes?

Should the standard specify that 316 SS be the most common material used in orifice plates unless material of higher quality is required by the process conditions?

Should the measuring element, where possible, be mounted above the orifice plate for gas measurement (taking care that condensibles do not influence the DP) and below the orifice plate for liquid, condensibles, and steam? Should the impulse lines be sloped 1 in. per foot? On condensibles and steam, do 1-1/2 in. tees provide sufficient capacity condensate pots?

Where condensation occurs in the measuring element on a steam line (or wet gas or vapor), should condensate chambers be fitted to the impulse points? Should both chambers be at the same level? Should impulse lines be insulated or heat traced?

Should the tap connections be vertical (i.e., from the top) for gases and horizontal for steam and liquids?

Does the orifice plate have a drain hole located at the bottom for steam and gas and one on top for liquids?

Should the orifice vendor supply a printout of the element calculation?

Since flow nozzles and venturi tubes tend to be more expensive than standard orifice plates, should the standard require that such devices may be specified provided they have a specific advantage for the particular application in question?

For slurry applications where differential pressure devices are required, will the segmental orifice provide a satisfactory measurement?

Where pressure drop must be minimized, should pitot tubes and pitot venturis be considered? Should the design allow for element removal while in service?

Should the standard recommend that flange taps are preferred for orifice plates?

Should a minimum of 20 straight pipe diameters be allocated upstream of the orifice and 5 diameters downstream?

On toxic or hazardous fluids, should the impulse lines be flanged or welded (instead of threaded)?

Vortex Shedding

Should the standard clearly state that such devices should not be used where:

- fluid viscosity may vary sufficiently to cause unacceptable errors;
- two-phase flow or emulsions may occur;
- viscous and fibrous liquids or abrasive slurries occur; and
- there are semifilled pipes?

Should upstream and downstream straight-pipe length requirements conform to meter supplier specifications?

Is the rangeability of around 15:1 acceptable?

Variable Area

Should the standard recommend that such flowmeters be used only on clean, nonerosive, noncrystallizing fluids?

Should the standard limit (or prevent) the use of these meters in lines that carry hazardous or corrosive fluids?

Is an accuracy of ±2% of span acceptable?

Should a material preference for the metering tube be stated (e.g., borosilicate glass)?

Should the tube have clearly legible scale graduations engraved directly on the glass?

Should plastic tubes be avoided unless the specific process application requires their use?

Where the fluid stream experiences strong pulsation, should flute-guided or rod-guided tubes be recommended?

Where necessary, should viscosity-compensating floats be used?

For safety reasons, should the standard recommended that the metering tube be statistically tested at 150% of normal working pressure?

Is the meter installed with sufficient clearance? Is it accessible? Is it mounted vertically?

Should the standard recommend horizontal connections where possible?

Is the piping such that no strain is imposed on the meter?

Is bypass piping required?

How is the calibration to be done? Does the vendor provide such a service?

Has the available pressure drop been considered?

If the process is hazardous, is the meter protected with a shield?

ISA has produced a series of four recommended practices that cover variable area flowmeters: ISA-RP16.1, 2, and 3; ISA-RP16.4; ISA-RP16.5; and ISA-RP16.6 (see Appendix B).

Magnetic

Should the standard recommend that a straight length of pipe equal in bore to the element and equivalent in length to five times bore diameter be provided upstream and downstream of the element? Or should such detail be left to the vendor's recommendations?

Should appropriate mechanical protection for the electrodes be provided?

Should the standard ensure that such meters be installed in lines:

- that remain full when the flow is zero;
- in which operating velocity is not less than 2 feet/sec (0.6 meters/second);
- in which the conductivity is within the meter's capabilities; and
- in which the line is always filled?

Is bypass piping required?

Should the standard ensure that proper grounding is in place? Have the vendor's recommendations been followed?

Turbine

Should a strainer be provided upstream of each turbine meter or positive displacement meter?

How many upstream pipe diameters are provided?

Should the standard state the straight length pipe requirements for turbine meters? Should it indicate values or leave that to the vendor's recommendations?

Should the standard recommend that such meters not be used for dirty, viscous, abrasive, and fibrous liquids; for semifilled pipes; for nonlubricating fluids; and for steam?

Is an accuracy of 0.25 to 1% acceptable? Is a rangeability of 10:1 acceptable?

Are strainers required?

Does the vendor have calibration facilities? What is the turnaround time for such activities?

Does the liquid contain entrained gases that may affect the accuracy?

On flanged meters, has it been checked that gaskets do not protrude into the flow stream?

Is bypass piping required? Are strainers required?

To prevent sudden hydraulic impact, is the flow increased gradually into the line?

Is the viscosity of the fluid constant? If not, how will the meter's performance respond to such changes?

To avoid the effect of electrical noise, is the transmission cable well protected?

ISA-RP31.1, Specification, Installation, and Calibration of Turbine Flowmeters, establishes for turbine flowmeters, especially those 2 inches in diameter and smaller;

1. the recommended minimum information to be specified in ordering;
2. the recommended acceptance and qualification test methods including calibration techniques;
3. uniform terminology and drawing symbols; and
4. the recommended installation techniques.

Level

Of the many types of level measurement, the following are a sample of common types:

1. Differential pressure (static head)
2. Displacement and float
3. Ultrasonic/sonic
4. Mechanical
5. Gage glasses
6. Radioactive (nuclear)
7. Bubbler
8. Capacitance
9. Conductivity

Differential Pressure (Static Head)

Should this type of level measurement be used only for liquids with fixed specific gravity or where errors due to varying specific gravities are acceptable?

Are all differential pressure level instruments, where feasible, isolated from the process by a shutoff valve? If not, how can the instrument be removed without affecting the operation? Should these valves conform to the process specifications to which they connect?

Has consideration been given to the possibility of condensation in the low pressure impulse line and, therefore, the need for filling tees? Is the fill fluid similar to the process fluid? Is it acceptable? Is it safe?

For vessel connections, should flanged differential pressure level instruments have, as a minimum, a 3 in. flange for both the flush type and the extended diaphragm type? Is there a need to standardize on the size and type of connections in the plant?

Is this type of measurement in general best suited for clean fluids? Could it be used in dirty and corrosive applications with the proper design? Should the standard recommend the applications best fitted for this type of measurement (and the ones that are not)?

For pressurized vessels, is a sealing fluid or purge required?

Can calibration be performed easily? Are special tools or training required?

Displacement and Float

Since these types of instruments may not be installed directly on the top of vessels, is it acceptable for the vessel to be taken out of service without shutting down the process? Is this acceptable to the operators?

Is a stilling well required? Is any turbulence generated by agitators or by the location of the discharge pipe into the tank?

Are external cage-type instruments preferred? Are they normally piped to the vessels with a minimum size (e.g., not less than 3/4 in.) screwed or flanged, in accordance with the piping specifications? Are exceptions to these requirements acceptable? Should these exceptions be first approved by the plant?

Are all external cage-type level instruments isolated from the process vessel by valves? Is such a design compatible with the process conditions? Is the piping arrangement designed to prevent the formation of sediment on the bottom of the float cage? Are the piping material and isolation valves compatible with the process fluid?

Is a suitable drain normally provided at the low point and a vent valve provided at the highest point?

Should this type of level measurement be used only:

- for liquids with fixed specific gravity and
- where the errors due to process variations are acceptable?

Since this type of measurement in general is best suited for clean fluids, could it be used in dirty and corrosive applications with the proper design? Should such application obtain the approval of the plant control engineer first?

Will the element be affected by coating, buildup, or dirt? If yes, is the frequency and accessibility of maintenance acceptable?

Is the movement of the float, linkages, or levers restricted? Has the tank designer been consulted for the location of the measurement connections and for the space required by the measuring device?

Would a change in process condition create crystallization or solids?

Ultrasonic/Sonic

Is the device mounted in such a manner as to minimize the effects of both continuous and intermittent vibration? Can such vibration be identified and estimated before installation?

Is there a surrounding production noise present (especially at high frequencies)? Will this noise affect the measuring device? Has this been checked with the instrument manufacturer?

Has it been ensured that the instrument is not in contact with process fluid? How is this ensured?

Have the maximum process temperature and pressure been compared with the limits of the sensor?

Since most operating spans range from 1 ft to 200 ft, is this within the process requirements? Would there be a need in the future to change the range of the instrument?

Is foam present in the liquid surface (which weakens the signal)? Has it been checked that there is no foam (however, it may be used on dusty applications)? Would coating occur (i.e., affecting its accuracy)? If coating is a problem, should another type of measurement be considered?

Is temperature compensation required?

Is vapor concentration changing (which affects calibration due to the modified speed of sound)? Is this variation in accuracy acceptable? Does it meet the requirements of the process?

Has care be exercised in the design of mounting flanges or nozzles for ultrasonic devices to avoid "ringing" or echoes during operation? The manufacturer normally provides recommendations in this area; these recommendations should be carefully followed.

Has it been ensured that there should no braces, stiffeners, or other cross members in the path of the ultrasonic beam of any ultrasonic device? Has the tank designer been consulted to ensure that such conditions will not occur?

In closed flat-top tanks, is it necessary to reduce the transmit repetition so that respective echoes have enough time to die out? Is this going to affect performance? Or should a sound-absorbing layer be installed to the underside of the tank top?

Mechanical (guided floats, chains, tapes, etc.)

Is the application for clean liquids only?

Has it been checked first that the application of other pneumatic or electronic instrumentation is not feasible and that no signal transmission is required?

In the case of outdoor installations, were proper measures taken to protect the mechanical parts of the level-measuring instruments from possible weather interference?

Is the vessel not agitated?

Gage Glasses

Are these devices provided with gage valves to facilitate removal of the gage glass during operation? Are these isolating valves in accordance with the piping specifications? Are they the right size?

Is this type of measurement used for clean fluids that require local indication only?

Is there a need for drain and vent valves? Are these valves in conformance with the piping standard of the application in question?

Is the fluid being measured nonhazardous?

Should an excess flow check valve be incorporated into the gage valve to stop the flow in the event of glass breakage?

Is there a possibility that the gage may be damaged or broken?

Has it been checked that it is safe to use tubular gage glasses? Are reflex gages permissible for low and medium pressure application? Are exceptions permitted? For high pressure application or where the fluid is toxic, should armored gages with magnetic dials be used?

For safety reasons, should gage glass lengths between process connections not exceed a fixed distance, e.g., 4 feet (1.25 meters)?

Is the location of the gage within visual range? Is it accessible?

For dark liquids, is the display visible? Should modifications or the considerations of another type of level measurement required?

It should be mentioned at this point that in certain services, such as steam drum service, glasses must conform to local code requirements (e.g., ASME Power Boiler Code). The standard should reflect such a requirement.

Radioactive (nuclear)

Has extreme care been taken to observe all safety measures in locating and installing the radioactive source? Have the manufacturer's recommendations been followed? Has the manufacturer been consulted to obtain optimum results and maximum safety?

Is there a requirement for a special license? How is this to be obtained?

Is calibration easy to perform? How often should the unit be tested? Is special training required?

Bubbler

Is the bubbler dip pipe installation capable of withstanding maximum air pressure that results from a blocked dip pipe? Does it incorporate a tee piece at the top of the pipe to enable rodding?

Is the introduction of a foreign material (usually instrument air) into the process acceptable? Should a special gas be used instead?

Is there a possibility for coating, freezing, or plugging, thereby affecting performance?

Has the cost of continuously using the bubbling gas been considered?

Are the materials of construction compatible with the process? Should this assessment also consider the effects on loss of gas pressure?

Is the frequency of maintenance acceptable?

Capacitance

Will coating occur, thereby affecting performance?

Is the calibration time deemed acceptable? Should a device with less calibration time be considered?

Is temperature compensation required?

Has the design ensured that the probe is vertical and not in contact with the tanks walls?

Is the fluid conductive? If not, is a counter-electrode required?

If the application requires an insulated probe, has the design considered the care required at installation to prevent damage to the insulating material?

Conductivity

Will coating occur, thereby affecting performance?

Is the fluid's conductivity acceptable? What are the effects of conductivity if the process temperature varies?

It is worth noting that special requirements must be observed when the application is for boiler drum level indications. They must conform to the codes applicable at the site (e.g., ASME Power Boiler Code). The corporate standard must reflect these requirements. Examples of such special requirements for boiler drum level, for example, are as follows:

1. A differential-type pressure level sensor should be used for level control.
2. High and low drum level alarms should be independently implemented on a separate vessel leg.
3. A local sight glass with backlighting derived from the emergency power supply system is required.
4. Discrete-type conductivity sensors with indication in the control room are essential.

Weight

The four main types of weight measuring devices are:

1. strain gage load cells,
2. pneumatic load cells,
3. hydraulic load cells, and
4. mechanical lever scales.

ISA-RP74.01, Application and Installation of Continuous-Belt Weighbridge Scales, furnishes design criteria to simplify specifications and to provide recommendations for installation, calibration, and maintenance of continuous-belt, weighbridging-type scales (see Appendix B).

The selection of such devices is based not only on the technical features but also on vendor support and maintenance capabilities. The evaluation of weight measuring devices needs to consider many parameters, and a corporate standard that would approach such a subject must consider accuracy, installation requirements, susceptibility to the working environment, etc. The following checklist is a guide when preparing a corporate standard on the subject. Again, as previously mentioned, vendors may have exceptions, additional features, and capabilities beyond those described in this text.

Strain gage load cells generally:

1. have a very wide range of measurements,
2. are highly accurate and sensitive,
3. are easy to install,
4. can be used in harsh environments, and
5. are temperature sensitive unless compensated.

Pneumatic load cells generally:

1. are used mainly for low weight measurements,
2. have average accuracy and sensitivity,
3. are easy to install, and
4. are not acceptable for outdoor installations unless protected.

Hydraulic load cells generally:

1. are used for medium to heavy weights,
2. have an acceptable accuracy and sensitivity, and
3. are relatively sensible to temperature changes.

Mechanical lever scales generally:

1. are used for low to medium weights,
2. have a very good accuracy and sensitivity,
3. have little sensitivity to temperature changes, and
4. are not used in corrosive environments unless well protected.

The standard may recommend the use of one type over another, or it may simply create a comparison table that lists the advantages and disadvantages of each type, leaving the decision to the designer.

Analyzers

There are many types of industrial process analyzers. pH and conductivity analyzers are the types most frequently used in the process industries. The following questions may help the producer of such a standard define the points to consider. It is based on pH measurement, which has been taken as an example case, but its concept could be applied to other types of measurement.

In addition, general analyzer requiurements, sampling systems, and anlyzer shelters are also considered.

Other common analyzers are chromatographs, oxygen, moisture, and infrared. In general, and because of the special nature of these instruments, discussions on individual installations are held between the supplier and the customer before preparing the specifications.

pH Measurement

To prevent the reference electrode from becoming dry, should it be immersed at all times? Should a source of city water be substituted when the process flow stops?

Should the location be downstream far enough to ensure proper mixing? Would the use of an agitator improve mixing?

Is pH control in pipes OK for small changes? On large and rapid fluctuations, is a tank needed?

Is the glass selected for the membranes of the electrodes compatible with the temperature and pH value of the process?

Is electrode cleaning a manual operation? Is it an automatic operation (ultrasonic, water jet, brushing, or chemical)?

Is the probe easily accessible?

Are spare electrodes required to allow the measurement to be preserved during maintenance? On critical measurements should a two out of three setup be designed?

The inclusion in the corporate standard of a section that deals with analyzers in general needs to consider:

1. some general requirements applicable to most analyzers,
2. sampling systems, and
3. analyzer shelters, since many analyzer applications are located outdoors (such as stacks) and require protection from the environment.

The following questions consider these three items.

General Requirements

Is the analyzer required to monitor a single stream or a multiple stream?

What are the components to be analyzed? What are their measuring ranges?

Should one analyzer monitor all the components, or are different analyzers required?

What is the required response time? Is this the time required by the process?

Where will the analyzer function be located (i.e., extractive or in situ)?

What are the process temperature, the pressure, and the gas composition? Do these conditions change? Any abrasion and corrosion problems?

Are there specific requirements from the local authority (e.g., EPA)? Is the analyzer performance acceptable (accuracy, drift, response time, etc.)?

Is the calibration of the analyzer simple and accurate? Is any special training or equipment required? Are automatic zeroing and calibration required features?

How much modification to the existing installation is required to install the transmitter?

Should the existing power supplies be upgraded? What is the effect of a power loss? Or a power restart?

What is the warmup time after restart? How frequent is it expected that the analyzer will shut down?

Are the displays to be analog or digital? Are these displays local to the analyzer (or remote)?

If the analyzer is remote, how is the operator advised of a malfunction?

Are the analyzer outputs to be sent to a recorder or to a computerized data logging system? If a computer connection is required, is the communication protocol to be developed or does it exist?

A logic is required to blowback and calibrate the system, where is it located? Is it supplied by the vendor? Can this logic be linked to the plant control system?

When installed, is the analyzer easily accessible for testing and repairs?

Is the analyzer (or analyzer probe) to be installed in an environment that is:

1. corrosive,
2. hazardous (electrical area classification),
3. subject to weather conditions, or
4. subject to vibration and/or shock?

Is blowback air clean, dry, and oil-free? Typically, instrument air regulated at 50 psig is used.

What type of warranty and maintenance contracts are available from the vendor?

Will the vendor supervise the installation? Will the vendor supply training?

What is the scheduled maintenance? What is the estimated cost of labor and material?

Is this a custom-built analyzer, or is it a time proven off-the-shelf device?

Should the complete system be tested at the vendor's facility before shipping to the site?

Sampling Systems

Sampling systems are, in many cases, essential and are part of the analyzer system. However, they can also be the most troublesome if not properly designed, installed, and maintained.

Does the sampling system comprise a flow loop, flow indications, pressure regulator, cooler, resistance orifice, filter, catch pot, and relief valve for the gas systems?

Does the sampling system alter the sample through condensation, polymerization, etc.? Does the sample line maintain the sample within a set temperature range?

Does it provide the capability for doing zero and span calibration to the analyzer to which it is connected?

Is the sampling line leak-free? How is this ensured?

Is the sampling line kept to a minimum length?

If continuous emission monitoring for a stack is required, is the sample point location in conformance with the local regulations? This location must be within a number of stack diameters downstream and upstream of any disturbance.

Once analyzed, where is the sample routed to? Is this location acceptable, safe, and secure? Is all venting in conformance with the requirements of the regulatory bodies?

Should the sample line be fitted with a restriction to limit the flow into the analyzer shelter in case of a fractured pipe?

Should sample lines that carry hazardous fluid have automatic isolation valves to shut off the sample line in case of ventilation failure?

Is the velocity of the fluid in the sample line adequate to allow sufficient speed of response (e.g., 5 to 10 ft/sec)?

Are the filters suitable for the physical and chemical composition of the sample? How easy is it for maintenance to replace the filter?

Will the materials in the complete sampling system:

1. react with the sample,
2. absorb components of the sample,
3. transfer contaminants through osmosis, or
4. create an unsafe or flammable condition?

Analyzer Shelters

Analyzer shelters are provided for the housing of on-line process analyzers and should be situated such that sampling time lags are kept to a minimum. These shelters, with all equipment installed, are in many cases shop-fabricated on skids.

There may be cases, especially given today's needs for analyzer data, to group analyzers in a single location — inside the analyzer house in a vendor-supplied cabinet for all the analyzers.

Does the analyzer shelter conform to the electrical code in effect at the site? Although analyzer shelters may be located in a Division 1 or Division 2 area with suitable ventilation, the inside can be regarded as a safe area. In this case, flammable gas indicators with annunciation in the central control room should be installed. It should be arranged that if ventilation were to stop or the gas indicator were to alarm, all electrical power to the analyzer would be cut and all inflows of flammable samples halted. In addition, analyzers that handle flammable samples must be air purged, and failure should cause the power to them to be cut. Purging requirements vary with the purge classification. Purge classifications are in ISA-S12.4 (see Appendix B).

Should the structure be able to withstand and maintain a slight positive pressure (e.g., 2 in. W.C.)?

Should the structure be insulated, heated, air conditioned, and condensation-free? Should it be of a material not affected by the environment surrounding it (e.g., corrosion)?

Should the structure be appropriately ventilated (natural or fan-forced)? Where is the ventilation air supplied from? Is this source safe and reliable? Are the ventilation motor and fan easily accessible for maintenance? Is an intake filter required? How many air changes per hour are required (e.g., 10)?

Should the calibration gas cylinders be located inside or outside the structure? If inside, should a restriction at the bottle limit the flow to a safe value as per the ventilation of the structure?

How many gas cylinders are required? How often will they be replaced?

Is high-quality bottled air required (e.g., for THC analyzers)? How much air is needed? How frequently will the air cylinders be replaced?

Is there a need for a desk, a chair, and maintenance manual storage?

Should hand-held fire extinguishers and/or sprinklers be specified?

Should hand-held transceivers (walkie-talkies) be prevented from being used in the structure due to generated noise (RFI) that will affect the microprocessor functions of the analyzers? Should a telephone be recommended instead?

Control Valves

Control valves, when properly selected and applied, will provide years of trouble-free operation. On the other hand, the best of control systems will not improve the performance of a poorly selected valve. Any corporate standard must address the subject of control valves and their application, keeping in mind that the requirements for control valves will obviously vary depending on the application.

As a starting point, ISA has produced the S75 series of standards and recommended practices that are related to control valves and of interest to design and maintenance activities. See Appendix B for titles and brief descriptions of these documents.

The preparer of a corporate standard for this subject needs to consider many parameters. The questions that follow provide a starting point for the topics to be considered. It is broken down in four parts, each covering an aspect of control valves:

1. General Requirements
2. Body
3. Trim
4. Actuator

General Requirements

Should the standard ensure that, as a general rule, it is expected that control valve material, connections, and pressure/temperature ratings, as a minimum, must conform to (or exceed) pipe line specifications and process requirements?

Should block and bypass valves be generally included where the control valve duty is rigorous (erosive, corrosive, large pressure drop) and where manual control on the bypass is practical? Where block and bypass valves are not used, should handwheels be considered for control valves?

When block valves are fitted on either side of a control valve, should they normally be the same nominal size as the line? Should the bypass valve be the same size as the control valve? Should a small shutoff cock be provided to permit depressurization of the line between block valves?

Are vent and drain valves required? Should they be of a minimum size (e.g., 1 in.)? Such valves are used as drains, vents, flushing, additional pressure taps, sample connections, or indicators of the absence of pressure at maintenance time.

Is there a need for the vendor to pressure test all control valves and have the test pressure stamped on the valve? Should the pressure test certificate be sent to the plant for records?

Should valves for special services (e.g., for liquid ammonia) be fully radiographed by the vendor? Should the results be sent to the plant for record keeping?

In cases where leakage is of concern, should it be required that all control valves be leak tested by the manufacturer? Also, should certified reports be submitted to the plant control engineer? Should reports indicate the actual test conditions? Is there a need to have the testing witnessed by the plant control engineer?

Should the design ensure that, for throttle-type control valves, the design pressure drop should be at least one third of the total system friction pressure drop, not including gravity head?

Should valves be sized to pass a maximum percentage of the expected design flow when wide open and at design pressure drop (e.g., 130%)?

If the valve is oversized, should the standard recommend the equal percentage (to provide better control than a linear valve)?

Should the design ensure that the noise level near any valve is no greater that 85 dBA measured at a distance of three feet from the source for an eight-hour exposure? Should the standard note that this level includes ambient noise from other sources and will also be affected by acoustics of nearby surfaces (e.g., walls)? Should the standard recommend that noise-absorbing insulation not be used but rather noise-reducing trims or downstream silencers?

Should radiating fins be used where flowing temperatures are high (e.g., 400°F or 200°C)? Should extension bonnets be used where flowing temperatures are low (e.g., 32°F or 0°C)?

Are solenoid valves acceptable as final control elements? Are they recommended only for instrument air applications or where the line size is 1/4 in. or less?

On self-actuating valves (temperature or pressure), should a gage be installed to indicate the process condition?

Will the speed at which the valve opens or closes cause water hammer? Is speed control required? In what format is it required? Is it available as a standard feature of the actuator?

Should the control valve that handles combustible fluids be kept away from hot pumps, lines, or equipment (in case leakage develops)?

Is the I/P approved for use under the applicable hazardous area classification? If not, could it be mounted remotely in a nonclassified area?

During start-up, has care been taken to keep scale, welding rods, construction boots, etc., from plugging or damaging the control valve? Is a spool piece used during flushing operations?

During pressure testing, should the control valve be put in the fully open position?

Has access been allowed for valve testing and maintenance?

Is heat tracing of the valve required?

Should line connections be flanged, threaded (generally used for small sizes under 1 in.), butt welded, or socket welded? Note: The weld-end types are generally used for high pressure, flammable, or toxic materials.

When the control valve size is smaller than the line size, reducers are normally used. Should these reducers be of the eccentric type for duties where condensibles or sludge could be trapped in the line immediately upstream of the valve?

Where alloy steel or lined material is required and piping specifications permit, should control valves be flanged in all sizes except 3/4 in. and smaller where threaded NPT or socket welds are used, depending on the application?

Should steel and alloy steel flanged valves have raised face flanges in accordance with the standards in effect at the site (for example, ANSI's B16.5)? Should cast iron valves have generally flat face flanges?

Should screwed control valves have flanges or unions immediately adjacent to the valve for removal purposes?

For toxic duties, should valves be normally flanged? Should the standard state that screwed valves or valves clamped between flanges are unacceptable?

What are the difficulties in maintaining the valves? Is lapping required (a high labor-intensive activity that requires special tooling)?

Should the standard ensure that valves used for oxygen service be degreased and be suitably protected during shipment and prior to installation?

Body

When specifying valve bodies and in addition to the following questions, some parameters must be considered:

1. Rangeability: Varies from $50:1$ for a split body valve to a $20:1$ for a globe valve, to a $15:1$ for a diaphragm valve. Valve rangeability means that it should handle the maximum flow at the minimum pressure drop and the minimum flow at the maximum pressure drop.
2. Maintenance: Low on split bodies where trims are easily removed; on angle valves maintenance cost is average.
3. Sizes: Limited with each type; angle valves, for example, are generally available in sizes of 1 to 6 inches.
4. Construction: Linked to valve options; split bodies, for example, are not available in jacketed construction, and globe valves with double-seated control valves should be top and bottom guided. Note that double-seated valves do not seat tightly due to machining tolerances.
5. Application: Valve construction is tied to the application. Angle valves and diaphragm valves, for example, are not used for cavitating and flashing services, but globe valves may be used for cavitating service. Diaphragm valves may be used for slurry service but are limited by temperature and pressure of the process.
6. Flow characteristics: Good for angle valves but poor for diaphragm valves.
7. Tight shutoff: Available with angle valves and diaphragm valves.
8. Cost: Low for butterfly valves, particularly for large sizes.
9. Fire-safe valves allow a small leakage when exposed to a fire; is there a need for fire-safe construction?

Such parameters may be included in the standard in a format similar to the one above or in a table.

Should the standard specify that, in general, the minimum valve body size for line sizes one inch and larger is generally specified at one inch and line size valve bodies are used for line sizes smaller than one inch? Should reduced trim be used if necessary?

Should all seat rings be, in most cases, of the renewable type?

On split body valves, should the standard ensure, for safety reasons, that split-body valves would not be used unless approved by the plant control engineer?

On ball valves, should the standard recommend the use of fire-safe seals and anti-static features where necessary? Where a ball valve body is welded into the line, should its construction allow removal of the ball with the body in-line?

Should the standard recommend that ball valves not be used for flashing or cavitating service?

Should valves on slurry lines be full-bore ball valves or diaphragm valves?

On butterfly valves, should the standard recommend they be sized for a maximum flow at 60 degrees? Is an exception permitted for characterized valves (such as the "fishtail") that may be sized at 90 degrees?

On highly erosive fluid, should the standard recommend full port valves with no obstruction?

If a single valve cannot provide both tight shutoff and good control, should the standard recommend the use of two separate valves, each doing a separate function?

When selecting a valve, should the standard ensure that the valves does not operate below its 10% opened position, since below this point valve characteristics tend to be unreliable?

If the valve is to operate under high pressure drops, should there be an investigation of the possible transient noise and cavitation?

Should each valve be capable of withstanding a test pressure equal to 1.5 times the maximum specified operating pressure under certain conditions (e.g., for 5 minutes at 70°F or 20°C) without any damage or signs of leakage?

To avoid corrosion problems, should cast iron and bronze bodies be used for air, steam, and water? For other applications, should the standard recommend that the plant's engineering group be consulted?

Should the standard recommend that valve packing material under the operating conditions be:

1. elastic and easily deformable,
2. chemically inert,
3. as frictionless as possible, and
4. easily accessible for maintenance?

Should the standard specifically state that for applications that are toxic or environmentally hazardous, bellows seals are required?

Trim

The three most common trims are the linear, the equal percentage, and the quick-opening. Should the standard recommend the following?

1. Linear trims may be used where
   - the pressure drop across the valve is always more than 45% of the total pressure drop,
   - the corrective action is to be linear with opening, or
   - the process lags are small.
2. Equal percentage trim be used where
   - the pressure drop across the valve at design conditions is less than 45% of the total drop,
   - the available overpressure drop varies widely
   - the process maximum pressure and maximum temperature occur at the same time (are these conditions transitional or continuous),

- the valve capacity required is not certain,
- considerable lags are present in the system, or
- the pressure drop across the valve varies more than about 2:1.

3. Quick-opening trim may be used only for on-off service.

The seat, plug, and stem should be generally of 316 S.S. for pressure drop up to 700 kPa and hardened alloy steel for higher pressure drops unless materials of higher quality are required by pipeline or vessel specifications.

Some corporate standards may include a table that gives a comparison of the different types of valves and their features to facilitate the selection process. Where acceptable to a corporation, and depending on the experience of its users, a standard may adapt a general recommendation that may simply state, for example:

1. linear valves are to be used where the measurement is linear and the pressure drop across the valve is relatively constant;
2. equal percentage valves are to be used where the valve pressure drop decreases as the flow increases; and
3. quick-opening valves are to be used for on-off operations only.

Actuators

Should all valve actuators normally operate on a 3–15 psig (20–100 kPag) signal? Are all diaphragms in the plant standardized to a 3–15 psig (20–100 kPag) signal?

Is an air vessel required to assist in the failure mode of the valve?

For cylinder-operated valves, should the cylinders be designed to operate with 60 psig (400 kPag) air pressure and withstand 100 psig (700 kPag)?

Should all tubing for cylinder-operated valves be specified to be 3/8 in. minimum? Is copper acceptable or should stainless steel (or other material) be used instead?

Should the standard contain a guide as to when to use valve positioners? For example, the standard may state that valve positioners (with integral bypass valve and three gages—supply, input, and output) are normally provided on control valves for the following:

1. Pressure differential of 1500 kPa and higher
2. Flashing liquids
3. Slurries or highly viscous liquids or whenever high valve stem forces are expected
4. Double-acting pistons used as actuators
5. Where tight valve shutoff is required
6. Valves used on split range (without positioner bypass)
7. Three-way, butterfly, and ball throttling valves
8. Valves 4 in. and larger
9. Valves with extended stems for radiating fins and extension bonnets .

Note: Exposed feedback linkages should be avoided wherever possible.

Since a valve positioner is a secondary loop that must be faster than its primary loop (i.e., the main control loop), valve positioners may in some cases be detrimental to the control loop. Should the standard also indicate when valve positioners should not be used? For example, the standard may state that on fast loops such as flow and liquid pressure, positioners degrade the performance since the secondary loop (the positioner) is slower than the primary loop. Should the standard recommend volume boosters in this case?

Note that when volume boosters are used

1. a local reservoir may be needed to ensure air supply at full instrument air pressure with a check valve to prevent air loss, and
2. a larger than 1/4 in. (for example, 1/2 in.) connection is required between the actuator and the booster.

Should the standard recommend that all actuators be mounted with their spindles vertical?

Is the opening or closing speed of importance to the process? Note that large valves fitted with positioners may take up to a minute to respond; small on-off valves can respond in less than a second.

Should the stroking speed of a control valve with positioner mounted be specified in the standard (e.g., not exceed 10 seconds for valves up to and including 6 inch nominal size, and 15 seconds for larger valves, except when other speeds are required by the process)?

Two common accessories of control valve actuators are position switches and solenoid valves. Should the standard specify that all position switches mounted on valves be of a certain type (e.g., proximity type and hermetically sealed)? Should the solenoid valves be capable of a satisfactory performance when the supply voltage drops below its nominal value (e.g., 85% of nominal value)?

If position-sensing switches are required, should they be integral to the positioner?

Should the standard recommend that valve action on air and power failure be to a fail-safe position?

What is the failure mode of the valve? This failure covers either pneumatic or electronic signals.

Should handwheels be limited to the few cases in which such a handwheel is essential to process operation? Should the design ensure that such handwheels are easily accessible and can be maneuvered by a single average-strength person?

Pressure-Relieving Devices

As a starting point, it is recommended that the standard clearly states the following:

1. All applicable codes must be followed without exception.
2. The design and application of all pressure relief systems must be in strict accordance with the codes and standards in effect at the site.

3. Safety/relief valves should be leak tested and pressure set by the manufacturer.
4. Certified reports (indicating the actual test conditions) must be submitted to the plant.

Should safety/relief valves installed on lines that carry inert gases (such as nitrogen or carbon dioxide) be normally piped to vent outside the process building (unless hazardous vapors may also be present)?

When relieving systems discharge into common headers (which should be minimized within practical limits), should the standard highlight the possibility of back pressures, the effects of which may be radically different on different types of devices?

Should all safety/relief valves be of the direct spring type, approved and stamped by the authority having site jurisdiction (e.g., ASME)?

Should the standard limit the use of certain materials? For example, bronze and cast iron body safety/relief valves would not be used except for air, steam, and water.

Should safety/relief valves have lifting levers for steam, water, and air services? Should a plain cap be generally used for all other conditions?

Should any changes to the application or setting be preceded by a hazard study and approved by a responsible plant engineer?

Should relief devices be sized only according to an approved calculation?

Should relief devices be inspected, tested, and maintained by authorized personnel only? Is training required?

Should the maintenance records of relief devices be available for auditing purposes? How long should the records be kept?

Should each relief device have a nameplate that shows model number, serial number, manufacturer's name, size (in × out), set pressure, certified capacity, and the code of authority (e.g, ASME)?

Is an isolating valve present in the piping between the protected process and the relief device? If yes, is it locked open? Are there clear procedures for closing the isolation valve?

Should the standard ensure that the relief device downstream piping is always

1. free from restriction,
2. well drained,
3. protected from freezing,
4. shielded from bird nests,
5. supported for thrusts,
6. directed to a safe area, and
7. free of any back pressure?

If the service is corrosive or dirty, is it possible to damage or clog the relief device?

Should the standard recommend that, on corrosive or clogging duties, rupture discs be installed between the relief valve and the process? Should the standard ensure that special rupture disks are used (standard ones may fragment and damage or clog the relief device)?

Should the space between the rupture disc and the relief device be monitored for pressure (check methods recommended by the code in effect at the site)? Should a local pressure gage and alarm be required between each disk and relief valve?

CONTROL ROOM INSTRUMENTATION

Modern control systems are mainly computer-based. This subject is covered later on this chapter under programmable electronic systems (PESs). However, stand-alone control room instruments such as controllers, recorders, and annunciators are still used. The designer and, hence, the developer of the corporate standard may need to keep in mind the following points.

Controllers

In many of the applications, controller functions are part of a larger machine such as a DCS or a PLC. This section addresses the individual, stand-alone controllers. Those controllers have evolved from being simple three-mode pneumatic controllers to microprocessor-based units with self-tuning, logic control capabilities, digital communication, etc. The following questions should prompt the developer of the corporate standard to consider the requirements when preparing a section in the standard for specifying such devices.

Is there a need to consider the effect the controller mode will have on the process (i.e., if left on manual)? Is this acceptable as a temporary condition? For how long? Should the transfer from auto mode to manual mode be a closely controlled activity?

How critical is the performance of the PID function? Should all control functions be well tuned? How are disturbances rectified? Should the stability of the process be checked against trends and recorder charts? Who does this checking?

To allow for future modifications, should all controllers of the PID type have switching devices for bumpless control transfer from automatic to manual and manual to automatic? Should this switching device be supplied with the instrument (rather than a future to-be-added option)?

Should all controllers have direct-reading scales (multipliers permitted) whenever possible?

Should level instruments indicate 0–100% level, while all other instrument scales be in engineering units? Should all controllers have a scale range approximately 30% greater than the expected operating range? Should all indications of controller outputs be 0 to 100% with 0 corresponding to valve closed?

Should all controllers that receive an electronic set point signal from an external source be equipped with a remote/local set point switch and permit bumpless transfer between set point sources?

In controllers that may develop reset wind-up because of their function, should they have a built-in external feedback connection (or anti-reset wind-up) to prevent such an occurrence?

In the rare cases where recording controllers are used, should indicating controllers plus separate recorders be required?

When specifying pneumatic controllers, should they be of the valve-mounted type? Should a maximum error of ±1% of span be specified to maintain good control?

Should power to field transmitters always be specified as part of the controller?

For panel-mounted controllers, do the cutout dimensions fit the existing panel space? Are the required power needs available?

Does the controller have sufficient input/output capabilities to handle the process requirements? What about future requirements?

Is the controller rated for the environment in which it operates?

For programmable controllers, is the programming simple to understand? Is special training required? Can the configuration/programming be documented?

Are specific communication requirements needed? Are they within the capabilities of the controller? If connection to a PC or to a DCS is required, is the software available? If not, what is involved in its development?

Is an external device needed for configuration and loop tuning? Is configuration retained on power loss? How is the configuration transferred to a new instrument?

Is the operation of the controller complicated? Will it potentially confuse the operator?

Should the controller include alarm annunciation in the form of LEDs? Are the alarms easy to understand? Are they secure from tampering?

How is the operation affected in case of controller failure? Is there a manual system that takes over or does a shutdown occur? Is the selected condition acceptable? Has the consequence of such failure been assessed and consider acceptable? Is this assessment made by one person, or is it the result of a team approach (for example, at a hazard study meeting)?

What is the action of the controller in case of power outage? Is this action selectable?

What is the action of the controller on sudden power restart? Is this action controllable?

Does the controller have internal diagnostics? Are they activated only on power-up? Or continuously?

What access protection is included for tuning parameters and configuration?

Is there a need to provide the capability to be able to manually operate the final control device (e.g., control valve) when the controller is removed (e.g., for maintenance)?

Recorders

General requirements for recorders, as for any other instrument, will vary according to plant needs. Having a section in the corporate standard that addresses these instruments will reduce errors and re-engineering, thereby increasing quality and reducing design time. In general, recorders may be broken down into two main types: continuous trace (the conventional type) and digital (microprocessor-based type), with some general requirements applying to both types. The following questions may help the producer of such a standard.

General Requirements

Should the standard clearly recommend that:

1. the chart scale be linear,
2. the visible chart portion in the closed instrument covers a minimum amount of time (e.g., 8 hours),
3. unless otherwise specified, the chart speed be of a certain speed (e.g., 20 mm/h), and
4. the chart length be sufficient for continuous service (e.g., for 32 days)?

Should alarm switches be specified to be independently adjustable? Should their range cover 100% of the scale length?

Is there a requirement for signal conditioning, such as attenuation, linearization, compensation, computation, filtering, etc.?

When the instrument is disconnected from its plug-in cable or when the power supply is switched off, should the control loop remain closed? Should this feature be automatic to protect the system from upsets that may occur during maintenance conditions? Is it acceptable that reconnection of the instrument to the control loop may cause upsets?

Is the instrument accuracy equal to or better than the least precise element in the measuring loop?

Is the maintenance of recorders a problem? Are charts and pens changed regularly?

Continuous Trace Recorders

Should the standard recommend that for such instruments a separate, non-clogging inking system be provided for each recorder pen?

Should sealed, replaceable ink cartridges be used? Should the ink level in the cartridge be clearly visible when the recorder door is open?

How much ink should the ink cartridges contain (e.g., four-month supply)? Should the cartridges be fitted with a means for starting the ink flow?

Should each pen circuit be independent? Is it a requirement to ensure that failure of one (or more) pen circuit must not affect operation of the remaining circuits?

Digital Recorders

Should the mechanism display the point number for each point as its value is being printed? Should the recorder support an indicator for the recorder scale?

Is there a need for an LED display of the data being printed? How many digits? Is the display in engineering units?

Should the instrument record a multiple number of different points at a minimum acceptable frequency (e.g., six seconds per cycle)?

Are mathematical calculations required such as $+$, $-$, $\times$, $/$, square root, etc.? Are there needs for averages or statistical functions?

Should any descriptive data be printed, such as date/time, scale range, chart speed, and/or user-defined messages?

How many types of inputs are required to be fed into the recorders (mA, mV, A, V, T/C, RTD, strain gage, etc.)?

Are self-diagnostics required?

Should the recorder be connected to a PC?

Are there requirements for password protection?

Annunciators

Does the operation of the annunciator require particularly high reliability?

Should the annunciator be regularly tested?

Should its sequence in accordance with ANSI/ISA-S18.1?

ALARM AND TRIP SYSTEMS

Alarm and trip systems (ATSs) protect only when they work; they are the safety net of a plant from a control system point of view. Not only should this net exist, it should also be functional. The designer and maintenance personnel have the responsibility of assuring that the plant is protected by such functionality. The corporate standard should state the guidelines to be met by all personnel to achieve the required reliability.

The purpose of a plant ATS is to provide warnings and to take protective or corrective action when a fault condition occurs. For example, an ATS could alarm and shut down the process in an orderly fashion, or it could switch over from some defective unit (such as a pump) to a standby unit.

There are many types of alarm and trip systems. They vary from electromechanical relays to solid-state relays, to programmable electronic systems (PESs). Each has its applications, advantages, and disadvantages.

The corporate standards should generally cover the following important aspects of ATSs:

1. Their design
2. Their reliability

3. Their documentation
4. Their testing and maintenance

The approach one takes in the handling and management of ATSs is very important. One such approach is to break them down into components. If they are considered as components, they become easier to handle from design to testing. This is the approach that is taken here; it could be the one used in the development of the corporate standard. A typical ATS consists of three basic components: input, logic, and output. Note: All components require a dependable power supply (and quite often a UPS to ensure reliable operation).

Input

The input converts process variables to the digital form that is required by the logic unit. For analog signals this conversion includes a comparison to a set point. Typical forms of inputs include self-contained devices, such as limit switches and push buttons, or systems that consist of a measuring element, a transmitter, a comparator, and a digital output. The following may need to be considered by the standard.

> Whenever possible, are the sensing elements installed in such a way that testing can be done without disconnecting wires or loosening pipe or tubing connections? For example, the impulse line between the process and a pressure switch may include a tee and a shutoff valve.

> Is it possible that "bouncing"may occur (such as on liquid levels)? If yes, this may cause annoying alarms and trips that may be disabled by the operator and lead to a dangerous situation. Is the introduction of a delay of a few seconds (or a deadband) acceptable?

> Are hermetically sealed contacts required (to avoid corrosion, dust, and contact film)?

> Should the logic output be fed back as an input to confirm the trip action (e.g., a limit switch on the stem of a trip valve)?

> Has the fail-safe mode vs. nuisance shutdowns been assessed?

Logic

The logic takes the input(s) and produces one or more output signals. The logic is performed by such devices as electromechanical relays or microprocessor-based programmable systems. Programmable systems are more reliable than relays, but typical programmable systems, due to the nature of solid-state electronics, have an unpredictable failure mode and, therefore, are generally not used in critical applications unless special precautions are taken. (The following section in this chapter provides further information on programmable electronic systems).

Programmable systems are also usually easier to use and modify than relays. In addition, the presentation of information and the logging of activities can be made clearer and more comprehensive, including monitoring any ATS overrides or defeats used during commissioning.

Another concern about programmable systems, in addition to their nonfail-safe feature, is the potential implementation of modifications to the software logic without discipline. The standard should cover this point and provide guidelines regarding any such modifications. All hardware and software modifications should be carefully controlled, their effects carefully studied, and their implementation carried out only by trained personnel. IEEE Std 730.1-1989, "IEEE Standard for Software Quality Assurance Plans," covers applications for the development and maintenance of software for critical applications. This standard may be used as a starting point where such a quality assurance plan is required.

Output

The output converts the results from the logic to one or more process variables. Typical forms of outputs include solenoid valves, trip relays, and so on.

The standard needs to ensure that most output devices should fail safe, i.e., a motor should stop on loss of control signals, a valve should fail in the safe process condition on failure of signal or air supply, etc. In addition, the failure mode of output devices must be carefully studied; both signal and power failure must be taken into account as well as the behavior of such output devices on sudden signal or power resumption.

Design

Most standards need a section on the design philosophy of ATSs. This ensures that basic requirements of performance and safety are understood and met. Obviously, and as a first step, the local legislative requirements in effect at the site must be followed.

A good design must consider many parameters. One of the most important is ATS failure. After the implementation under the best conditions from design to testing and maintenance, failure of ATSs will still occur due to their life expectancy. To increase reliability, dual and triple ATSs may be used in parallel. In this case, a key factor to watch for is common mode failure. For example, if a float is used to detect high level in a tank, there is a relatively high probability that with a second switch of the same type (i.e., float) failure will occur within a close time frame. A quick answer to this is to have, where possible, two different methods of measurements. For example, if one switch is a float, the other could be a capacitance probe.

The questions that follow provide a guide to producing such a design philosophy for the corporate standard. Obviously, some modifications will be required to adjust for plant needs and working conditions.

> Has it been checked that, for all processes, the failure of alarms and control systems will not result in hazardous conditions?
>
> Is there a need to incorporate in the design prewarning alarms, so that the operator could be notified prior to a shutdown? This is good practice, especially in today's modern control systems where this requirement could easily be implemented at minimum cost.
>
> Is the design based on the most direct measurement, logic, and output action?
>
> Are these processes provided with two systems of control — one control system for normal operation and one for ATS? Should the standard recommended that these two systems be as separate as possible to minimize the possibility that a common failure would affect both? For example, if a probe is used for level control, it might be appropriate to use a floatswitch for the ATS.

In very critical conditions, does the ATS require a two-out-of-three vote from the sensor all the way to the final control element? Is this decision based on a reliability calculation?

Can trip bypasses be avoided, particularly on critical trips? If bypasses are required, should they be automatically reset by timers?

How does the plant ensure the proper functioning and reliability of the ATSs (including their power supply system)?

Has it been assessed that the failure of the ATS could result in significant material damage, harm to the environment, and, more importantly, loss of life?

Is the ATS scheduled to be tested on a regular basis to ensure functionality? How is this testing frequency determined?

Is the design to be done such that the ATS will fail-safe?

- Does sensor failure cause the alarm or trip to activate and go to the fail-safe condition?
- If a high process value is the trip condition, is the sensor reverse acting (i.e., high value generates a low signal)?
- Is electrical isolation required? A grounded temperaure element without isolation may fail in an unsafe mode (stray currents).
- Do the initiating contacts energize to close during normal operation and deenergize to open when the alarm or trip condition occurs?
- Do solenoid valves energize under normal operating conditions but deenergize to trip?
- Do pneumatically operated trip valves move to a safe trip position on air supply failure? Where positioners are used in control valves, should the standard recommend the solenoid be located between the positioner and the actuator?
- Does the ATS failure cause an alarm or trip (i.e., it draws attention to itself and to the need for correction before operation can be resumed)?

It should be noted here that a system cannot be safe unless it fails in a safe mode.

Where electromechanical relays are used, should the standard ensure that:

1. they are of a specific make,
2. the contacts are hermetically sealed,
3. arc suppression is used where required, and
4. the effects of coil spring failure have been assessed?

Has the reliability of ATSs been achieved through:

1. their fundamental design,
2. the conditions under which they operate,
3. the capabilities of plant personnel through proper training, and
4. the frequency at which they are tested?

Are the ATSs designed to fail safe?

Is there a description of the different elements and actions of all ATS points (the ATS description)? Does the description meet the plant requirements? Does the description conform to other documents?

Do all documents convey the same message (i.e., no contradiction between logic diagrams, interlock diagrams, program printouts, etc.)?

Have all the ATS components been identified (i.e., inputs, logic, and outputs)? Are the components and their interaction clearly described? What documents describe them?

Reliability

Is reliability analysis part of the design process?

Should the design consider the possibility of errors by operations and maintenance? Should the design be independently reviewed upon completion?

Should the design use different methods of measurements? Are these methods of measurement as close as possible to the parameters to be identified?

Does the ATS use also different input/output channels? Are they physically segregated?

Are all ATS systems fail-safe wherever possible?

Are calibration adjustments limited to prevent adjustments into the dangerous range?

During testing and maintenance, should an ATS with a 2-out-of-3 vote be switched to operate as a 1-out-of-2?

Should common points such as junction boxes, cable runs, etc., be protected from outside hazards such as fire, heat sources, etc.?

Should the standard recommend the use of a proven design for at least one of the channels? Should innovative designs be allowed only for the remaining two (or more) channels?

Should the equipment selected operate under conditions well below their maximum limits?

Are the operating, testing, and maintenance procedures (which are prepared at the design stage) as simple as possible?

Are multirange instruments avoided?

Are design and displays as simple as possible?

Does the standard recommend that only quality components be used?

Should the standard recommend procedures so that calibration and testing will not cause or introduce any unrevealed faults?

Should an independent team review the design, the reliability calculations, the guidelines and procedures for construction, the operation, and the maintenance and testing procedures?

Documentation

As was mentioned earlier, the testing of ATSs is essential to their functionality and, therefore, their reliability. The implementation of such reliability, from a documentation point of view, is through two items of ATS documentation: the ATS description and the ATS testing procedure.

Good documentation begins during design and carries through the commissioning, the start-up, and the lifetime of a plant. During design, the hazards that require alarms or trips may be identified in the front-end engineering, in the hazard analysis studies, and in drawings such as interlock diagrams and logic diagrams. In all cases, ATSs must be clearly identified and should be kept up to date as the system evolves.

The key document that results from this process and should be audited is the ATS description. On this document, and for each alarm and trip function in the plant, the standard may require that the following data be recorded:

1. Tag number of each input (initiator), and the normal, alarm, and trip values for each input
2. Trip logic (actions generated by the trip logic)
3. Output actions of the trip (as well as other trips connected to this one)

This document in most cases is prepared jointly by the process engineer and the control engineer.

The alarm and trip description is an essential starting point for any process with ATSs. This document is needed not only for testing purposes but also for normal plant operation and, in most cases, is incorporated into the plant operating manuals. On very small applications, the ATS description could be part of the logic diagrams (additional information on logic diagrams can be found in Chapter 4). It is recommended that the ATS description be a separate document to provide quick and clear information to plant operating personnel the moment they need it. It is worth noting that the ATS description is not complete; it does not include the reasons for having a particular alarm or trip or why a trip is set at a particular value. This information may be found in other documents such as design notes and plant operating manuals. Two additional points must be considered by a corporate standard:

1. Will all these documents be accessible?
2. Will they always be maintained up to date?

An example of a completed ATS description is shown as Figure 6-3. The measurement column indicates that a flow transmitter (FT-127) is measuring flow with a range of 0–100 l/h. A switch set at 15 l/h acts as a warning for the trip function. The third column describes the trip initiators FSLL-127 (set at 7 l/h) and PSL-139 (set at 5 kPa). When both occur (AND gate), the interlock I-2 is activated, closing FV-128, which then stops the flow into tank T25. It is recommended that each trip action (in the case of this example, the tripping of FV-128) be described on a separate sheet of the ATS description and be given a number (in this case, I2).

Testing and Maintenance

Testing is essential in ensuring the functionality of ATSs, in particular those that protect the plant from critical events. The following questions could be used to assess the efficiency of the testing and maintenance activities.

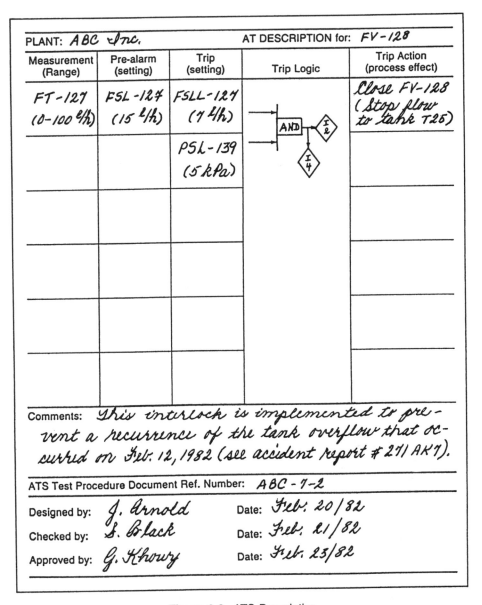

Figure 6-3. ATS Description

Is there a description of the different elements and actions of all ATS points (the ATS description)? Does it meet the plant requirements? Does it conform with other documents?

Is there a procedure for performing the testing of ATSs? Does the procedure conform to good engineering practices? Are the ATS test results recorded? Do the records describe the test, deficiencies, and corrective actions? Where are the records kept?

Is the ATS testing performed by plant personnel and/or outside contractors?

How is the frequency of ATS testing for all points determined? Is there a procedure for modifying this frequency? Is the procedure documented? Where is the document(s)?

Can the ATS be deactivated or bypassed? Does this occur during testing or maintenance only? Who controls the deactivation or bypassing of ATSs? Are procedures provided?

Should the maintenance of the ATS be done only one channel at a time?

Should the standard ensure that operations and maintenance preserve the design intent and reliability of the system (including assumed environmental conditions)?

Has the training covered the ATS and its operation/function?

Should modifications and maintenance be strictly controlled and monitored? Are they authorized by a responsible person?

Should maintenance and testing activities and results be recorded to measure equipment reliability and adjust the test frequency?

Should all maintenance activities be followed by an independent test?

Should failed components be repaired as soon as possible? Are they repaired to their original design (including identical components)?

An example of a completed test procedure is shown in Figure 6-4.

PROGRAMMABLE ELECTRONIC SYSTEMS

With the majority of modern control systems incorporating computers and their communication networks, the use of programmable electronic systems (PESs) as control systems is increasing at a substantial rate. Corporations or their engineering groups may decide to cover the activities related to such systems in a corporate standard. The successful implementation, system selection, design, testing, and maintenance of such systems are, even for the experienced, a difficult activity.

The definition of a PES, as used in control systems, is a broad one that includes a variety of devices such as distributed control systems, microprocessor-based stand-alone PID controllers, programmable controllers (PLCs), personal computers (PCs), distributed control systems (DCSs), direct digital control (DDC), and display systems that consist of CRTs, keyboards, printers, and communication links.

Those elements that are required for compatible interconnection of stations by way of a local area network (LAN) using the token-bus access method in an industrial environment are described in ISA-S72.01, PROWAY-LAN, Industrial Data Highway (see Appendix B),

System Implementation

The implementation of PESs as control systems must be well thought out before equipment purchase and installation. The standard is a good vehicle to provide such guidelines on the selection process. However, it should be kept in mind that with the ever-changing technology, it is very difficult to pinpoint a clear guide as to what

PLANT: ABC, Inc.   ATS TEST PROCEDURE for: *FV-128*

Test Frequency: *Yearly*

Hazards: Highly corrosive (refer to safety procedures SP7215)

Reference Information: Instrument Index sheet # *ABC-7-2*

Requirements—Personnel: 2 maintenance (1 piping and 1 instrument);
Equipment: 2 pressure testers, model AK78, and stand, tool box.

Test Procedures:
1. Advise operator and get work permit.
2. Activate I2 bypass switch (SW7) on control panel and ensure bypass light is ON.
3. Isolate FSLL-127 (a diff. press. switch) from process, open tee shut-off valve V36 and drain fluid in impulse line.
4. Inject regulated air signal into FSLL-127, bring to diff. press. of 5″ WC (= to 7 l/hr)—check that trip switch activates.
5. Isolate PSL-139 from process, open tee shut-off valve V37, and drain fluid in impulse line.
6. Inject regulated air into PSL-139 and bring to 5 kPa—check that trip switch activates.
7. Now that both switches are activated, check that logic has activated, and send a command to trip FV-128 (but bypassed by SW7).
8. Close the two isolation valves for FSLL-17 and PSL-139 (V36 + V37) and reconnect to process.
9. Deactivate I2 bypass switch SW7.
10. Advise control room operator of completion and return work permit.
End of Test Procedure.

ATS Description Document Ref. Number: *ABC-7-1*

Designed by: *S. Black*   Date: *6 Mar. 82*

Checked by: *K. Red*   Date: *6 Mar. 82*

Approved by: *J. Smith*   Date: *10 Mar. 82*

Figure 6-4. Completed ATS Test Procedure

type of PES to use in which control application. The standard may define general guidelines; however, the experience and knowledge of the user is essential.

The standard should help its users follow a systematic approach. A key tool for such an activity is the preparation of a system specification before purchasing. Such a document needs to be reviewed and accepted by all involved. The reason for such a document is that, with such a variety of products and functions to be matched between the plant needs on one hand and the available equipment from vendors on the other hand, errors can easily occur. The result of such errors is either a system that cannot perform its intended function or an oversized system that is a waste of money. A checklist that shows the content of such a system specification is shown in Appendix G. Such a checklist acts as a memory jogger when identifying the requirements of a PES.

As part of the selection activities in the implementation process, the standard may need to define the basic types of typical PES-based control systems. The two main reasons for such a definition are: (1) to have an agreed upon terminology and definitions and (2) to have a vehicle (the standard) for highlighting the advantages and disadvantages of the different types and for recommending the selection of one type over the other. Obviously, such a decision is dependent upon the type of industry in question, on the application and its requirements, on the corporate culture, and on the company's past experience.

The implementation of PESs is accomplished through a number of steps that are described in the following sections:

1. An understanding of definition and terminology
2. A selection of the best PES type suited for the application
3. Consideration of the design requirements
4. Considerations for testing and maintenance

The following is an example of how such a definition may look in the standard. It is a suggested format that should be adjusted to reflect the particular needs of the corporation.

PES Definition

Control systems using PESs can generally be classified into two major types: distributed control (such as PLC/PC and DCS) and centralized control (such as DDC). In distributed control systems, the control and input/output functions are located in equipment that is situated close to the process it controls, while the operator interface is in a remote control room. Typically, distributed controls can be distributed control systems (DCSs) or programmable controller/personal computer (PLC/PC) combinations with a PC-based operator interface software package (in many cases, from a third-party supplier). In numerous cases, a combination of PLCs and DCSs are used for plant control, utilizing the advantages of each type. However, as time goes by, the demarcation line between DCSs and PLCs/PCs is becoming harder to define. It is quite possible that in the near future little or no difference will exist between the two as their architecture and functionalities become similar.

In the case of centralized control, the inputs and outputs may be remotely located, but all control functions as well as the operator interface are centrally located. In most cases, these I/O racks have no intelligence, and their sole purpose is I/O signal handling between the process and the computer. Centralized control (also sometimes known as direct digital control (DDC)) consists of a mainframe, a minicomputer, or a microcomputer to which are connected remote or local I/O terminals.

In addition to defining the types of controls and depending on the level of technology and expertise available within a corporation, the standard may need a definition of system components. The following shows how the typical PES may be broken down into hardware and software components. A corporate standard may easily follow this same breakdown.

□ HARDWARE

The hardware for such systems consists, in general, of four basic functional components: inputs/outputs, processor (CPU), memory, and power supply. These components can be localized, distributed, duplicated, and/or combined. (The standard may then expand on the functionality of each of these components, depending on the level of expertise and culture of the company.)

When computer devices communicate with each other, each requires a communication port. The data is transmitted from port to port according to a well defined protocol. The link between ports is established through networks. Many types of networks are available, each with its advantages and disadvantages. They vary physically (twisted-pair, coaxial, fiber optics, wireless) as well as functionally (token passing, star, Ethernet). In some instances, to ensure signal transmission reliability, redundant communication networks are implemented to protect the operation in case of failure. In such a case the standard may recommend that each of the two networks be routed through separate routes to minimize the chance of a break in the line, which would shut down both communication links. The standard may request that diagnostics capabilities for network systems (and for the entire computer system as well) should be available and should be as simple as possible to understand and use.

□ SOFTWARE

The system software consists of two main parts: the operating software and the application software. The first is a basic requirement that tells the computer how to function; the second is related to the application for which the computer is used (i.e., the generation of graphics, alarms, etc.). The system software, in most cases, includes certain built-in capabilities (sometimes known as firmware). These capabilities include input/output signal linearization and conversion, filtration and digitizing of analog input signals, out-of-range signal detection (e.g., open input circuit), etc.

System Selection

The standard may also recommend a direction to take (i.e., DCS or PLC/PC or DDC). However, the debate over the pros and cons of each philosophy is an ongoing activity, and, with the technology changing at such a fast pace, it is best left to the discretion of experienced control engineers. Nevertheless, and as a starting point, the comparison that follows summarizes some of the present differences between DCSs, PLC/PCs, and DDCs. Such a comparison, or a similar one tailored to the needs of a specific business and process, may be developed and included in the standard as a guide to the selection process. It should be noted that these points carry different weights under different conditions. For example, if the process is very intricate and involves the handling of massive data at high speeds and the performance of sophisticated calculations, then a DDC is the obvious choice. The number of disadvantages under DDC would take a back seat in this case.

Regardless of which system is selected, the standard may need to ensure that the interface between the operator and the process is to be maintained at all times. Therefore, there may be a need in the standard to recommend that, for day-to-day operation, a minimum of two CRTs are to be used. They would operate in parallel with individual operator keyboards. The operator keyboard is more rugged than the engineering keyboard, and its layout is more friendly and simpler to use for operators.

Distributed Control System

☐ **ADVANTAGES:**

A. DCSs in most cases interface with smart transmitters.
B. Ease of implementation and modification, since configuration rather than programming is the typical implementation method.

☐ **DISADVANTAGES:**

A. DCS costs are high when compared with the PLC/PC combination.
B. Specialized support from engineering personnel is generally required.
C. The simplicity of configuration advantage creates a limited functionality versus PLC/PCs and DDC.
D. DCSs require a reasonably clean control room environment.
E. Tied up to a specific vendor.

Programmable Logic Controller/Personal Computer Combination

☐ **ADVANTAGES:**

A. PLC/PC systems are relatively low in cost.
B. They have a versatile line of I/Os.
C. Operator acceptance is easier to achieve.
D. Some PLCs interface with smart transmitters.
E. PLC programming software may allow different programming languages
F. The PLC programming software may be used to simulate the PLC in operation with the process — a very useful feature when debugging the program.
G. The PLC and the PC offer an affordable increase in functionality if a future need arises, such as multiple processors for dedicated and high-speed control or built-in microcomputers to perform high-speed communication and reduce the interference problems.

☐ **DISADVANTAGES:**

A. Sometimes separate suppliers for hardware/software create problems in identifying the responsibilities for malfunctions or for establishing communication links.
B. PLC/PCs have limited capabilities versus DDC for advanced control strategies.
C. If more than one PC connects to the PLC (which is highly recommended), creating a common database between the two PCs is difficult.
D. Implementing advanced control strategies in a PLC is difficult.

Two more points must be considered in the case of PLC/PC systems:

1. The line of functional demarcation between these two devices. This has been (and still is) a point of debate, but some corporate standards have been using the following philosophy: PLC is for process control and data collection (PID, logic, simple mathematics); PC is for PLC programming and documentation

and the operator interface (graphics, alarms, trends, reports, batch recipes) so that if the PC fails, the process is still under control. This philosophy ensures that on failure of the supervisory equipment, the independent controllers and/or PLCs maintain full control of the process. In the case of DCSs and DDCs, the decision about where the control functions are performed is preset and cannot be changed.

2. The PLC program documentation (also know as program description). Such documentation must be well implemented. Without it, program modifications become difficult tasks that are prone to errors and misinterpretations. The content of the documentation will vary depending on the complexity of the application and the familiarity of the support staff with the program. In the particular case of PLCs, their flexibility gives them the power required for many applications. However, such flexibility must be governed by a set standard on how to document the program; otherwise, a mishmash of hard to decipher codes are left for the person required to implement modifications (a messy and costly activity). Guidelines for what is to be contained and how the documentation should look is essential. Some corporations even clearly specify which programming software must be used.

Typical PLC program documentation may have to conform, as an example, to the following requirements:

1. The programming shall be developed on an IBM^{TM}-compatible PC and be written in format as requested by the plant.
2. The CRT shall display a minimum of 8 programming lines.
3. The individual I/O description at the rung shall show:
   - on the first line, the tag number (e.g., LSH-123);
   - on the second line, a description (e.g., TANK 17); and
   - on the third line, any notes. In addition, all outputs/inputs shall be cross-referenced to the rung(s) to which they connect.
4. Each rung and each section of the program (containing many rungs) shall be clearly explained. Up to 16 lines can be used for each rung. The ability to display or not to display the rung descriptions shall be available.
5. The PLC program will be simulated on the PC prior to commissioning, and the software used will have the ability to compare two programs and flag the differences.
6. The software used must comply with the plant requirements.

In some cases, computers (for the most part personal computers) and conventional instrumentation equipment (e.g., stand-alone PID controller) operate in tandem. In such cases, the PC generally acts as a supervisor, performing such tasks as set point adjustments, data collection, report generation, and data storage. Stand-alone PID controllers are dedicated to the control of the process according to their set points and/or set programs. In other cases, PID controllers are sometimes complemented (and sometimes altogether replaced) by programmable controllers (PLCs). The choice between the stand-alone PID controller and the PLC is generally based on the process control requirements. This choice would be hard to define in a corporate standard due to the ever-changing technology and available equipment.

Direct Digital Control

☐ **ADVANTAGES:**

A. The most powerful of control systems and the most flexible.
B. Provides custom control strategies not achievable with most DCSs and PLC/PC combinations.

☐ **DISADVANTAGES:**

A. DDC requires specialized support in the form of computer personnel.
B. DDC provides the highest implementation and maintenance costs.
C. They require more time to implement than a DCS or a PLC/PC combination.
D. They require a very clean control room environment.

Two standards for industrial control systems using FORTRAN procedures are ISA-S61.1, Industrial Computer System FORTRAN Procedures for Executive Functions, Process Input/Output, and Bit Manipulation, and ISA-S61.2, Industrial Computer System FORTRAN Procedures for File Access and the Control of File Contention (see Appendix B).

In addition, the requirements to be implemented in a corporate standard may include some specific points. The following questions may help in preparing these requirements.

If the control of equipment requires logic or sequencing, are PLCs systems preferred over relay systems because of their flexibility and reliability? Should they always be considered when logic or sequencing is required?

When PLCs are selected, can they be used for alarms and trips? Should the standard clearly limit the use of conventional PLCs for safety alarm and trips (refer to the section on alarm and trips)?

When implementing PESs as control systems, should the control equipment be supplied with a minimum amount of spare memory and spare input/output capabilities (e.g., 30% for each)?

Should all PES installations provide accessibility and conform to vendor's requirements?

Should the behavior of PESs on power failure be defined? Should the need for battery backup, UPS power supply, etc., be also defined?

Should the standard request that for applications in which safety is in question, any system must fail in a predicable way and the need for UPS power must be considered? In addition, should emergency circuits used for stopping the operation always be routed outside the PES? For example, devices such as end of travel limit switches, emergency stops, or pull cord switches should operate motor starters directly without being processed through PES logic. Should the standard stipulate that such critical circuits be implemented using a minimum number of simple, highly dependable components of an electromechanical nature, if possible?

Is the system designed to provide a convenient means of disconnecting the machine from the controller for use during troubleshooting or setup following maintenance?

□ CRT INTERFACE:

The standard may identify the required points to consider when designing CRT displays.

ISA-S5.3 indicates the requirements for symbolically representing the functions of distributed control or shared display systems (see Appendix B). This standard is applicable to all industries that use process control and instrumentation systems.

The CRT interface has many advantages over conventional control panels. However, the system designer should remember that CRTs provide a limited amount of available information at any one time (the information is serial instead of parallel). Therefore, the distribution of information, its relevance, the number of CRTs, and the final cost and operation should be balanced. Depending on the way a corporation does its work and on the process involved, the standard may need to address this point and provide guidance.

The following questions may help identify some of the key points to be considered when producing a standard on this topic.

Is the operator supplied with all the display and controls required? Has this been checked with the operator?

Is the display information directly related to the information to be represented? Is unrequired information displayed?

Is the displayed information used by other than the operator?

Could the information cause confusion or distraction?

Under stress conditions, is the operator capable of handling all the displayed information?

Has the operator been involved in display development/layout (including color selection)? Are any of the operators color blind?

Is the terminology displayed the same throughout?

Are there sufficient CRTs so that at a certain time a given decision can be taken (consider failure of one CRT, alarms, overviews, etc.)?

For critical actions, should the operator depend on a single key stroke? Is a confirmation key required?

Should error messages be clarified? For example, instead of displaying "entry error," display "entry error: range is between 40 to 60%"?

On critical systems, can instrument failure be identified quickly?

Can the operator check and ensure that the action just taken at the CRT keyboard is the intended one? Can this action be corrected? Is the correction a simple reversing of command?

Has the operator's understanding been checked to ensure that the displays are clear?

Are the displays in a logical/standard sequence?

Design Considerations

Design considerations may be the most critical part of computer- based control systems. This activity generally follows system definition and selection. Its importance stems from the fact that at the design stage, many considerations must be evaluated and decisions taken that, if incorrect, will affect the performance of the control system and eventually of the whole process. Design considerations will eventually be followed by maintenance considerations, which are developed at the design stages in many corporations.

Many of the implementation errors can be minimized and in many cases almost eliminated with a corporate standard that covers the requirements for a well designed, properly installed, and well managed application. At the design stage, some of the items to be considered are:

1. safety and system failure,
2. software development,
3. master safety relay and external watchdog,
4. environmental conditions,
5. documentation, and
6. additional general design considerations.

After the completion of the design activities, a functional testing of the PES is carried out.

□ SAFETY AND SYSTEM FAILURE:

The designer must ensure that such systems are applied safely. The first item to consider is the application; the more critical it is, the more precautions and safety features are required, and vice versa. Second, it is important that vendors' instructions be closely followed to ensure operation within the limits of the control system. Included in these instructions are the grounding and shielding of power and signal wiring as well as the grounding of enclosures.

Without addressing the legal question, the standard must underline the fact that there is a responsibility to ensure the safe application of these control systems, particularly where loss of life and property are possible. Control functions that protect from potentially hazardous conditions are defined as emergency circuits. The standard should address these applications. The following questions help prepare a section on this subject.

> For relay-based trip circuits, are these circuits routed outside the micro-computer-based control system, using a minimum number of simple, highly reliable electromechanical relays? To ensure proper operation, are these relays carefully selected to ensure that the contacts will never weld due to high in-rush currents, therefore maintaining their inherently safe design?

> For the cases in which relays do not meet the requirements, is a programmable electronic system required, such as redundant or triple redundant systems? It should be noted that such systems must be installed in compliance with any regulations in effect at the site, according to good installation practices, and in compliance with the vendor's requirements.

The standard needs to ensure that PESs are implemented to provide a reliable system and minimize system failure. These computer-based control systems are quite reliable by design, but the reliability of such systems has no bearing on whether they will fail in an acceptable mode. No matter how reliable a control system is, it will eventually fail; what must be determined is whether such a failure will cause an unacceptable condition. Code and regulations in effect at the site (e.g., NFPA) will govern the application of PESs in critical applications such as in burner management systems.

It is quite difficult to anticipate the failure mode of a PES. This is due to the nature of solid-state circuitry used in these systems. The following is a listing of the main components of a typical control system with potential problems that could be encountered in each of these components. It is not, however, a presentation of all the potential problems (just to make life more difficult for the person preparing a corporate standard). Of these components, the inputs and outputs are the most vulnerable to damage since they are directly exposed to external influences.

A. Input modules (normally solid-state devices)
- Can the failure mode be ensured?
- Would failure of an input circuit cause a false input into the control system? Would this result in various outputs responding accordingly?

B. Outputs (also normally solid-state devices)
- Could they fail shorted? Would this condition cause the external load to be continuously energized?

C. Control units (comprised of elements such as the CPU and memory boards)
- Could the be affected and even destroyed by electromagnetic or electrostatic interference?
- Would this cause a total shutdown of the control system or, even worse, a partially defective program with the system still in operation?

D. Power supply
- What are the problems encountered on the loss of power supply?
- Are these problems compounded by the sudden reactivation of power, causing often erratic action at the output modules?

Note: In some cases, outputs may operate erratically for a short time immediately after applying or removing power, resulting in hazardous conditions. A means to inhibit outputs through an operator-initiated action until power supplies reach their specified voltage may be required. Behavior on power failure generally needs to be defined, together with any need for a UPS. For critical applications, control systems must fail in a predictable way, and the need for UPS power is a requirement in such cases.

E. Cables interconnecting the different components of a control system
- Could they affect its safe operation if they are removed or short circuited while the system is ON?
- Could these cables pick up electric noise from their surroundings, causing erratic malfunctions within the control system (these problems are generally hard to diagnose)?

F. Communication modules
- If they fail, would this cause an interruption in the communication link and isolation of the affected components from the control system?
- Is such failure more a nuisance than a critical failure?

G. Software
- Will it may fail either due to erroneous programming or due to an involuntary introduced error (for example, electrical noise transmitted to memory)?
- Have the effects been assessed?

As a general rule, corporate standards recommend that the failure mode of loads connected to the output of the control system must be fail-safe. For example, the loss of power or the cutting of a signal cable must maintain the process in a safe mode.

To improve the safe operation and maintenance of a PES-based control system, good monitoring and diagnostics of that system and its functions are recommended. The standard may recommend that this can be accomplished by:

1. displaying all internal faults and status on a dedicated display at the CRT,
2. monitoring the critical output functions through feedback from the process and alarming any discrepancies, and
3. monitoring the status of the power supply.

In some cases, safety functions are too complex to be carried out with hardwired electromechanical relays, yet the use of a standard computer-based control system is not sufficiently safe. In these cases, the standard may recommend the need for a fault-tolerant PES-based ATS. It should be kept in mind that there is a design responsibility to ensure both the legal and safety aspects of such applications.

The justification of a PES-based fault-tolerant system is generally due to their:

1. capability for implementing complex logic,
2. ease of modification, maintenance, and troubleshooting,
3. communication with computer systems, and
4. reporting of shutdown history.

However, it should be mentioned that such systems must be protected from unauthorized changes. In addition, it is good practice to have the PES be able to directly display programmed functions. This allows a true indication of the implemented ATS without the chance of a designer error when developing a graphic.

The standard frequently will define the different types of fault-tolerant systems and may even recommend one type over another. A descriptive direction in the standard (such as the following) could be used as a starting point.

At present, two commercially available and field-proven techniques will achieve these requirements: duplication and triplication. Since both techniques are costly, they are used only where economic and safety considerations are justifiable.

In a control system duplication, two similar computer-based systems operate in parallel, the controlling one and a backup one. The backup system monitors the controlling one and determines its status and health. If the controlling one fails, the backup system takes over immediately. However, in critical applications, a shutdown of the process is initiated if a disagreement develops between the two control systems, since the backup cannot always guarantee which of the two control systems is good.

Control system triplication, also known as triple redundancy, is used where the shutdown of a process can have unacceptable consequences. This method consists of three complete control systems that operate in parallel in such a way that if only one control system fails, safety shutdown does not occur. All control and I/O functions are the result of a two-out-of-three vote and, therefore, at least two of the three channels are functional and perform their control functions. Each of the three control systems has its own monitoring and input/output devices, allowing the failure to be identified and aiding in the repair of faulty components. Triplicated control systems normally offer a repair feature in which faulty components can be replaced on-line without affecting the process.

Control system triplication with fault tolerance is the safest form of industrial PES-based alarm and trip system presently available.

□ SOFTWARE DEVELOPMENT:

The application software is generally the item most prone to errors. This is due to its flexibility and to its "hidden"presence. The standard may recommend basic steps and the assignment of responsibilities to be able to control this problem. The following questions may help the preparer of such a standard identify the points to consider.

Should a software quality assurance manual be developed?

At what stages of software development should the programming/configuration be reviewed?

Should a specific person (or persons) in the organization be responsible for the management of software?

Should the standard specify the method for testing the software? Note: Generally, this can be done with hardwired test equipment (i.e., test switches, lamps, etc.) or with computer-based simulation, which may be the recommended method for medium to large applications.

Are all software (and hardware) changes closely controlled?

Where a subcontractor is developing the software:

- how are the requirements transmitted to the subcontractor, and
- how is the quality of the final product ensured?

□ MASTER SAFETY RELAY AND EXTERNAL WATCHDOG:

To ensure instant control over the system outputs, the standard may recommend the use of a master safety relay. This relay, when deenergized, cuts the power supply to the output modules, thus disabling them.

The relay should be energized by a dedicated enable push button and deenergized by shutdown functions such as emergency push buttons and partial power loss. In many cases this relay would have no effect on the remaining components of the control system. The reason is to maintain the supply of information from the process to the control system and to the operator.

Some microcomputer control systems include an internal watchdog that monitors the operation of the internal components, in most cases excluding the input/output modules. The output from the internal watchdog must then be connected to the master safety relay in such a way that it is deenergized in case of an internal failure, disabling the outputs to a safe condition.

To ensure that the software runs in a normal mode, the standard may recommend the implementation of an external watchdog. This is a check function that is incorporated into the program and checked with an external timing function. The standard may, for example, state that this check consists of a software exercise in which values or statuses are changing with each scan to make sure that the PES memory is not stuck in a logic state (for example, a square wave ON–OFF where the output is ON for one cycle and OFF for the next cycle, or one ON timer and one OFF timer working in unison). The check function activates a timer outside the control system. The outside timer is adjusted to a time that corresponds to three or four scans of the program, and if within these scans the timer does not reset, a set of contacts will open, deenergizing the master safety relay.

□ ENVIRONMENTAL CONDITIONS:

PESs are susceptible to environmental effects that are detrimental to the system, such as temperature, dust, corrosion, humidity, shock, and vibration. In addition, and to complicate matters, these control systems are also affected by the presence of strong electromagnetic and electrostatic energy.

The standard must ensure that all installations are protected from such environmental effects. The best approach for the standard is to strongly recommend that the vendor's instructions be followed.

As a general rule, high-powered walkie-talkies emit large amounts of electrical noise. Therefore, when they are close to PESs, all signal wiring in and out of the control system acts as an antenna, triggering unwanted signals. To avoid this type of problem, the standard may recommended that a base station with an antenna on the roof and a telephone hand set (or a movable microphone) in the control room be used.

In many industrial applications, the use of an office-type PC is often avoided unless it is located in a clean environment. Drawbacks in using such nonhardened equipment include poor tolerance for humidity, temperature, and vibration extremes as well as sensitivity to power supply fluctuations. The standard may recommend that in most cases the additional cost of a hardened PC more than justifies the cost of additional maintenance and shutdown losses. Equipment cost is sometimes a major factor, since industrial equipment could cost as much as 20 to 50% more than commercial-type equipment.

The standard should clearly indicate that humidity, condensation, seepage, dust, and dirt must be avoided, since they tend to create short circuits (and sometimes corrosion) within the electronic components, resulting in shutdowns (or even more dangerously, spurious malfunctions in the operation that are difficult to diagnose). Equipment protection is provided by enclosures that are rated accordingly (see Tables 6-4, 6-5, and 6-6). The standard may describe the most common types of enclosures for computer equipment and recommend which types should be used. An example of such a description follows.

A. General-purpose for indoor use. Typically used for office equipment and clean control rooms to prevent accidental contact between personnel and equipment.
B. Dripproof type for indoor use. This enclosure protects the equipment from falling dirt and light splash and is typically used in most control rooms, clean production environments, and warehouses.
C. Watertight and dusttight enclosures for indoor and outdoor locations. These enclosures protect against hosedown and are generally used in the plant environment close to the production equipment.

Temperature plays an important role in the life of all microcomputer-based equipment. Most such equipment has a temperature range of 32–130°F (0–55°C). The standard should ensure that:

1. proper temperature dissipation and the avoidance of hot spots must be ensured through either air cooling (natural convection or fan-forced) or air conditioning equipment, and
2. vibration and shock levels protection must be provided. In most cases, this cannot be easily predicted at the design phase, so this is usually an after-the-fact discovery.

The power supply in many industrial plants is of low quality due to the fluctuating demand of large electrical loads, ground loops, voltage frequency noise, and miscellaneous voltage dips. Microcomputer-based equipment can generally accept voltage dips as low as 90 V AC; however, dips below this level, in addition to the other sources of poor power quality, could cause system shutdowns or, even worse, transients that could affect system performance without the operator's being aware of such a malfunction until it is too late. The standard may recommend a solution to this kind of problem through the use of on-line UPSs. A properly sized and selected UPS will cancel this type of nuisance and avoid the destruction of data, damage to computer equipment, and system shutdowns.

□ DOCUMENTATION:

Once the design is completed for all hardware and software, the standard should recommend that all documentation that supports these systems be prepared. This documentation should typically have an overall description of the system, individual descriptions of the main components (inputs/outputs, communications, etc.), and the necessary documentation to support all the changes implemented in the system. This documentation was described in detail earlier.

□ ADDITIONAL GENERAL DESIGN CONSIDERATIONS:

In addition to all the design topics previously discussed, some specific items may require consideration as noted by the following questions.

Was a study conducted on the computer system to define the effects of malfunctions and/or shutdowns (inputs, outputs, power supply)?

Are records of this study available? Were the recommendations implemented?

Is the PES installed according to the vendor's recommendations?

Are there external alarms to indicate PES malfunctions and failures?

Does the operator know what to do in the event of a system or network failure or malfunction?

How reliable is the power supply? Is there any backup?

What is the type of communication between the control center and the rest of the site (telephones, walkie-talkies, etc.)?

Are hardware and software modifications strictly controlled? Are procedures in place?

Are spares readily available?

Has training been provided for hardware and software support and maintenance?

Is there a maintenance contract for the hardware, or is it performed by site personnel?

Testing and Maintenance

System testing, the final step of a design function, is an essential activity. When performed well, it saves time prior to commissioning and start-up. The standard should recommend that the control system be fully checked, all inputs simulated, and all outputs monitored. This ensures that the control system operates as designed, thereby improving its reliability. In addition, creating simulated short or open circuits at the inputs with systematic observation of the outputs give results about the behavior of a control system in case of individual failure. This will help confirm previous studies and assumptions.

ISA-RP55.1, Hardware Testing of Digital Process Computers, establishes a basis for evaluating functional hardware performance of computer-based control systems. This recommended practice can be used as a basic medium of communication between vendor and user (see Appendix B).

One of the main advantages, and also one of the main risks, of PESs is the ease with which the system (hardware and software) can be modified. Changes to the hardware and software should be implemented according to clear procedures (also known as self-discipline). These procedures ensure that checking, approval, and implementation of the changes to the system are done properly.

The handling of system modifications needs to be tightly controlled and, therefore, should be covered in any corporate standard. Otherwise, as modifications are implemented and people are transferred into other activities, the internals of the system become a nightmare to decipher. Tight control is achieved through good documentation (see Appendix F) and a clear procedure for the logistics behind implementing changes. The standard needs to address the following:

1. Who implements modifications?
2. How are they implemented?
3. Are they checked?
4. Where are the latest disk copies kept?
5. Are they all identical?

In addition to the effects of direct uncontrolled modifications, there is a need to maintain software security as well as to prevent damage from microcomputer viruses. The standard should guide the designers and users of computer-based control systems to good practice. The following may be used for such a purpose.

1. Use security keys and/or passwords to prevent easy access to the computer-based control system.
2. Wait till the bugs are out and avoid first versions of new software.
3. Write-protect all disks except those to be written to.

4. Boot from hard-disk or from the same write-protected disk.
5. Never use pirated software; use only copyrighted software.
6. Perform frequent backups to disk.
7. Keep system programs on program disks and production data on data disks.

CHAPTER 7

Installation

OVERVIEW

The installation specification is an important part of any corporate standard on instrumentation and control. It provides the requirements for the installation of instruments, control systems, and their accessories. As a basic rule, all equipment and installation must comply with all code and plant requirements in effect at the site, which is a criteria that must be enforced. It is the responsibility of the installing contractor to ensure and meet compliance.

It is imperative to underline the fact that the content of this chapter is only a memory jogger and should not be taken "as is" since statutory, technical, and corporate needs vary from one site to the other.

An installation specification may be comprised of the following sections:

1. A scope of the installation requirements. This is a general overview and a description of the scope of work.
2. A description of the installation and mounting of the instruments. This section covers the requirements for the correct position and bolting of the instruments. Items such as instrument height and access are described.
3. The process tubing requirements. This section covers the connection of the instruments to the process following its installation in the previous step.
4. An explanation of the wiring needs and criteria. This section covers the electronic/electrical connections to the installed instruments.
5. A description of air tubing requirements. In addition to (or instead of) step 4 above, instrument air connections may be required and are covered under this section.
6. Checkout and acceptance of the installation. This is the final step of the installation section, in which the completed installation is checked for functionality and accepted.

ISA-RP42.1, Nomenclature for Instrument Tube Fittings, can aid in the proper specification and application of instrument tube fittings through standardization of the nomenclature (see Appendix B).

The questionnaire format used throughout this book is maintained in this chapter. This provides guidelines for the preparer of the standard by questioning the contents and specifications that should be contained in the installation specification. A completed installation specification example is shown in Appendix I.

SCOPE

Does this section, once completed, provide and define the overall requirements for the installation of instruments, control systems, and their accessories?

Has the scope underlined that all equipment and installation must comply with all code, statutory, and plant requirements in effect at the site? Is it the responsibility of the contractor to ensure and meet compliance?

Should the standard recommend that the contractor visit the site prior to tendering to become familiar with all conditions and requirements to be met in carrying out the work under this contract? Does this include a review and understanding of the safety requirements in effect at the plant?

Should the scope state the documentation that describes the contractor's scope of work? The following list is shown as an example of such documentation:

- Scope of Work (i.e., the Installation Standard)
- Instrument Index
- Specification Sheets
- Loop Drawing
- Electrical Schematics
- Typical Installation Details
- Vendors' Data

Are the exceptions to the scope of work separately identified by the owner? Should it be mentioned that all instrumentation devices, including those supplied directly by the owner, will be mounted and connected by the contractor?

Since a manufacturer, such as a panel fabricator, may for shipping purposes ship pieces of the equipment and instrumentation separately, are these pieces to be installed and connected by the contractor to form an operating unit?

Should the standard require the contractor become familiar with all furnished data before commencing the installation work?

If there are questions or inconsistencies between any of the documents, should the contractor notify the owner, who then determines which portions of specifications are applicable? Or should the contractor decide the best solution?

Should the contractor be responsible for the correct installation and assembly of all items or equipment listed or shown on the above documents? Or should some of that responsibility rest with the owner? What is the line of demarcation for responsibilities?

Should it be clearly stated to the contractor that any damage that results from failure to observe the manufacturer's instructions or failure to understand how a particular job is to be done will be the contractor's responsibility? Does this mean that the contractor will have to make good any resulting loss or damage?

Because it is important that the installation specification contain a definition of the quality of the personnel doing the installation, how specific does the standard need to be? Should the standard insist that the work under an installation contract must be carried out by a team of certified and trained tradesmen? Should this team have adequate supervision at all times? Would the contractor be required by the owner to produce evidence of such certification and training?

Execution

General

Should the standard note, at the beginning of such a specification, that the instrument installation specification and its reference documents do not cover each and every detail?

Is the contractor expected to be familiar with current good practice for the installation of the instruments and hardware indicated? Is the contractor expected to provide and install all items such as clips, supports, clamps, brackets, stands, etc., as well as all necessary welding, painting, wiring, junction boxes, tubing, fittings, etc., that are required to complete the installation and connection of instruments as they are acquired from suppliers?

On the instrument index, some of the instruments may be noted as "Supplied by Contractor." Are these the responsibility of the contractor to purchase and install? Items that may fall under such a heading are air sets and 3-valve manifolds (if not supplied with the instrument).

Should the standard clearly mention that all items supplied by the contractor must be suitable for the process area concerned?

Is the contractor responsible for the receiving, unloading, safekeeping, and storage of all materials and equipment supplied by the customer or by the contractor?

When accepting deliveries, should the contractor inspect the equipment and materials against the instrument index, specifications, and purchase orders to ensure that quantity, type, ranges, etc., are as specified? By certification of the suppliers' packing list, would the contractor be deemed to have acknowledged that all equipment and materials are complete and satisfactory in every respect?

If the contractor is required to store the received instruments and control systems, should the contractor therefore provide adequate storage space, indoors, secure, protected from unauthorized tampering, free from fire hazard, clean, and dry? Should this facility be heated or air-conditioned depending on the type of equipment to be stored and on the geographical area of the installation?

Should all instruments, wherever possible, be kept in their original shipping carton until they are installed? To avoid damage to the instruments, most of which are sensitive devices, should this separate storage space be maintained apart from areas in which large piping items and equipment are stored?

If the contractor is storing all instrumentation and control systems, is it then the contractor's responsibility to issue all stored equipment whether they are to be installed by the contractor or by other disciplines? Should the contractor be required to maintain accurate records showing equipment and material received, stored, issued, and installed?

Where the owner of the plant requires an ongoing analysis of the project status from an installation point of view and to facilitate such an interaction and the transfer of status information between the installer and the owner, should a table with such information be generated on a regular basis? The table, looking slightly similar to an instrument index, may be either manually generated or on a computer database. It lists all the items covered under the scope of work on the vertical side, and on the horizontal side it lists the different activities at each step for each device such as:

- receiving,
- calibration,
- installation process hookup,
- electronic hookup to instrument (enter tag number),
- conduit run,
- cable run/wire pulled,
- wires connected,
- panel connection power supply connection,
- pneumatic air supply,
- tubing connected,
- tested,
- commissioning, and
- start-up.

Work Specifically Excluded

Should the installation of all in-line devices be the responsibility of the mechanical contractor? Such in-line devices are:

- control valves,
- orifice flanges,
- orifice plates,
- in-line flowmeters,
- thermowells,
- process shutoff valves,
- safety relief valves,
- rupture discs, and
- venturis.

Is the air header supply piping normally part of the mechanical contractor's scope of work?

Is the installation of all impulse piping from the process up to and including the first block valve part of the process/utility piping contract and, therefore, detailed on the piping drawings?

Should the standard state that, to avoid damaging the instruments or reduce their accuracy, all in-line devices except thermowells are to be removed when the piping is being flushed, cleaned, or pressure tested? Should this philosophy also apply to control valves (in which case the valve is replaced by a spool piece)? Should all in-line devices then be installed after the flushing, cleaning, or pressure testing is completed?

Reference Codes and Standards

The standards in the ISA-S75 series are a valuable source of information to the piping/mechanical engineer at design time and to the contractor at installation time; they give face-to-face dimensions for valves (see Appendix B).

As a basic rule, and to comply legal and insurance requirements, should it be noted in the installation specification that all electrically operated instruments, or the electrical components incorporated in an instrument, shall be approved and bear the approval label of the local electrical authority? Should this apply to all items supplied by the owner or by the contractor?

Should it be stated in the installation specification that wherever the drawings or specifications call for material, workmanship, arrangement, or construction of a superior quality than required by any applicable codes and standards, the drawings and specifications shall prevail? Otherwise, should there be a conflict between any codes and standards and the drawings and specifications, the applicable codes and standards prevail. Note: The purpose of such a statement ensures that errors in the documentation provided to the contractor will not result in substandard installations.

To reduce equipment variety on site and to facilitate future inspection and maintenance of instruments and control equipment, should uniformity of manufacture be maintained for any particular item throughout the project?

Permits

On completion of the installation, should the contractor furnish to the owner a certificate of final inspection and approval certifying unconditional approval from the local electrical inspection department?

Should the contractor normally pay all fees required to furnish such certification?

Where the local authorities require additional certificates of compliance for the installation work, should the contractor acquire them and pay all fees required to furnish such certificates?

Inspections

Should the contractor have the responsibility to inspect and note apparent damage or defect at time of receipt and during storage, handling, or installation? Should such discrepancies be immediately reported to the owner to allow sufficient time to either get a replacement or get the defective unit repaired?

Should the standard recommend that it be stated in the installation specification that all material supplied and installed by the contractor must be new? (This sounds obvious, but unless it is stated there is no guarantee that it would be the case.)

Panels

Unless otherwise specified in the installation agreement between the owner and the contractor, control panels for control room and for field installation, as well as interlock panels, are normally supplied piped and wired, ready for installation, with plug-in or slide-in instruments packaged separately.

Is the contractor then required to install plug-in and slide-in instruments correctly in their respective panels?

Is it the responsibility of the contractor to move the panel from the delivery vehicle, when it reaches the plant boundaries, to the control room? (This item is often overlooked in the preparation of installation specification.)

Is the contractor responsible for the installation of all panels, as specified in the reference documents? In general, control panels are not installed in the control room until the room is enclosed and finished and all structural and painting work is completed.

INSTALLATION AND MOUNTING

This section covers the requirements for the mounting and installation of the instruments.

Should the standard recommend that in the installation specification all field-mounted instruments should be installed and connected in such a way that the instrument can be maintained and removed for servicing without having to break fittings, cut wires, or pull hot wires through metal conduit (rigid or flexible)?

Should the contractor provide the necessary unions and tubing connections to all instruments to allow removal?

Is sufficient clearance provided above, below, or in front of instruments to permit removal without disturbing other equipment?

Is the cutting of concrete or structural members done only by the contractor after the written approval by the customer's construction manager located on site?

Should the contractor be responsible for reasonable protection of all installed instruments from damage by inclement conditions or physical damage?

Should the contractor ensure that, after installation, care is taken to protect any instruments, conduits, tubing, and control valves from dirt, water, insulation, debris, and paint?

Should all field-mounted instruments such as transmitters, controllers, and transducers be protected by heavy plastic bags until final plant acceptance by the owner?

Should the contractor ensure that wherever dry air purging and/or heating may be specified for an outdoor instrument enclosure, these are activated as early as possible for the protection of instruments?

Should the installation specification clearly state that the contractor will bear all costs of repair or replacement of any instruments prior to acceptance by the owner?

Is it the responsibility of the contractor to ensure that all instruments and control equipment, including junction boxes, are identified with stainless steel tags embossed or stamped with the equipment identification number? Should this identification number be complete and read the same in all respects as the number given on the instrument index?

If any tags are missing, should they be supplied and installed by the contractor? Should the specification require that the tag should be attached to the instrument body or housing wherever possible and to the instrument support or adjacent tubing only when unavoidable? Also, should the specification recommend that the contractor should not place the tag where routine maintenance would require the tag's removal?

To avoid the effect of rust, is stainless steel wire recommended to be used for tag attachment?

Is the contractor or the owner responsible to check all controllers for correct action (i.e., direct or reverse)?

Should seal fluids, where required, be installed by the contractor?

Instrument Enclosures

The following field equipment is generally mounted in instrument enclosures: instruments that are not weatherproof (except certain explosionproof equipment), instruments that are likely to be subjected to excessive dust or external corrosion, and recording instruments and other similar equipment.

Should instrument protection be provided where necessary to protect from freezing, corrosion, and other adverse conditions by housing, purging, insulating, protective heating, etc., as appropriate to the specified environment? Is the contractor or the owner responsible to ensure that the enclosure fits a defined space?

Should the standard ensure that all enclosures meet the area classification? Should these enclosures be selected to protect against the ingress of liquids and solids and against electrical, chemical, thermal, and mechanical influences in the environment? Is cooling or heating required? Is there a need to perform a heat study to ensure proper air flow? Is shock isolation for internal components required?

Should the installation specification recommend that, when deciding for the location of an enclosed instrument, the complete instrument access must be maintained with the enclosure installed?

Junction Boxes

Should the contractor have the responsibility to ensure that, for both pneumatic and electrical boxes, they meet the needs of the applications and conform to the environment they operate under?

Should these boxes be of a minimum designation? For example:

These junction boxes are of a watertight construction to prevent a stream of water from a hose from entering the enclosure. Such enclosures also tend to be dusttight for indoor and outdoor locations. Where corrosion is a factor, these boxes are required to be resistant to its effects.

Is there a need to standardize in the plant on enclosures with a hinged, scratch-resistant window?

Should cable entries be only through resilient seals in the bottom of the box, with a drip loop? Should all conduit entries be located also in the bottom or side of the box and provided with a drip loop and a bugproof drain?

Should the terminal strips be mounted on metallic standoff to allow condensation on the colder metal walls?

Should each cable be grounded at one end only?

Should the design minimize the possibility of accidental grounding of the shield or drain wire?

Should shield drain wires be connected on the terminal strip?

Should a checklist be included to facilitate the selection of boxes? For example, the factors to consider in box selection and design are:

- size of box (terminal strips involved, wiring space, entry/exit of cables, etc.),
- location (indoors,outdoors),
- electrical area classification,
- atmosphere (corrosive, hazardous),
- materials of construction (including the hardware such as hinges),
- security (lock),
- access to box (number of doors, type), and
- fire or last protection.

If the contractor is installing terminal strips, such as in junction boxes, should the plant preference always be taken into account to avoid introducing non-compatible hardware in the plant? In all cases, should at least 20% or 6 spare terminal points, whichever is greater, be provided on each strip unless otherwise specified by the plant?

Mounting

It must be decided whether to produce installation and mounting details for each instrument to be installed or whether to expect the contractor to ensure that all items of instrumentation are mounted according to good instrument installation practices with reference to maintenance, freedom from vibration, and damage by process fluids.

Note: The installation of most instruments should be achieved, when using a good installing contractor, by having a good description and relying on the contractor's knowledge. However, the need for detail installation drawings may be required for special installations. Some corporations still prefer the use of typical installation details for the most common installations. This philosophy ensures a clear understanding of the owner's requirements by the contractor. Such typical installations can be broken down into two types:

1. one for gases, where the condensate or any liquids should flow back to the process (see Figure 7-1), and
2. one for liquids and condensates (such as steam), where a leg of liquid is to be maintained and where bubbles (or entrapped gases) should go back to the process (see Figure 7-2).

In each of these two cases, the instruments may be mounted either above or below the process connections. It is recommended that, in case of the gases (or liquids with suspended solids), the instruments should be mounted above the process connection. In the case of liquids and condensible fluids they should be mounted below the process connections.

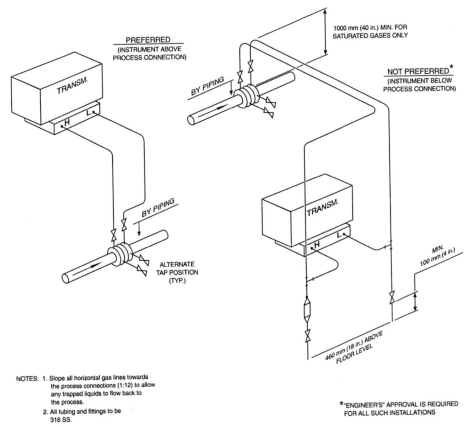

Figure 7-1. Typical Instrument Installation for Gas Service

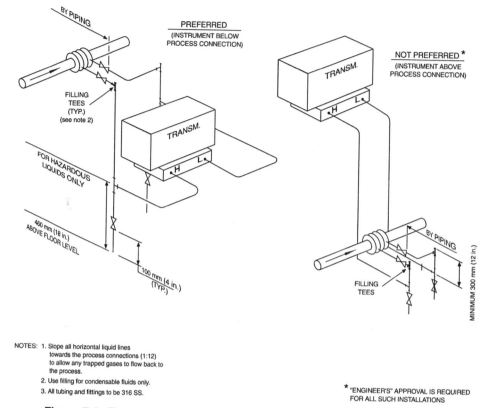

NOTES: 1. Slope all horizontal liquid lines
          towards the process connections (1:12)
          to allow any trapped gases to flow back to
          the process.
       2. Use filling for condensable fluids only.
       3. All tubing and fittings to be 316 SS.

* "ENGINEER'S" APPROVAL IS REQUIRED
   FOR ALL SUCH INSTALLATIONS

Figure 7-2. Typical Instrument Installation for Liquid and Condensable Fluids
(e.g., Steam)

Should such instruments, when mounted, be allowed to obstruct or present a personnel hazard in an access passage or aisle or create an unsafe condition such as sharp edges or protrusions? Note: It is good practice to include in the installation specification a clause to cover doubts that may exist regarding these requirements, asking the contractor to contact the owner for a decision.

When mounted, should all instruments and junction boxes be accessible so that personnel may service or remove any instrument or instrument auxiliary without danger of falls, burns, or hazards?

What are the accessibility requirements to be identified in the installation specification? For example:

- Accessibility requirements are based on having each instrument installed so that it may be serviced by one man.
- The height of instrument equipment and associated installations is normally acceptable where it is 4.5 feet (1.4 meters) ±10% above grade, floor, or walkway.
- Headroom clearance for all instrumentation items should be maintained at no less than 7.5 feet (2.3 meters) from grade in all areas of normal personnel access unless specifically specified to the contractor for rare cases.

- Two-foot clearance should be provided to allow for rodding out if needed.
- Minimum height above grade or platform is one foot to the bottom of the instrument.

Should all instruments and junction boxes be mounted level and plumb and in such a manner as to provide accessibility and protection from mechanical damage, heat, shock, and vibration?

Once installed, should these instruments be allowed to interfere with or be interfered with by any structure, other equipment, piping, or electrical work? Should these instruments be allowed to obstruct walkways or other means of access provided for maintenance or process use (such as forklift truck access and access for cranes).

To avoid damage during the construction phase of a project, should the specification recommend that instruments not be installed until all heavy mechanical work adjacent to their installation has been completed?

Should, as much as possible, field-mounted items of instrumentation and junction boxes be mounted on building columns and walls where such building columns or walls are accessible? Should support stands be provided when the mounting of instruments on columns and walls is not practical? Should the specification clearly state that these stands should not be fixed to floor grating?

How are these stands to be fabricated? For example:

> The support stands are in most cases fabricated from 2-in. mild steel pipe and painted in accordance with the painting specifications used on the project.

Should the specification recommend that instruments be mounted using the brackets supplied with the instruments wherever possible rather than be fabricated on site?

Should supports and stands be attached to the building structure, beams, columns, or other permanent structural members and not be attached to handrails, process equipment, piping, vessels, conduit, or instruments? Should the contractor ensure that all supports and stands are mounted perpendicular to the supporting structure and are finished so as no sharp edges, points, or irregular angles exist?

Are there clear instructions that welding or drilling of any structural steel, piping, equipment, or vessel so as to mount or support items of instrumentation should be done only after the contractor has obtained acceptance from the owner? (This approach may prevent costly damages.)

Are all supports and stands to be fabricated so they will not become a trough or trap for spilled liquids? Should they be painted to match the supporting structure?

Where welds are allowed, should they be ground smooth, preprimed, and painted in accordance with the painting specifications used on the project to match support or stand, prior to installation of tubing tray or instrument?

Unless approved by the owner and only where no other means are practical, should the specification ensure that instruments, impulse lines, tubing, or wiring must not be attached to process lines or process equipment? (Exceptions to this requirement may be for equipment designed specifically for pipe or flange mounting, such as pressure and temperature gages, and for control valve mounted items, such as limit switches and positioners.)

Should the contractor ensure that instrument items connected to piping or equipment are not installed in such a way so as to place damaging or undesirable stress on the piping, equipment, or instruments? As obvious as it may sound, the owner may also need to ensure that piping and equipment must not be supported on or from items of instrumentation or their accessories.

Where no other suitable means of support exists, should the contractor supply and install a channel, angle, or tubing tray to provide support for individual tubing runs? Should such support be of a material and finish that is suitable for the process area concerned? Should these supports be installed so as to minimize any catch place for rainwater, snow, process drippings, or dust accumulation?

Should the installation specification state that indicating gages, either as part of an indicating transmitter or as a stand-alone device such as a pressure gage, be positioned so as to be easily read from a normal operating area? What is the definition of visible? For example:

> Plainly visible is defined as line of sight not exceeding 14 feet (4.25 meters).

Should tubing and/or conduit penetrations through walls or floors be properly sealed, watertight, and dusttight?

Should the holes or slots in walls, floors, or ceilings where cables or tubing pass through between hazardous and nonhazardous areas be sealed after installation of the cables or tubing in accordance with the electrical code in effect at the site?

Should the specification recommend that atmospheric vents on items of instrumentation such as solenoid valves must be arranged so as to prevent the entry of foreign materials such as rain, dirt buildup, etc.? Should the direction of the vent aiming downward be sufficient (in other cases, a small piece of tube would perform this function)?

Purging

Since purging prevents the process fluid from reaching the instrument, has the proper purging fluid been selected? (It is being added to the process stream and cannot always be air.) Is the suitable purge fluid available at a pressure higher than the process pressure? Is it clean and noncontaminating to the process fluid? Is it supplied from a reliable source?

Should the supply of the purging fluid be independent of the process (to ensure supply when the process is not operational)?

How easy (or difficult) is it to maintain the purging system?

Is the purging fluid injected at the instrument or at the process connection?

Is winterizing needed for the purging fluid?

Is the purging fluid fed continuously and at a fixed rate? Is this accomplished with a rotameter set at the correct flow range? Is there a need for a restriction orifice? Is a pressure regulator needed if the supply pressure is too high?

Sealing

Since sealing is another positive means of preventing the process fluid from coming in contact with the instrument that is measuring the process, have the proper diaphragm seals been selected?

Is the liquid used in the seal the correct one? Will it withstand the pressure and temperature of the process? Also, in case of seal rupture, will the seal liquid react with the process fluid to cause a hazardous condition?

Are the capillaries between the seals and the instruments of the correct length?

Due to sometimes widely varying ambient temperature conditions affecting the pressure inside the capillaries, is temperature compensation required?

Winterization

Is heating protection (electrical or steam) self-regulating to prevent overheating?

Where electrical tracing is used:

- Is loss of power alarms provided?
- Is it thermostatically controlled to meet the exact requirements?
- Is it installed according to the local electrical codes and the vendor's recommendations?
- Is the thermostat set at the correct set point?
- Is the location of the thermostat appropriate?
- Is self-limiting tape used?
- Is UPS backup required?
- If the heating cable has been pre-engineered and prefabricated (which is hard to determine before installation) to a specific length, how is the extra cabling handled? Note: The cable should not cross over itself; otherwise, overheating occurs.
- If short lengths were ordered, are dedicated step-down transformers required?

Where steam tracing is used:

- Is the steam heater fitted with shutoff valves? Are these valves located at a high point on the header? Are these valves provided with a tag that shows the tag number of the instrument it serves?
- Is a separate trap and condensate-isolating valve provided for each traced instrument?

- Is the tubing material used in conjunction with the plant requirements? Should the use of copper or (stainless steel) tubing be standardized to minimize corrosion and rusting?
- Has the installation ensured that no electronic components are located near the steam line?

PROCESS TUBING

Process tubing connects the process to the measuring instrument and is, therefore, subject to the same conditions that the process itself sees.

Do the process tubing and fittings meet the criteria of the process? Do all process tubing and fittings conform to, or exceed, the process/utility piping code specification with respect to design temperature and pressure and materials of construction? Are the tubing and fittings used to connect the process to the instrument used at temperatures and pressures that do not exceed the manufacturer's recommendations?

Since such connections are generally dead-ended, will the process fluid cause clogging and freezing? Is tubing that contains liquids subject to freezing protected by heat tracing? Is the contractor responsible for the supply and installation of heat tracing?

Have service conditions, such as vibration and thermal cycling, been considered in the application?

Should the tubing connected to the process be tested as part of and under the same conditions as the process/utility piping system? Before and after testing, are lines flushed and blown down with water or air to remove all contamination? Prior to testing and cleaning, should all lines be disconnected from the instrument and blanked off?

Does the specification ensure that in no case shall any instrument, other than control valves and thermowells, be subject to test pressures?

Should a test device such as a "tee" be located between the instrument isolating valve (the shutoff valve) and the instrument so that calibration and occasional checks on the instrument's output may be made without disconnecting the instrument? Is this test device required for pressure gages?

On typical gas installations with no condensable fluids, should the process tubing be routed such that the measuring device is above the process line? Are all horizontal lines sloped 1 : 10 to allow any trapped liquids to flow back to the process? Note: Sloping ensures that the gas and liquid go to predictable locations in the tubing; on steam lines, the tubing must remain horizontal to ensure a steady liquid head.

On typical liquid or condensable fluid, such as steam, is the measuring device located below the process line? Are all horizontal lines sloped 1 : 10 to allow trapped gases to flow back to the process? On condensable fluids, are filling tees required to allow for the creation of a stable static head?

What is the size of the process tubing? Note: Process tubing that connects the process to the instrument is generally either 1/2 in. OD or 3/4 in. OD, the 3/4 in. is used for mechanical strength where the potential exists for a person to stand on it, since it is common (but not recommended) that people step on a process connection tube to reach something else. Some plants have used the 1/2 in. as a standard and have clear (and enforced) procedures for not stepping on these tubes.

Has the standard defined that process tubing, under the scope of an instrument contractor, originates at the shutoff valve? Note: From the process to the shutoff valve is generally the responsibility of the process/utility piping contractor.

Are field instruments to be located as close as possible to their process connection, while allowing for convenient access for operation and maintenance?

On dirty applications in which process tubing is subject to plugging, are suitable connections for cleaning provided? Also, on process tubing that (1) handles gases that contain moisture or other extraneous matter or (2) handles hazardous liquids are such applications provided with suitable drains, settling chambers, or traps?

ISA-RP42.1 defines the nomenclature for tube fittings most commonly used in instrumentation. It applies to mechanical flared and flareless tube fittings as commonly used in instrument tubing systems (see Appendix B).

WIRING

Overview

Wiring has two main functions in the world of instrumentation: to supply power or to connect devices for the transfer of signals. All installations must closely conform to the electrical code in effect at the site.

Is there a need for the standard to define different levels of wiring? For example:

Instrumentation and control wiring can be divided into four basic types:

1. Very low level DC analog signals such as thermocouples, strain gages, pH sensing, etc.
2. Low level DC analog signals (4–20 mA at 24 V DC)
3. Low voltage discrete signals and low voltage power wiring (24 V DC)
4. High voltage discrete signals and high voltage power wiring (120 V AC)

Should it be common practice for the contractor to run each type in a dedicated multiconductor or conduit?

Should the specification recommend that shielded wiring be used for types 1, 2, and 3?

Should a minimum parallel separation of 1-1/2 ft (0.45 m) between the types of multiconductors or conduits be maintained to avoid electrical noise?

When the separation is vertical, is it recommended that the signal wiring be in the top tray and the high voltage in the bottom tray? Note: With this arrangement, the signal wires are not in the electric field that exists between the high voltage lines and ground.

Should the specification recommend that special wiring be installed according to equipment vendor recommendations?

Should the separation follow a company approved recommendation? For example:

If power wiring is under 20 A (which is the common condition limited by the fuse size) then, the following may be used:

- 6 in. (15 cm) for tray to tray spacing
- 4 in. (10 cm) for tray to conduit spacing
- 3 in. (7 cm) for conduit to conduit spacing

If the power is greater than 20 A, multiply the spacing stated above by 5.

Are installed trays to have solid bottoms and tops for better shielding?

Should the spacing between high power (> 100 kVA) and instrument wiring (types 2 and 3):

- be routed parallel to the instrument wiring,
- have a distance greater than 5 ft (1.5 m) for trays, and
- have a distance greater than 2-1/2 ft (1 m) for conduits?

Should the exposed conduit joints be coated with an electrically conductive sealant that is also a corrosion inhibiter and is not harmful to the wire insulation? Should the installation specification state that aluminum conduits must use compounds specifically made for aluminum?

Should power cables placed in a single layer with a ventilation space between the cables and control cables require no extra spacing? Should the laying of control cables allow for 20 to 30% future cable capacity to be provided?

Should trays be supported to limit deflection? For example:

Conduit Size:	Support Interval:
1 in. and smaller	10 ft
1-1/4 in. to 2-1/2 in.	15 ft
3 in. and larger	20 ft

In addition, all conduits will be supported within 3 ft of each junction box or instrument.

Should tray routing be such that routes where damage and fire hazards may occur must be avoided?

Should all cable routing be:

- kept away from hot piping as well as corrosive environments (unless designed for such applications), and
- routed such that it: (1) does not pass over mechanical equipment or

allow enough overhead clearance and (2) ensures that there is no inter-ference with maintenance space?

Should the routing of cables consider that if a fire or damage occurs in a spot, the remaining system is not completely shut down? Should separate routes be implemented for separate trays?

Should the trays be fireproofed?

Should the standard recommend the material of conduits? Should nonmetal-lic conduit be not recommended for usage for instrument cabling (since they do not provide electrical shielding)?

Should the inside of conduits be cleaned before the installation of wires/cables? (A conduit can be cleaned by pulling a rag through it.)

Should the specification recommend that conduits are not to be supported from piping? Would exceptions be tolerated?

Should the thermal expansion and swaying of high towers in winds be con-sidered when routing conduits?

Should conduits have a drain at low points?

Wiring

Should all wiring be identified with suitable nonconductive abrasion and sol-vent resistant markers? Should these markers bear the wire numbers shown on the documentation?

Is color coding of the different types of wiring required? Should the standard state that such coding comply with the requirements of the electrical code in effect at the site and also meet the requirements of maintenance personnel at the plant? An example of such a color distribution could be as follows:

For 120 V AC power and 120 V AC discrete control signals:
Phase or hot conductor (L1 or H) — black
Neutral conductor (L2 or N) — white
Intermediate conductors — brown

For 24 V DC power and 24 V DC discrete control signals:
Positive conductor — black
Negative conductor — white
Intermediate conductors — brown

For 4–20 mA (24 V DC) analog signals:
Positive conductor — black
Negative conductor — white

For thermocouple extension wires, use ANSI color code. For other spe-cialized wiring, either follow the manufacturer's color on the lead wires or refer to the plant control engineer.

For earth ground (if insulated) — green

For intrinsically safe wiring — bright blue
Note: Raceways, wireways, terminal blocks, and field junction boxes should also be identified with a bright blue label bearing the legend

INTRINSICALLY SAFE. In addition, when numbering the wires and to avoid the problems of color blindness, a specific ID is required (e.g., IS preceding the number).

For temporary jumpers — orange
Note: Minimum length should be 2 feet (70 cm)

Wire identification

Should all wires and cables be identified using a number or a color code (or a combination of the two)? Note: Number code avoids the problems of color blindness and facilitates wire stocking and supply.

Should the wire numbering take the number of the loop it is for, followed by a dash, followed by the number of the wire starting at the power supply (see loop diagrams)?

Size of Cable and Wiring

Requirements for cable and wiring sizes will vary depending on the requirements of the electrical authority in effect at the site and with the needs and preferences of plant personnel. The following is an example used in many plants.

Power and control cabling, 120 V AC:
Minimum wire size is #12 AWG for power supplies and #14 AWG for discrete control signals.

Power and control cabling 24 V DC:
(1) Individual cabling — For 24 V DC power and 24 V DC discrete control signals, the minimum wire size for single pair in conduits is 16 gage cables. For 4–20 mA (24 V DC) analog signals, 18 gage is the minimum size (16 gage is preferred).
(2) For multipair cables, 20 gage should be the minimum size. All multipair cables should be of the same construction and each should terminate in an individual junction box. In addition, each cable should contain a minimum of 20% spare pairs.

Note: It may be necessary to require, for mechanical strength, that all wires 18 gage and smaller have lugs, since fine wire could be cut when tightening that terminal and not be detected.

Special Cabling

Where instruments require special cables (e.g., pH electrode cable and data highway cables), the instrument manufacturer's requirements must be followed. Load cell cables, another example of special cabling, are factory matched for resistance and must not be cut. The designer, when specifying the instrument, must ensure that sufficient length is available, and the installer, when mounting the instrument, must coil and neatly tie any cable excess in a well protected area.

Cable Runs

Where multiconductor cables and single wires in conduit are run from the control room to local junction boxes, should a certain percentage (e.g., 20%)

of spare wires be normally provided? If no spares are included, would the cost saved warrant the higher premiums for future additions?

Does the choice between conduit and multiconductor depend on the economics of each situation? Is the decision left to the contractor or to the designer?

Should signal wiring be run in conduit or in armored cables? Would armored cables be preferred in larger installations with a central control room?

Termination

To allow for expansions and contractions due to changing temperatures and to avoid stressing both the instruments and the conduits, should all final connections to field-mounted instruments be made with liquidtight flexible steel conduit (generally, single pair is provided from the junction boxes to the individual instruments)? Should there be some exceptions in the case of explosionproof enclosures? In all cases, should the specification again underline that all installations must comply with the requirement of the local electrical authority?

Should the specification underline the fact that wires should not be spliced in conduit runs or anywhere in the field except on identified terminal blocks in approved junction boxes?

Should the termination of cable cores and single conductors be by either crimped (normally preferred) or soldered pins? Should the makeup of all crimped connection be carried out with the connector manufacturer's approved tools? Should the wire to spade connector junctions and the screened pairs in the area where the individual foil screens are cut back be protected with an adhesive-lined heat shrink tubing or sleeve of suitable diameter? Can preformed sleeves or caps of the same material be used?

Grounding

Should the specification recommend that the individual shields in a multiconductor cable be connected to the shields of the individual pair of cable they connect to? At the same time, is it important that the shields are not otherwise grounded to the structure or to each other at the junction box? At the instrument end, should the standard advise that no connection is to be made to any shield, foil, or drain wire?

Should the specification ensure that at the field instrument, the shield and drain wire are cut off and protected from possible ground contact?

How is the ground continuity of electrical equipment housed in nonmetallic enclosures maintained? Is this done by bonding together the armor or metallic sheath of all incoming and outgoing cables? In addition, are the bonding connections suitably protected against weather and corrosion?

Cable Routing

Is cable entry in equipment, wherever practical, located on the underside of equipment to reduce the risk of water or other liquids entering the equipment? Where side entry is unavoidable, are cables inclined downwards away from the equipment to ensure that water does not flow towards the cable entry?

Should good routing practice be followed by the contractor to ensure that cables neatly run either vertically or horizontally but not diagonally across walls, ceilings, or floors?

Should cable runs be accessible for maintenance and not be positioned directly over or under large plant items, in close proximity to moving machinery, immediately above or adjacent to steam or other hot pipes, or directly below pipes that carry corrosive liquids? Should there be a minimum distance (e.g., 16 in. or 400 mm) between any cable and the lagging of steam or hot process lines? Should cables be positioned clear of process pipes, service pipes, ventilation ducts, hoist blocks, overhead cranes, and other similar services?

Are main cable routes defined in the installation specification? When the routing of the cables is not indicated on a drawing or described in the installation specification, should the contractor submit details of the proposed routing to the owner for approval prior to commencing the installation?

Should the specification state that armored multiconductor cables and conduits shall not be bent to a radius less than those stated by the vendor recommendations? Unless otherwise specified, should armored multiconductor cables rising from the ground be protected to a minimum height (e.g., at least 6 ft or 2 m) by galvanized steel casing or other approved means to suit the particular situation? Note: This will protect the cable from damage due to impact or abrasion over the years.

Wiring in Hazardous Areas

Such wiring must always conform to the requirements of the electrical code in effect at the site. Therefore, should additional descriptions of the owner's needs provide additional guidance to the contractor doing the installation work?

Since the safety of equipment used in hazardous areas can be seriously jeopardized if the wiring requirements are not strictly followed, should the contractor be held responsible for all code and specification implementation?

Since only certified equipment should be installed in hazardous areas, in cases where certified apparatus is not available should the design be changed or should the contractor discuss first with the owner?

Should all intrinsically safe cables, wiring, junction boxes, and other equipment be positively identified in accordance with the engineering documentation provided to the contractor? In addition, should junction boxes be identified inside and outside?

Should unarmored cables that carry intrinsically safe circuits not be run alongside other unarmored cables? Note: They should be run either in separate conduits or in separate armored cables.

Should the installation specification recommend the following?

1. No intrinsically safe circuit cable should be terminated in a junction box that houses nonintrinsically safe wiring. Field wiring terminals for intrinsically safe circuits in control room areas, panels, etc., must be segregated from other nonintrinsically safe field wiring terminals. They should be located in separate enclosures.
2. Where a conduit, raceway, cable, or other conductor system crosses a boundary between hazardous areas of different classification or between a hazardous area and a nonhazardous area, vents or seals or both must be provided to ensure that no flammable atmospheres or substances can be transmitted through the conduit or cable across such a boundary. Areas of high fire risk should be avoided, particularly for junction boxes and cable runs.
3. Intrinsically safe, redundant, or temporarily redundant circuit cables should be disconnected and removed from equipment at both ends, at the supply end bonded together and to ground, and at the plant end bonded between cores and insulated from ground. Spare cores in a multicore cable should be connected to the intrinsically safe ground in the safe area only and elsewhere must be fully insulated.
4. To minimize the total number of electrical enclosures in hazardous areas, the contractor should not provide and install extra junction boxes or other equipment except with the specific approval of the owner.
5. The cabling connections and other work carried out by the contractor on equipment for use in hazardous areas should be such as to maintain the validation of the equipment certification.
6. Cables and wiring of IS circuits must be identified as such. Permanently attached bright blue colored labels shall be used with the following information shown as a minimum:
   - Manufacturer's name and model number
   - Hazardous location class, division, and group
   - Operating temperature or temperature code
   - Maximum safe area voltage (for IS barriers assemblies)

Where pressurization of enclosures is used for protection:

1. Should, for safety reasons, dry air be the only gas used?
2. Are individual regulators for each enclosure preferred?
3. Is it desirable to have two regulators operating in parallel to ensure pressurization in case one regulator fails?
4. In cases where the density of the hazardous gas differs from that of air, should advantage be taken of the displacement effect to ensure efficient purging (i.e., if air is heavier, air inlet should be at the bottom of the enclosure and vice versa)?

Where explosionproof enclosures are used for protection, should the restrictions and requirements of the manufacturer be closely adhered to? Should these enclosures be mounted so as to minimize dust accumulation and facilitate cleaning?

Since a major hazard in some hazardous processes is the entry of loose metal parts into process machinery, should all equipment be securely fixed through special measures? Note: These special measure include the "wiring" of bolts. (The free part of the bolt is drilled and a continuous stainless steel wire is threaded through all bolts to be secured. The two ends of the wire are then joined through a high integrity joint.)

AIR TUBING

Air tubing carries the supply of instrument air and the transfer of signals between pneumatic instruments. Some of the following questions suggest the owner's needs and can be used to provide additional guidance to the contractor doing the installation work.

Should the standard recommend that the installation specification require that all tubing be identified by a stainless steel tag at all instrument terminations and at all fittings? Should the identification conform to the data shown on the engineering documentation provided to the contractor? In the absence of this identification number, should the tag bear the identification number and the function of the instrument to which it connects (i.e., input, output, air supply, etc.)?

The identification of the function of a tube could be done using colors. Should the same color standard be used throughout the plant? In the absence of such a standard, should the following ISA-based color coding be used (from ISA-RP60.9)?

    Air supply to instrument — red
    Transmitted measurement — orange
    Controller output to valve — yellow
    All other signals — natural

Should any deviations from these requirements by the contractor first be approved by the owner?

Should the individual instrument air supply and pneumatic field transmission lines to individual instruments from the air supply header, field junction boxes, or control panels be of a specific type? For example:

    Seamless type 316 SS tubing, 1/4 in. O.D., 0.030 in. min. wall thickness unless otherwise specified.

Should the panel instrument air supply and field air supply subheader be of a specific type? For example:

    Seamless type 316 SS tubing, 1/2 in. O.D., 0.030 in. min. wall thickness unless otherwise specified.

Should the contractor ensure that multitube bundles have the mechanical protection needed to prevent damage? Should these bundles terminate in individual junction boxes or bulkhead? Should each bundle contain a minimum 20% spare tubes, and should all spares be terminated?

Should all tubing fittings for instrument air supply and pneumatic field transmission be of the flareless compression type?

Should all tubing should be installed in continuous length from:

- the instrument to the instrument air supply valve,
- the instrument to a pneumatic junction box fitting or bulk head fitting, and
- the instrument to another instrument.

Should the specification recommend that in no case would union fittings or splices be permitted in tubing runs (all splices and connections must be made accessible in junction boxes or at the instruments)?

Multitube bundles of plastic instrument tubing are normally installed between control panels and field-mounted junction boxes. Should these bundles have 20% spare tubes? Should these bundles not be bent to a radius less than that recommended by their manufacturer?

Could field instruments, which require an air supply as well as a signal line, be connected to the junction box by two-tube bundles? Should an air supply shutoff valve be supplied inside the box? When more than one instrument is supplied from a single takeoff, should an individual shutoff valve be supplied for each user in a manner that allows independent shutoff of each user?

Should the takeoff from the major supply header be made from the top or side of the header or branch? Should the takeoff terminate within 1-1/2 feet (0.4 meters) of the user instrument with a 1/2 in. quarter-turn ball valve consistent with the piping specifications?

Should the termination of pneumatic tubing be by bulkhead connectors suitably mounted within the junction box?

To avoid plugging pneumatic components, should the use of Teflon^{TM} (tape or paste) or any pipe sealant in tube fittings be restricted?

Should all tubing be clean and free of oil, grease, dirt, and other foreign materials? Should it be blown out with clean instrument air before being connected to other tubing or devices?

Should all tube ends be cut square and deburred so that they remain perfectly round? Should tubing be routed and formed so that it may be removed or disconnected without dismounting the instrument (bends, loops, offsets, etc.)? Can fittings be installed excessively close to a bend? Should tubing sections be fitted properly to prevent springing or side stresses on fittings? Can metal tubing be bent only by using a suitable bending tool and with a bend radius that prevents crimping, cracking, or collapsing of tube?

Should tubing trays be used to support three or more tube lines? Could tube clips be used to support single- or double-tube lines? Should tube clips, whether used on horizontal or vertical runs, be installed every 2 feet (0.7 meter), at changes in direction, and where the tube leaves supports for connection to instruments?

Are supports provided to protect the tubing from its own weight, vibration, wind, external mechanical injury, and exposure to unusual service conditions such as operator handholds and footholds? Should supports allow tubing movement as a result of device motion and thermal expansion where applicable?

Should all tubing be installed with loops or bends so as not to transmit stress or vibration to the instrument it is serving and so that it may be disconnected without bending, twisting, or distortion? For example:

A tubing loop shall consist of one coil turn of 4 to 6 in. (100 to 150 mm) diameter.

Should the contractor ensure that the installation of all tubing is in such a way as to allow for thermal expansion over runs and strain relief at all fittings or connections?

Should tubing and tubing bundles be run above ground and be adequately supported on racking or trays?

Should the specification ensure that unless otherwise specified, multitube bundles rising from the ground must be protected to a height of at least 3 feet (1 meter) by galvanized steel casing or other means approved by the owner to suit the particular situation?

Should multitube bundle routes be defined in the installation specification? If the routing is not indicated on a drawing or described in a drawing, should the contractor submit details of the proposed routing to the owner for approval prior to commencing the installation?

Should all tubing be routed neatly to run either vertically or horizontally but not diagonally across walls, ceilings, or floors?

Should multitube bundle runs be:

- accessible for maintenance,
- not positioned directly over or under large plant items,
- in close proximity to moving machinery,
- immediately above or adjacent to steam or other hot pipes, or
- directly below pipes carrying corrosive liquids?

Should the contractor ensure that there should be a minimum distance (e.g., 16 inches or 400 mm) between any multitube bundles and the lagging of insulated hot process lines on hot surfaces? Should multitube bundles be positioned clear of process pipes, service pipes, ventilation ducts, hoist blocks, overhead cranes, and other similar services?

Should all air headers be of welded construction with takeoff points mounted on the top of horizontal headers?

Should drain valves be fitted to the low points of each header? Should ten percent or three (whichever is greater) spare takeoff points with block valves be provided on each instrument air header?

Should each instrument air user in the field be purchased with a nonbleed type of separate filter/regulator complete with a 0–30 psig (0–200 kPag) output pressure gage? Should all filter/regulators be of the same manufacturer and model number to avoid confusion and reduce parts inventory?

CHECKOUT

The checkout activity ensures that the control system is ready for operation when the plant is ready to start. In general, checkout not only includes the items installed by the contractor under the scope of work but also the controls and instruments supplied as packaged units, e.g., compressors, boilers, water treatment units, etc.

Since most instruments have been factory calibrated or factory set before shipping to the site, should the contractor be allowed to adjust or tamper with the calibration or settings of any instrument or instrument accessory until checkout time?

Prior to final inspection, should the contractor supply a number of copies of wiring diagrams, operating and maintenance instructions, and renewal parts lists for each piece of equipment purchased and installed by him or her as part of the work? Should the number of copies be set according to the plant needs and procedures?

Should all authorized changes and deviations from the drawings made by the contractor be recorded by him or her on a set of drawings, which then should be handed over to the owner before final inspection of the work?

Should the contractor ensure that every instrument and control component bears its tag with identifying tag number? If any of these tags have been removed or lost during installation or not supplied, should the contractor replace the missing tags with others similar to those originally supplied?

After completion of the installation, should the contractor perform the following work?

1. Check the entire instrument installation, including the instrumentation of packaged systems, to confirm that all instruments and associated equipment and accessories have been correctly installed and connected.
2. Clean the control tubing by blowing out with clean dry air.
3. Perform tubing pressure tests for leaks as per ISA-RP7.1 (see Appendix B) and ensure that all connections have been made correctly.
4. Ring out all wiring to ensure that all connections have been made correctly. High voltage devices are not to be used for such checks. No circuits may be energized without the prior approval of the owner.

Should all post-installation calibration, if required by the owner, be done by the contractor in the presence of the owner? Should the contractor ensure that his or her equipment installation is complete, correct, and ready for calibration?

What does calibration consist of? For example:

1. The contractor should calibrate all field instruments at five points (0, 25, 50, 75, and 100%) and ensure that each individual instrument is in good working order. The contractor should then check that all control valves are in good working order, are lubricated where required, and that the control valve input signal matches the corresponding valve

section. Control valves, like the instruments, should be stroked at five points (0, 25, 50, 75, and 100%) with a simulated input signal.

(An example of the forms used for recording the calibration of instruments and valves is shown in Figure 7-3.)

TRANSMITTER CHECK

TAG NO.: _____

INPUT RANGE: _____

OUTPUT RANGE: _____

CHECKED BY: _____

DATE: _____

INPUT	RANGE %	INDICATION (OUTPUT)
	0	
	25	
	50	
	75	
	100	

(A) TRANSMITTER FORM

RECEIVER CHECK

TAG NO.: _____

INPUT RANGE: _____

OUTPUT RANGE: _____

CHECKED BY: _____

DATE: _____

INPUT	RANGE %	INDICATION (OUTPUT)
	0	
	25	
	50	
	75	
	100	

(B) RECEIVER FORM

Figure 7-3. Typical Calibration Recording Form

TOTALIZER CHECK

TAG NO.: _____

INPUT RANGE: _____

UNITS: _____

FACTOR: _____

CHECKED BY: _____

DATE: _____

INPUT	RANGE %	TOTAL COUNTS PER HOUR
	0	
	25	
	50	
	75	
	100	

(C) TOTALIZER FORM

CONTROL VALVE CHECK

TAG NO.: _____

INPUT RANGE: _____

ACTION: F_O ____ F_C ____ F_L ____

VALVE POSITION
         OPEN AT: _____mA

         CLOSE AT: _____mA

CHECKED BY: _____

DATE: _____

INPUT	RANGE %	VALVE POSITION %
	0	
	25	
	50	
	75	
	100	

(D) CONTROL VALVE FORM

Figure 7-3. (*Continued*)

2. The contractor should calibrate filled thermal systems at two points and ensure that the instrument is in good working order. Two temperature baths may be used for calibration.
3. The contractor should calibrate direct-operated alarms and shutdown switches at their set value (as per the engineering documents supplied).

Note: Obviously, test equipment must have a better accuracy than the instrument that is being calibrated. As a rule of thumb, all test equipment necessary to properly calibrate instruments must be within its manufacturer's specified accuracy, or 0.25%, if unspecified. These testing devices are normally provided by the contractor and are certified by the test equipment manufacturer within six months prior to use. It is recommended that all equipment and procedures used for calibration should meet the approval of the owner prior to checkout. In order to prevent delays of the project, such approval should be obtained about two months before the beginning of calibration activities.

Should the contractor maintain complete and accurate records of final calibrations and adjustments to instruments and control systems? Should these records be signed off by the contractor and the owner? (See Figure 7-3.)

Will the final acceptance of the functionality of the instrument loops be based on the owner's representative checking the functionality of each individual completed loop by simulating process and events? Should this simulation be determined by the owner?

Upon receipt of the final calibration records and signatures of both the owner's representative and the contractor's representative on the loop checksheet, would acceptance be completed, signifying transfer of jurisdiction?

Note: There will be cases in which the dynamic response of a loop requires testing. ISA-S26, Dynamic Response Testing, establishes the basis for dynamic response testing of measurement and control equipment. Methods for sine wave, step, and pulse-type signals are included in this standard.

CHAPTER 8

Maintenance

INTRODUCTION

Maintenance follows the rule that, since no product is absolutely perfect, everything eventually fails. The function of maintenance is to ensure the continued, reliable operation of the equipment on demand. It should be mentioned at this point that ISO 9000 states: "Sufficient control should be maintained over all measurement systems used in the development, manufacture, installation, and servicing of a product to provide confidence in decisions or actions based on measurement data." The above definition of measurement systems includes related computer software.

In addition, the preparer of a corporate standard should keep in mind that not only is the maintenance to be done correctly but also that any alterations must comply with all established codes such as the electrical code in effect at the site. Maintenance personnel should keep in mind that modifications to approved equipment may void the approval of such equipment.

Post-installation and maintenance requirements vary with plant needs and specifics. Maintenance activities in general, and in particular for instruments and control systems, are comprised of a large portion of human interrelations and teamwork. Maintenance will be accomplished successfully through a combination of technical know-how and experience.

Since not all maintenance activities for all possible plant applications can be covered in a single chapter, four items that are common to many applications will be examined here:

1. General maintenance needs and procedures
2. The testing of alarm and trip systems (ATSs)
3. The testing of electrical control equipment in hazardous (explosive/flammable) locations
4. Instrument calibration

Corporate standards for maintenance and post-installation activities will widely vary from corporation to corporation. Even within the same corporation, variations from site to site will occur. However, a good maintenance program would generally include:

1. a good understanding of the maintenance activities,
2. a clear definition of the maintenance organization,
3. a set of good procedures used in maintaining equipment in general and in particular the ones located in hazardous areas, and
4. a good system for maintenance records.

It is imperative to underline that the content of this chapter is only a memory jogger and should not be taken "as is" since statutory, technical, and corporate needs vary from one site to the other.

A typical standard covering the subject of maintenance must ensure that all activities comply with code requirements and good engineering practices. In addition, the standard must ensure that good engineering practice includes the following:

1. Engineering data is always kept up to date with the site modifications (for example, the loop drawings and the cable number on the drawing match the one on the cable).
2. The vendor's instructions are followed when maintenance is done.

The corporate standard in many cases may describe the relationship (authorities/ responsibilities) between maintenance and their two main links—purchasing and production. Such a requirement will vary depending on the corporate culture and on the size of the sites in question.

ISA-S82.01, ISA-S82.02, and ISA-S82.03 are related to the safety of electrical and electronic equipment (see Appendix B). In addition, ISA distributes ANSI C100.6, Voltage or Current Reference Devices: Solid-State Devices.

Types of Maintenance

A good maintenance program will:

1. reduce downtime by avoiding or reducing the unexpected problems,
2. provide sound data for decision making related to the frequency of shutdowns and preventive maintenance (PM), and
3. minimize product variation by maintaining the plant in good running order, i.e., higher quality products.

The two main types of maintenance are corrective maintenance and preventive maintenance. The two main activities of the maintenance team are plant improvements or modifications (generally a preplanned activity) and plant maintenance (generally combining corrective and preventive types).

Corrective maintenance is performed when breakdowns occur (or are about to occur) and is obviously not scheduled. Another type of maintenance, known as predictive maintenance, relies on the monitoring sensors (vibration, temperature, pressure, etc.) to tell if maintenance is soon required. In many cases, predictive maintenance is considered part of corrective maintenance.

Preventive maintenance (PM) is predictable since it is scheduled ahead of time and is performed generally at preset time intervals. The method by which the intervals are determined should be based on past maintenance records.

The debate over the advantages and disadvantages of PM vs. corrective maintenance is interesting and is still going on in many plants. On one hand, failures that could occur at the wrong time (they generally do, according to Murphy's law) could create loss in production or, even more importantly, affect human safety. On the other hand, if PM is scheduled over too long a period, breakdown will occur before the preset maintenance interval. If it is scheduled over too short a period, it will waste money and might even increase breakdown due to the infant mortality of the replaced parts. To have the PM set at the correct schedule is quite difficult;

therefore, the dilemma still exists and the debate goes on. In any case, PM should not be established just for its own sake. The reasons for it should be based on facts and figures.

PM is based on frequency; therefore, in plants using PM, the frequency of maintenance should be established (anything over two years should be suspicious). This frequency requires review on a regular basis (annually seems to be a norm). PM could, for example, be scheduled every quarter or so and is generally timed to coincide with plant shutdowns. In most cases, the frequency of maintenance is based on the manufacturer's recommendations and on past experience through analyzing maintenance records. If, after a number of consecutive inspections, the equipment is consistently in good condition, then the frequency of maintenance could be eased. A good maintenance program should indicate how PM is scheduled and planned (including spare parts requirements).

Personnel

Some corporate standards may find the need to identify the maintenance organization by establishing who does what, how they interface, and what are the official lines of authority and responsibility.

The need to have this as part of the standards is dependent on the corporate philosophy and the way a company does business. In many cases it is not required. In addition, other items such as job requirements and skills required, may be included (e.g., the loop tuning capabilities of maintenance personnel, and the frequency of the changing of filters on the air supply systems).

All maintenance activities must be performed only by competent personnel, including inspection and testing. Competency is achieved through proper training and includes instructions on the various types of protection and installation practices and on the general principles of area classification. In addition, suitable refresher training must be incorporated as required.

Records

Maintenance activities must be recorded. Complete maintenance records are required to support all maintenance activities, regardless of whether they are corrective or preventive. They are used as historical data for reasons that vary from setting the frequency of PM to legal and insurance documentation. They should also be kept at a minimum.

ISO 9000 states: "Procedures should be established to monitor and maintain the measurement process itself under statistical control, including equipment, procedures, and operator skills."

Sometimes maintenance records are coded to facilitate entry into computer systems where data collection and retrieval are handled by database managers or spreadsheets. Maintenance records vary from one organization to the other, but maintenance data that is generally required, regardless of the format, includes:

1. the tag number or description of the device,
2. corrective/maintenance actions on the device,
3. spare parts used,
4. the name of the person doing the maintenance, and
5. the date of the maintenance.

PLANT: *ABC Inc.*   INSTRUMENT TAG NUMBER: *PV·33-1*

Complaint/Behavior of instrument:

PV 33-1 unstable at low flows

Date: *June 13/88*   by: *HJ Smith*

Diagnostics/Symptoms:

Valve checked -all components function-ing as per specifications

Setup time [S]: *1:10* (hrs:min)   Diagnostic time [D]: *0:20* (hrs:min)

Corrective action: *1- recalculate valve sizing 2 - valve oversized 3- change valve trim to correct size 4- valve tested and works O.K. through full range*

Repair time [R]: *4:50* (hrs:min)

Total maintenance time [T]=S+D+R= *6:20* (hrs:min)

Parts used: *New trim kit part # 72158HV9*

Comments: *none*

Maintenance by: *Doug White*   Date: *June 18/88*
Approved by: *Joe Doe*   Date: *June 18/88*

Figure 8-1. Typical Corrective Maintenance Form

In addition, in the case of corrective maintenance, two additional items are needed: a description of the complaint or failure and a description of the diagnostics.

Figure 8-1 shows a typical example of a completed form used for corrective maintenance. The auditor needs to ensure the existence and use of such records.

GENERAL PROCEDURE

The needs will vary from plant to plant, but in general, the minimum required documentation must be up to date and may include:

1. a set of maintenance records,
2. a copy of all P&IDs,
3. a copy of all instrumentation and control documentation, and
4. a copy of an area classification document.

Maintenance may be broken down into different steps; this breakdown may be required for estimates, scope of work, and job descriptions. The following breakdown is tentative, and preparers of corporate standards will have to adjust these according to their particular application and needs.

1. Receive a request for maintenance.
2. Select the required procedures, tools, and manpower to do the job.
3. Get a work permit from the operator.
4. Isolate the process.
5. Remove the instrument from the process.
6. Decontaminate the instrument.
7. Perform the maintenance activity, part of which is the diagnosis of the problem.
8. Recalibrate the instrument, which includes
   - collecting the required technical information,
   - ensuring it is the correct information for the instrument in question,
   - selecting the calibration equipment,
   - connecting the instrument to be calibrated,
   - calibrating, and
   - disconnecting the calibrated instrument.
9. Prepare for instrument reinstallation (similarity with step 2 above).
10. Reinstall the instrument.
11. Check its correct operation.
12. Advise the operator.
13. Complete the required paperwork.

The requirements and precautions for maintenance in hazardous locations must be kept in mind when setting the guidelines for maintenance. The corporate standard should specify that a work permit approved by the operator must always be obtained.

Maintenance work in hazardous areas is generally limited to the following:

1. Disconnection, removal, or replacement of instruments and control equipment and cabling
2. Calibration of the instruments
3. Using test instruments

The standard may have to note that electrically powered test equipment (including uncertified batteries) should not be used in a hazardous area unless the area is covered by a gas-free work permit.

Also, where repair has been done on personnel safety-related equipment, it is good plant policy to have a second person inspect the work. If this is not done, how else can the safety and the quality of work be ensured? After all, anyone can make a mistake, but no one can afford deadly ones.

The following questions and descriptions focus on four key items:

1. Electrical isolation
2. Maintenance of programmable electronic systems (PESs)
3. Batteries
4. Pressure relief valves

Obviously, not all items to be considered are covered here. Others (such as grounding, etc.) are to be included when the standard is being prepared. The selected items in this chapter should give the preparer of the corporate standard a good understanding of the requirements to be covered.

Electrical Isolation

Should the standard recommend that, except for intrinsically safe circuits, instruments and control systems that contain electrically energized components and are located in a hazardous area should not be opened? To be opened, should the electrical energy be first isolated through fuse removal or opening and locking the breaker in the open position?

If the absence of a hazardous atmosphere can be guaranteed for the area where maintenance is to be performed, may some of the stringent requirements be relaxed and the area be treated as nonhazardous? Should this guarantee be first approved by the highest authority, considering the risk involved?

For circuit identification, is it necessary to confirm for all instrumentation and control loops that the circuit identification information is correct? Note: The main reason for this requirement is to ensure that equipment can be safely isolated whenever maintenance is done. This is done by checking that the actual tag numbers on the equipment and cables conform to the available documentation.

Should cables close to the equipment be checked for obvious damage as part of the equipment check? Is the checking of the complete length of cable required only if damage is suspected due to major modifications?

Should the standard ensure that all alterations and repairs comply with the local electrical code in effect at the site? Note: It must be kept in mind that modifications to approved equipment may void original equipment or system approval and should always be reviewed with the manufacturer.

Should the standard recommend that the repair of devices that provide safety in hazardous environments be performed only by the original manufacturer of such devices?

PESs

Do the frequency and type of maintenance meet the requirements of the facility? Is this in accordance with the vendor's recommendations?

Is maintenance performed by competent personnel who are trained to do this type of work?

Is PES hardware maintenance performed with the equipment off-line and the power supply disconnected?

Are ventilation passages left clean and clear of obstructions at all times?

Is the condition of enclosures and of grounding checked as part of routine maintenance?

Are lithium batteries, commonly used for memory retention, handled according to the vendor's recommendations?

Is the replacement of components and modules done in strict accordance with the vendor's recommendations?

Batteries

The following is an example that may be used in a corporate maintenance standard.

Only certified equipment for the area in question shall be used. Uncertified batteries (and battery-powered equipment) shall be taken through a Div. 2 area only if the equipment is adequately protected (for example, in its case, switched off with leads disconnected). Such equipment shall not be taken through a Div. 1 area unless the route is covered by a gas-free work permit or the equipment is so enclosed that the risk of it being surrounded by a hazardous atmosphere is insignificant (for example, by enclosing it in a sealed bag). Note that it is permissible to use an uncertified voltage indicator to prove the effectiveness of an isolation, provided that the voltage indicator does not contain a voltage source.

Pressure Relief Valves

These should be installed and maintained to the requirements of the codes and regulations in effect at the site, keeping in mind the type of process materials the relief valves will handle. However, in general, the following questions will help identify the overall requirements.

Upon receipt, should relief valves be tested in a shop that has the correct equipment? Should the valve then be sealed by the test shop (and, in some cases, color coded)? Should a test certificate be produced by the person doing the testing and approved by the plant safety inspector? Should copies of this certificate be kept in a specific area (e.g., the test department, plant engineering, and the safety department)?

Should repair and adjustments to relief valves be done only by qualified persons? After repairs and adjustments, should the relief valve be tested again and a certificate issued?

Should the standard state that relief valves be tested at fixed intervals in compliance with the local code requirements? Should exceptions to such requirements be implemented (for example, if the regulatory authorities require a more frequent testing or if the relief valve experiences operating conditions that require frequent maintenance)?

Other Items

As a final check in the preparation of a corporate standard, the preparer may refer to the following questions. It should be mentioned at this point that the subject of maintenance, more than any another covered in this book, is subject to the needs and corporate culture of the company for which these standards are being prepared.

What is the required overall quality of the maintenance program? How are costs monitored? Are they on budget? How close? Is there a procedure for handling the maintenance work (verbal, written)?

Is there a need for a preventive maintenance (PM) program for all items of control? What should be the frequency of the PM program? How is the frequency of maintenance to be determined? Should there be an analysis of equipment histories that examines repeated failures?

Should the standard recommend a procedure on how to perform calibration and maintenance? Does it conform with vendors' recommendations?

Are maintenance manuals to be available for all items of control? Where are the maintenance manuals to be kept?

Are calibration and maintenance results to be recorded? Are the records to be prepared according to good engineering practice? Where are the records to be kept?

What spares are to be available in stock? Is this sufficient?

Should the standard require the identification of a maintenance organization? Is training to be identified?

Is all maintenance to be done by plant personnel, and/or is the help of outside contractors requested? Should there be a contract maintenance program with an outside contractor? Is this approach effective? How is unplanned maintenance handled?

What should the general condition of the maintenance shop be? Should the standard recommend a minimum requirement, or should it be left to the discretion of the maintenance personnel?

Is the calibrating equipment to be kept in good condition at all times (or only at PM time)? What is the required accuracy in comparison to the equipment being calibrated?

Should the standard ensure that the equipment is correctly used and that its use agree with the maintenance manuals? Should this requirement instead be left to the discretion of maintenance personnel?

Is a special maintenance procedure to be observed where safety is involved?

When equipment is withdrawn from service, should the standard ensure that exposed wires are:

- terminated in an appropriate enclosure,
- insulated, and
- not left hanging loose?

Should maintenance records be available to maintenance personnel and up to date? Should their location be specified in the standard?

Are there means of recalling (or assessing) product that has been checked with instruments found to be out of calibration?

Should all test hardware (and software) verified before use and periodically checked?

Should the desired measurement accuracy be known to the maintenance personnel? If not, how can they ensure that the instrument "as left" condition is what is required?

Should the standard ensure that records show that instruments were calibrated before being put in service?

THE TESTING OF ALARM AND TRIP SYSTEMS

Every alarm and trip system (ATS) will fail sooner or later. Therefore, and to reduce the possibility of such failures, testing is required. It is quite common that a corporate standard will address this subject, which may be broken into the following items:

1. Purpose of testing
2. Testing
3. Testing methods
4. Frequency of testing
5. Testing procedures

The following questions will help the preparer of such a standard identify many of the items required for consideration.

Purpose of Testing

Does the corporate standard ensure that the testing of ATSs and the appropriate equipment needed are considered at the design stage?

Does the design documentation provide a clear explanation of the intended method of testing and the assumptions on which the test method is based?

Since failures can happen either as "fail-safe" or "fail-to-danger," is the testing of ATSs designed to reveal all faults? Note: When the failure of an ATS causes a spurious alarm or trip, it is said to be "fail-safe" or "fail-to-safety." This is because it draws attention to its malfunction and must generally be corrected before operation is restarted. If, however, a fault occurs that does not reveal itself, then when the system is called upon to alarm or trip, no alarm or trip will occur, and a sometimes dangerous occurrence may follow. Such faults are called "fail-to-danger." If a "fail-to-danger" fault occurs, the affected system will remain in a risk condition until the failure is revealed and corrected.

How has the design considered that faults are to be revealed? Note: The existence of a fault may be revealed either by failure of the system to operate when required (an unwanted condition in most cases) or by testing (obviously the preferred method).

How is the reliability of ATSs achieved? Note: This is generally accomplished first through their fundamental design, then through the conditions under which they operate in the plant, and finally through the frequency at which they are tested.

Should the operator always be advised of (and agree with) an upcoming test? Have provisions been made for a safe manual intervention by the operator should a genuine emergency arise while the testing is being performed?

Testing

What is the testing philosophy? Note: Generally, testing should be based on the use of artificially generated process signals, since this would check the functionality of the ATS starting at the measuring element.

In some cases when exception to the above philosophy may be required, would testing be performed by intentionally bringing the process to the actual trip condition and observing the response of the ATS? Note: This method, if used, should be performed under controlled conditions and should be avoided for routine testing of ATSs wherever possible.

In critical cases, are redundant output components (e.g., trip valves) used? Note: This is to allow testing on one while the other is fully functional. In other cases, generally critical ones, complete redundant ATSs are implemented to provide very high reliabilities and allow the complete testing of an ATS while maintaining the process under another ATS.

Are there cases in which testing of the ATS is done by bringing the process towards a hazardous condition and checking that the trip system operates? Does this approach create a potentially dangerous condition? Should it be carefully evaluated before following such a route? Note: Such dangers may arise from two main reasons. First, additional real demands could be imposed on the trip system when it is disabled for testing. Second, in the event of other process measurements being defective, the plant may be inadvertently brought into a hazardous condition.

Is it possible to accommodate adequate testing during routine shutdowns? Would the test prove the ability of the ATS to work under the required process conditions (e.g., at temperatures and pressures that will prevail when the plant is required to alarm or trip)? Note: This may be difficult if extreme conditions must be simulated by maintenance personnel.

In extreme cases, is the installation of redundant trip valves required to allow full on-line testing?

Would normal testing reveal all possible faults, such as wear that prevents tight shutoff or plugged process isolation valves? Has consideration been given to testing so as to reveal these faults or to routine equipment removal for maintenance and checking at appropriate intervals?

Testing Methods

The most common method of testing an ATS is by breaking down the system into its three main components — input, logic, and output — and testing them individually. The advantage of this method versus testing as a complete unit is the ability to promptly isolate problems.

Inputs are tested by finding out if they respond correctly to a simulated or a real change in process conditions. Many methods of testing are used; the most common in order of preference are:

1. isolating the impulse line (after closing the isolation valve) to the switch/transmitter and injecting a simulated signal (while testing, the trip set point should be verified);

2. altering the set point to cause a trip; and
3. altering the switch/transmitter output by altering its range or zero point.

Logic systems are tested by simulating action at the input and verifying that the output(s) is responding correctly. This may require the use of defeat or bypass switches to enable section-by-section testing.

Outputs are tested by finding out if they respond correctly to a simulated or a real command from the logic. The most common output device for alarm functions is a light, and for trip functions, motors and trip valves. The testing of lights and motors is a straightforward activity; the testing of trip valves may require careful planning in some cases, because a trip valve may also be a modulating control valve.

The most common methods of testing valve-based trips, in order of preference, are:

1. allowing a valve to trip;
2. using a chock (a travel-limiting device) to limit valve movement and allow the valve to trip to chock;
3. bypassing the trip solenoid valve; and
4. injecting a suitable signal into the solenoid valve vent to control the movement of the main valve.

When fitting a valve with a handwheel, has extreme care been taken to ensure that there is no interference with the normal operation of the valve if not fully disengaged?

Who performs the ATS testing? Is there a preference if it is to be performed by plant personnel, by outside organizations, or by a combination of both?

Frequency of Testing

The dependability of an ATS depends on the proof test frequency and on the reliability of the equipment used. The frequency of testing ATSs is generally determined by a number of factors:

1. How critical is a particular point to personnel safety and plant performance?
2. What is the result of previous testing? Was maintenance required?
3. Do any regulations require specific testing?

How is the modification of frequency testing done? Are all modifications and the reasons behind them carefully recorded?

What is the testing frequency? Note: Too much testing is a waste of human and financial resources; not enough testing defeats the whole purpose of ATS reliability. As a starting point, should ATS testing for critical points that relate to safety or environmental needs be carried out at 3- to 6-month inter-vals? Should analyzers be an exception and require testing more frequently? Should testing frequency not exceed 12-month intervals and not be at less than 1-week intervals?

In cases in which some plant production units run for long periods of time, should their ATSs be tested while the plant is running? Should the methods of doing this without interruption of the process be considered at the detailed design stage? On the other hand, for processes that shut down relatively frequently, may their ATSs be tested by using them to shut down the plant?

Is there a reason to increase the reliability of ATS equipment through the use of levels of redundancy and diversity in measuring sensors?

Testing Procedures

Testing procedures must maintain the safety of maintenance personnel and the production facilities and must be designed to minimize the risk of initiating a spurious trip. The corporate standard should reflect this philosophy and/or any additional philosophies agreed upon at the earlier stages of this activity.

Were the decisions related to the testing of ATSs closely developed with key plant personnel? Has the procedure assessed that the testing will not jeopardize the safety of personnel who perform the testing and the regular safety norms set for the operation of a plant?

Have the tests been designed to minimize the risk of spurious trips and to allow safe manual overrides to intervene when plant emergency conditions develop during testing?

Have key documents been prepared? Note: The key documents that include key information are the ATS test procedure and the ATS description.

Has the ATS test procedure been worked out and agreed upon by the various responsible persons in the plant? Does an ATS test procedure exist for every alarm and trip in the plant? Does it exist at least for the critical ones? Are the procedures kept up to date? Note: A simplified example for a completed ATS test procedure is shown in Figure 5-10. In it, the points related to the procedure of testing the ATS are indicated. As a guide, the following steps could be used in the generation of test procedures:

1. The process engineer identifies the conditions that trigger an alarm or trip point (ATS description).
2. The control and process engineers jointly prepare the procedures for testing.
3. The ATS test procedure is then reviewed and approved by operations and maintenance.
4. The control engineer makes a final review and approves or disapproves.

Through the preparation, review, and approval of the ATS test procedure, the following points must be indicated:

1. Alarm/trip test frequency
2. Hazards to personnel and to equipment
3. Reference information (i.e., drawings, specifications, etc.)
4. Equipment and personnel required
5. Test procedures

How is the testing to be performed (i.e., on-line vs. off-line)? Note: The testing of ATSs should be done with the minimum of disturbance to the plant. The choice is between on-line, off-line, and shutdown. On-line testing requires great care to avoid shutting down the whole plant; even then it is limited to those trips that can be defeated for a period without undue risk. Off-line testing is limited because scheduled shutdowns or turnarounds tend to be infrequent, of short duration, and very busy. Thus, off-line testing is limited to the more critical systems such as turbine low oil pressure, compressor trips, etc. Shutdown trips are seldom used, except in the case of batch systems where the cycle frequency is relatively short. These methods do test a complete system. They are usually done under the guidance of the operator.

INSPECTION OF ELECTRICAL CONTROL EQUIPMENT IN HAZARDOUS (CLASSIFIED) LOCATIONS

The corporate standards being developed should ascertain the procedures used in maintaining equipment used in hazardous environments.

The person who prepares the corporate standard must remember that maintenance of equipment in hazardous areas should be done only if power is removed from the system and only if the plant is free from hazard. With modern control systems, these two conditions can usually be met only during major plant shutdowns. Part of the function of a corporate standard is to set the conditions under which the plant maintains equipment in hazardous locations.

In addition, when addressing the subject of the equipment used for testing in hazardous environments, the standard needs to determine that the test equipment is approved for such use and that it is in good working condition. The following questions may help the preparer of the corporate standard.

Since much test equipment is battery operated, should the standard recommend that the batteries be certified for such an environment? If not, do the maintenance people obtain a "hazardous-free" work permit before going into these hazardous locations with uncertified equipment?

Is there a need to identify procedures to ensure that test equipment is used properly?

Should the equipment be checked frequently to ensure reliable operation? How frequently?

Where pressurized enclosures are used, the standard may recommend the type of gas to be used. If it is anything but air, what is its effect on personnel in case of malfunction (i.e., sudden releases)?

Is the installation in accordance with the codes in effect at the site and in accordance with ISA standards? (See Appendix B)

The following are points that may require specific highlighting in the standard:

1. Since equipment used in such hazardous environments possesses special features, these features must be maintained (for example, explosionproof boxes should not be altered or even repaired on-site, intrinsic barriers should be used as recommended by the vendor, etc.).
2. The seemingly correct operation of such equipment does not mean that its integrity is protected (for example, explosionproof boxes with dirty or corroded joints or intrinsic barriers that are not grounded).

Area Classification

It is important that all the appropriate data regarding area classification be available to maintenance personnel. The most common document is a plant layout, which shows the different electrical area classifications.

Since there are special maintenance procedures where safety is involved, it is important for the preparer of the corporate standard to ensure some general requirements. The following questions may be used as a starting point. Further details are supplied later in this chapter.

Are the inspection, testing, and maintenance of control systems for use in hazardous locations in accordance with good engineering practice?

Are maintenance records available? Are they up to date? Where are the records kept?

Is the equipment used appropriate to the area classification? Are there any unauthorized modifications?

Are the equipment and their circuits identified correctly on the drawings?

Are flange faces on explosionproof boxes clean and undamaged? Is the gap within the permitted maximum?

Are the cables of the correct type for the area classification? Any damage? Is the cable installation (including boxes) as per the electrical code?

Are the grounding connections satisfactory? Is the ground loop resistance satisfactory?

For pressurized enclosures, is the protective gas relatively free from contaminants? Are the pressure and flow adequate? Are the alarms and interlocks functional? Is the enclosure gasket in good condition?

On systems with intrinsic barriers, are the barriers of the approved type? Are they installed correctly? Is segregation maintained between intrinsically safe and nonintrinsically safe circuits?

Inspection

A regular routine inspection of instruments and control systems is the first step for effective maintenance. One of the main components of such a scheme is the keeping of good maintenance records. The standard may provide guidelines and even typical forms for the generation of such records.

The timing and frequency of inspections will vary depending on the plant needs. In general, inspections are carried out:

1. prior to commissioning and after modifications to the system,
2. periodically on a regular basis — a kind of PM (it is good practice to have the frequency of this periodic inspection set according to the records from previous inspections), and
3. on a random basis.

The results of all inspections should be recorded. This information is a valuable tool in determining the frequency of regular inspections.

In general, the preparer of the corporate standard will find inspection requirements specific to a particular industry or site. These requirements must be developed to accommodate the needs of the users. The following points may help to emphasize this process:

1. Inspect all installation prior to start-up and at selected time frequencies.
2. Ensure that control systems are in a condition that allows them to operate as expected and designed.
3. Inspect carefully for damage and faults on equipment that has just been maintained.
4. Eliminate sources of error that may occur during installation and maintenance due to poor workmanship, incorrect type of equipment being used, or damage caused by others.
5. Save time and maintain quality by performing all inspections in a systematic manner, using competent personnel.
6. Determine the detail of inspection activities based on how critical the system being inspected is and how much maintenance is done to it.

Inspection may vary in complexity. The following two types give an indication of the range:

1. Visual inspections determine without the use of tools or specialized equipment those defects that are obvious to the naked eye.
2. Detailed inspections determine defects that can be identified only by using tools and/or specialized equipment.

The standard may identify when and where each type is used, or this decision may be left to the plant maintenance staff.

This chapter will consider four types of equipment inspection:

1. Explosionproof Enclosures
2. Protection by Pressurization and Dilution
3. Intrinsically Safe
4. Enclosures for Combustible Dusts or Fibers

Inspection of Explosionproof Enclosures

The inspection of such enclosures may be a requirement of the standard. Writing this part of the standard can be accomplished by answering the following questions.

☐ **ENVIRONMENT:**

Is the enclosure protected from adverse conditions?

Is there any unnecessary accumulation of dirt and dust?

If weatherproofed, is it installed correctly?

☐ **EQUIPMENT:**

Is the circuit identification correct?

Are there any unauthorized modifications?

How is the opening of an explosionproof boox performed?

How is the absence of power ensured?

Do maintenance personnel wait for stored electrical energy to dissipate before opening?

Do they allow the equipment surface temperature to come down first?

What is done if maintenance is required yet power cannot be cut off?

Are bolts and connectors of the correct type, complete and tight?

Are flange faces clean and undamaged? Note: Cleaning and clearances should be in accordance with the recommendation from the enclosure supplier.

Are flange gap dimensions within the range?

Are the enclosure, glasses, and glass/metal seals satisfactory? Note: It is normal, from usage, for the seal between the glass and the body of the enclosure metal to have some damage from environmental conditions. This seal is part of the enclosure and repairs to it should not be done on site. It is recommended that a complete replacement assembly be used.

Is it appropriate to the classification of the area in question?

Is the equipment surface temperature class correct?

☐ **INSTALLATION:**

Is the installation in compliance with the electrical code in effect at the site?

Are the electrical protective devices functional and correctly sized?

Is the type of cable appropriate? Any cable damage?

Are the grounding connections satisfactory?

Is the ground loop resistance acceptable?

Are the cable boxes correctly filled?

Are there any obstacles near the flange joints?

Inspection of Equipment Protected by Pressurization and Continuous Dilution

The inspection of such enclosures could be specified in the standard, which can be accomplished by answering the following questions. Such installations should conform to ISA-S12.4 (see Appendix B).

☐ **ENVIRONMENT:**

Is the enclosure protected from adverse conditions?

Is there any unnecessary accumulation of dirt and dust?

If weatherproofed, is it installed correctly?

□ EQUIPMENT:

Is the identification of the enclosure and of the circuits correct?

Are there any unauthorized modifications?

Is the equipment appropriate to the classification of the area in question?

Is the equipment surface temperature class correct?

□ INSTALLATION:

Is the installation in compliance with the electrical code in effect at the site?

Are the electrical protective devices functional and correctly sized?

Is the type of cable appropriate? Any cable damage?

Are the grounding connections satisfactory?

Are the pipes/tubes for the supply of the protective gas in good condition?

Is the protective gas safe? Is it free from contaminants? Note: It is recommended that, where process conditions permit, air be the only gas used for pressurization.

Are the pressure and flow settings adequate? Note: It is recommended that pressurized enclosures, including pressurized control rooms, be tested before commissioning and afterwards on a regular basis.

Is the inlet temperature acceptable? Note: The air temperature should not exceed 100°F (40°C) at the inlet of the enclosure.

Are the indicators, alarms, and interlocks operating correctly?

Is the pre-energizing purge period adequate?

If flammable gas detectors are installed, are they functional?

Inspection of Intrinsically Safe Equipment and Systems

The inspection of such equipment and systems may be specified in the standard. This can be accomplished by answering the following questions.

□ ENVIRONMENT:

Is the enclosure protected from adverse conditions?

Is there any unnecessary accumulation of dirt and dust?

If weatherproofed, is it installed correctly?

□ INTRINSICALLY SAFE (IS) EQUIPMENT AND SYSTEMS:

Is the equipment appropriate to the classification of the area in question?

Are there any visible unauthorized modifications?

Is all equipment identified as per the engineering data (including the length of signal cables)?

Are the IS barriers of the type approved by the electrical authority having jurisdiction at the site?

☐ **INSTALLATION:**

Are all the electrical connections tight and clean?

Is the complete installation (including IS barriers, grounding, and cables) installed per the approved documentation?

Is there any obvious damage to cables?

Is the IS ground continuity adequate? Is it grounded at one point only?

Is the testing of ground resistance made according to the vendor's recommended methods and equipment? Note: The resistance of the ground connection between all intrinsically safe circuits and the ground reference point should be measured to ensure that it is less than 1 ohm. The conductor used for the connection should be equivalent to a copper conductor of 4 mm^2 minimum cross-sectional area. The measurement should be made using a tester for intrinsically safe circuits. In order to carry out these tests, the normal ground connection should be disconnected. This can be done only if either the plant is free from hazard or power is removed completely from the system. These conditions on modern integrated control systems can be met only at major shutdowns.

Is segregation maintained between IS and non-IS circuits in common junction boxes and panels?

Is the IS system inspected following any maintenance work?

Inspection of Equipment Protected by Enclosure for Use in the Presence of Combustible Dusts or Fibers

The inspection of such enclosures may be required in the standard, which can be accomplished by answering the following questions.

☐ **ENVIRONMENT:**

Is the enclosure protected from adverse conditions?

Is there any unnecessary accumulation of dirt and dust?

If weatherproofed, is it installed correctly?

☐ **EQUIPMENT:**

Is the identification of the enclosure and of the circuits correct?

Are there any unauthorized modifications?

Is the equipment appropriate to the classification of the area in quesiton?

Is the equipment surface temperature class correct?

Are the electrical connections clean and tight?

Is the enclosure gasket in good conditions?

☐ **INSTALLATION:**

Is the installation in compliance with the electrical code in effect at the site?

Are the electrical protective devices functional and correctly sized?

Is the type of cable appropriate? Any cable damage?

Are the grounding connections satisfactory?

Is the ground loop resistance acceptable?

INSTRUMENT CALIBRATION

A primary activity in maintenance is the calibration of equipment. Quite often this activity is performed in a calibration shop where most of the calibrating equipment is located. The quality of the calibration shop, the quality and accuracy of the instruments used for calibration (obviously they must be better than the instruments being calibrated), and the calibration records kept for all instruments are extremely important. In addition, it is good practice to calibrate control equipment prior to first use in order to confirm all settings (an ISO 9000 recommendation). A typical calibration report is shown in Figure 8-2.

CALIBRATION REPORT

INSTRUMENT TAG NUMBER:

MAKE: MODEL NUMBER:
              SERIAL NUMBER:

TEST PROCEDURE NUMBER:

CALIBRATION DATA

INPUT UNITS %	OUTPUT UNITS AS FOUND		% FULL SCALE ERROR	INPUT UNITS %	OUTPUT UNITS AS LEFT		% FULL SCALE ERROR
	UP	DOWN			UP	DOWN	
0				0			
*25				*25			
50				50			
*75				*75			
100				100			

* = Minimum check points

DATE TESTED: TESTED BY:

APPROVAL DATE: APPROVED BY:

Figure 8-2. A Typical Calibration Report

The calibration of instruments is needed to ensure that the accuracy designed into the control system as a whole is maintained.

When corporate standards are being developed, questions of instrument priority, degree of calibration, and required accuracy are raised. Instrument priority looks at critical vs. noncritical equipment and its effect on safety, health, and the environment. Such a priority may also have to consider the results due to loss of performance or even loss of the instrument's required accuracy. The degree of calibration looks at the extent of the required equipment and the technology that are required to perform the expected calibration to ensure that the instruments are in compliance with their design intent. Required accuracy looks at the need of the process rather than the capabilities of the instrument; for example, if an instrument can operate with an error of ±0.25%, but the process requires only a ±1%, should extra effort be spent to reach the 0.25% capability? Would 0.5% be sufficient? The answer must consider the effects of calibration time, highly precise calibrating equipment, specially trained manpower, etc. — all of which reflect unnecessary additional costs.

Note: In some cases manometers are used for instrument calibration. ISA-RP2.1 facilitates and standardizes the use of manometers and U-tubes (see Appendix B). This document also includes a discussion on the more frequent and more important sources of error in manometric measurements together with correction tables for mercury and water columns.

For the purposes of this book, and as a starting point for the generator of such a standard, instruments in a plant may be divided into four types.

1. Type 1 are the plant calibration standards. These types of instruments are used to calibrate type 2 and are generally traceable to an outside standards or calibration organization that is nationally recognized. ISA-RP52.1 serves as a guideline for the operation of standards laboratories.
2. Type 2 are the instrument calibration standards. These instruments are used by maintenance personnel to calibrate types 3 and 4.
3. Type 3 are the critical process instruments that prevent situations that are life- and environment-threatening.
4. Type 4 are the instruments used for production and represent the majority of the instrumentation and control equipment in a plant.

Sometimes instrument calibration standards reside in a quality assurance manual in a plant rather than in its corporate standards for control engineering. It all depends on the way a plant does business and runs its operation. In either case, the results should be the same; i.e., there are procedures to follow to ensure good maintenance and the preservation of the control functions as intended.

The following is a simulated example of how such a procedure may look for each of the four types. This example should give a good indication of the contents of the corporate standard on this subject. This example should be modified to reflect the needs of the site and to comply with the local regulations and/or meet certain quality standards such as ISO 9000.

CP No.: 123abc   P.1 of xx

Author: J.J. Black   Issue Date 93.04.20

Approvals: M.M. White   Approval Date: 93.05.16
            K.H. Green   Approval Date: 93.05.17
            M.S. Brown   Approval Date: 93.05.16

Revision number: 2
Revised by: J.J. Smith   Revision Date: 93.12.02
Approved by: J.T. Doe   Approval Date: 93.12.03

General Procedures

This procedure is to establish the guidelines for the calibration of plant instruments.

Each week a list of instruments to be calibrated will be issued. The maintenance supervisor will then assign the calibration to a trained instrument mechanic or will send the equipment out if it is of the Type 1 or if the workload in the instrument maintenance shop is high.

Each month a list of instruments that were not calibrated as per schedule will be issued and immediate action taken to tag this equipment out of service until such time that calibration is correctly performed.

The maintenance foreman and the quality manager shall semiannually review the PM schedule and decide, based on past instrument performance, whether maintenance frequency should be changed.

Every calibrated instrument should have a calibration sticker indicating:

- the date of calibration,
- the initials of the person who performed the calibration, and
- the due date for the next calibration.

It is preferable, where possible, to place the calibration sticker across the seal or over the calibration access to the equipment.

No instrument (all types) should be put back in service if it does not meet the calibration standards.

On all calibration reports, the instrument mechanic will note on the completed form the ``as found'' and ``as left'' conditions. If the ``as found'' and ``as left'' conditions deviate by more than the specified acceptable value, the quality manager will try to access the time during which the instrument was out of calibra-

Figure 8-3. Example 4-Type Calibration Report

tion and the effect this may have had. This information must then be immediately provided in writing to the maintenance foreman and the production manager. The quality manager and the maintenance foreman will then review the maintenance and calibration records for the instrument in question and decide whether the calibration frequency should be changed or any corrective action is needed.

All records pertaining to calibration of instruments (all types) must be retained for a period of six years.

All manufacturer's maintenance manuals will be kept in the maintenance shop in a dedicated area.

All calibrating instruments must be identified by individual tag numbers to facilitate identification and historically record keeping.

Instruments Type 1 (Plant Calibration Standards)

These instruments are used to calibrate Type 2 instruments. They consist of:

- two XY123 calibrators, tag numbers X1 and X2, and
- two WYZKID gages, tag numbers X3 and X4.

They are to be calibrated annually by ABC Independent Calibration Labs. After each calibration, they are to be returned to the plant with a documentation of certification approved by ABC Labs. They should be sent and received back within 30 days of the anniversary due date.

In the event that a Type 1 instrument is found out of tolerance, ABC Labs should immediately advise the plant. The maintenance supervisor at the plant will then assess the effect this out of tolerance may have had on Types 2, 3, and 4 instruments.

The anniversary date of these instruments will be staggered to ensure the presence of a working and calibrated set in the maintenancae shop at all times.

When the calibration equipment is received back, it shall be checked for obvious shipping damage. If there is damage, the equipment must not be used and must be immediately returned to ABC Labs for repair and/or recalibration.

These instruments are to be kept in the maintenance shop in an environmentally controlled area that meets the manufacturer's specifications.

Figure 8-3. (*Continued*)

Instruments Type 2 (Instrument Calibration Standards)

These instruments are used to calibrate Types 3 and 4. They consist of:

- two NIK13 gages, tag numbers Y1 and Y2;
- four GIG05 digital multimeters, tag numbers Y3, Y4, Y10, and Y11;
- two BEB01 thermometer calibration kits, tag numbers Y5 and Y9
- two BIJ01 lab test weights, tag numbers Y6 and Y8; and
- two PUN06 air regulators, tag numbers Y12 and Y13.

They are to be calibrated semiannually by plant maintenance using Type 1 equipment. In addition to the scheduled annual check, calibration may be performed whenever the accuracy of an instrument Type 2 is questionable.

Calibration form CF12 must be completed for each instrument every time a calibration is performed. These forms are then signed by and filed with the supervisor of plant maintenance.

Instruments Type 3 (Critical Instruments)

Type 3 are the critical process instruments that prevent life- and environment-threatening situations. The following list identifies such equipment:

- FSH-123A, FV-123A
- TSH-456, TV-456

Calibration is done every six months (as part of PM), when the instrument is replaced, or when its accuracy is questioned (for example, when its reading is compared against other indicators).

Calibration form CF13 must be completed for each instrument every time a calibration is performed. These forms are then signed by and filed with the supervisor of plant maintenance.

Calibration of Type 3 instruments is performed as follows:

- Identify tag number at the instrument.
- Obtain copy of its up-to-date instrument specification sheet
- Retrieve the manufacturer's maintenance manual for this instrument.
- Obtain a blank CF13 form.
- Calibrate instrument as per manufacturer's recommendations.
- Complete calibration form CF13 and return to the supervisor of plant maintenance.

Figure 8-3. (*Continued*)

- Return manufacturer's maintenance manuals to their storage location.

Instruments Type 4 (Noncritical Instruments)

Calibration of Type 4 instruments will be done on a yearly basis as a starting point. After 4 years of service, the records will checked to determine if the yearly frequency is adequate.

Calibration form CF14 must be completed for each instrument every time a calibration is performed. These forms are then signed by and filed with the supervisor of plant maintenance.

Calibration of Type 3 instruments is performed as follows:

- Identify tag number at the instrument.
- Obtain copy of its up-to-date instrument specification sheet.
- Retrieve the manufacturer's maintenance manual for this instrument.
- Obtain a blank CF14 form.
- Calibrate instrument as per manufacturer's recommendations.
- Complete calibration form CF14 and return to the supervisor of plant maintenance.
- Return manufacturer's maintenance manuals to their storage location.

Figure 8-3. (*Continued*)

APPENDIX A

National and International Developers of Standards for Instrumentation and Control

Acoustical Society of America (ASA)
Air-Conditioning and Refrigeration Institute (ARI)
Air Movement and Control Association (AMCA)
Aluminum Association (AA)
American Association of Textile Chemists and Colorists (AATCC)
American Boiler Manufacturers Association (ABMA)
American Chemical Society (ACS)
American Conference of Government Industrial Hygienists (ACGIH)
American Gas Association (AGA)
American Leather Chemists Association (ALCA)
American National Standards Institute (ANSI)
American Nuclear Society (ANS)
American Petroleum Institute (API)
American Society for Quality Control (ASQC)
American Society for Testing and Materials (ASTM)
American Society of Agricultural Engineers (ASAE)
American Society of Heating, Refrigerating, and Air-Conditioning Engineers, Inc. (ASHRAE)
American Society of Mechanical Engineers (ASME)
American Vacuum Society (AVS)
American Water Works Association (AWWA)
American Welding Society (AWS)
Anti-Friction Bearing Manufacturers Association, Inc. (AFBMA)
Association for the Advancement of Medical Instrumentation (AAMI)
Association of Official Analytical Chemists (AOAC)
The Chlorine Institute (CI)
Cooling Tower Institute (CTI)
Dairy and Food, 3A Sanitary Standards Committees (DFSSC)
Electronic Industries Association (EIA)
Factory Mutual System (FM)
Fluid Controls Institute, Inc. (FCI)
Gas Processors Association (GPA)

Industrial Fasteners Institute (IFI)
Industrial Risk Insurers (IRI)
Institute of Electrical and Electronics Engineers (IEEE)
Institute of Environmental Sciences (IES)
Institute of Interconnecting and Packaging Electronic Circuits (IPC)
Instrument Society of America (ISA)
Insulated Cable Engineers Association, Inc. (ICEA)
International Association of Plumbing and Mechanical Officials (IAPMO)
International Conference of Building Officials (ICBO)
International Electrotechnical Commission (IEC)
International Organization for Standardization (ISO)
Manufacturers Standardization Society of the Valve and Fitting Industry (MSS)
Metal Powder Industries Federation (MPIF)
National Association of Pipe Coating Applicators (NAPCA)
National Association of Relay Manufacturers (NARM)
National Board of Boiler and Pressure Vessel Inspectors (NBBI)
National Cable Television Association (NCTA)
National Council of Radiation Protection and Measurements (NCRP)
National Electrical Manufacturers Association (NEMA)
National Environmental Balancing Bureau (NEBB)
National Fire Protection Association (NFPA)
National Fluid Power Association (NFLDP)
National Institute of Standards and Technology (NIST)
Pipe Fabrication Institute (PFI)
Plumbing and Drainage Institute (PDI)
Radio Technical Commission for Aeronautics (RTCA)
Range Commanders Council (RCC)
Resistance Welder Manufacturers Association (RWMA)
Scientific Apparatus Makers Association (SAMA)
Society of Automotive Engineers, Inc. (SAE)
The Society of Naval Architects and Marine Engineers (SNAME)
Spring Manufacturers Institute, Inc. (SMI)
Technical Association of the Pulp and Paper Industry (TAPPI)
Ultrasonic Industry Association, Inc. (UIA)
Underwriters Laboratories, Inc. (UL)

APPENDIX B

ISA's Standards and Recommended Practices for Instrumentation and Control

The following is the list of " Standards and Recommended Practices for Instrumentation and Control".

The following ISA Standards and Recommended Practices are available from the Instrument Society of America, 67 Alexander Drive, P.O. Box 12277, Research Triangle Park, NC 27709.

ISA-RP2.1, Manometer Tables, Reaffirmed 1985, 31 pp.
Presents abbreviations and fundamental conversion factors commonly used in manometry, recommended definitions of pressure in terms of a column of mercury and water, and for a large number of liquids, tables of pressures indicated by, or equivalent to, heights of columns at various temperatures.

ISA-S5.1, (ANSI/ISA-1984), Instrumentation Symbols and Identification (Formerly ANSI Y32.20), 1984, 52 pp.
Establishes a uniform means of designating instruments and instrumentation systems used for measurement and control. The differing established procedural needs of various organizations are recognized (where not inconsistent with the objectives of the standard) by providing alternative symbolism methods. A number of options are provided for adding information or simplifying the symbolism, if desired. Includes additional information on symbolism for function blocks, function designations, computer functions, and programmable logic control.

ISA-S5.2, (ANSI/ISA-1796, R 1981), Binary Logic Diagrams for Process Operations, R1981, 19 pp.
Provides symbols, both basic and non-basic, for binary operating functions. Intended to symbolize the binary operating functions of a system in a manner that can be applied to any class of hardware, whether electronic, electrical, fluidic, pneumatic, hydraulic, mechanical, manual, optical, or other.

ISA-S5.3, Graphic Symbols for Distributed Control/Shared Display Instrumentation, Logic and Computer Systems, 1982, 14 pp.
Establishes documentation for that class of instrumentation consisting of computers, programmable controllers, minicomputers and microprocessor based systems that have shared control, shared display or other interface features. Symbols are

provided for interfacing field instrumentation, control room instrumentation and other hardware to the above.

ISA-S5.4, (ANSI/ISA-1976, R 1989), Instrument Loop Diagrams, 1989, 11 pp.

Provides a method and practice for the preparation and use of instrument loop diagrams in the design, construction, checkout, startup, operation, maintenance, and reconstruction of instrument systems in industrial plants.

ISA-S5.5, (ANSI/ISA-1986), Graphic Symbols for Process Displays, 1986, 40 pp.

Provides a system of graphic symbols for conveying information on visual display units (VDUs) used for process monitoring and control. Intended to ensure compatibility of symbols on process VDUs with related symbols used in other disciplines. The standard applies to computers, distributed control systems, etc., and covers both color and monochromatic displays. It supplements ISA-S5.1 and ISA-S5.3.

ISA-RP7.1 Pneumatic Control Circuit Pressure Test, 1956, 6 pp.

Intended to provide a satisfactory procedure for the testing of pneumatic control circuits for leaks together with reasonable criteria for acceptance of work done and suitable aids for performance.

ISA-S7.3 (ANSI/ISA-1975, R 1981), Quality Standard for Instrument Air, R 1981, 6 pp.

Establishes a maximum allowable moisture content at which the instruments will function satisfactorily; a maximum entrained particle size which will avoid plugging and wear/erosion of air passages and orifices, a maximum allowable oil content which will avoid malfunction due to clogging and wear of the components; an awareness of a possible source of corrosive or toxic contamination entering the air system; through the compressor suction, plant air system cross connections, or instrument air connections directly connected to processes.

ISA-S7.4 (ANSI/ISA-1981), Air Pressures for Pneumatic Controllers, Transmitters, and Transmission Systems, 1981, 4 pp.

Purpose is to establish standard operating pressure ranges for pneumatic intelligence transmission systems; and standard air supply pressures (with limit values) for operation of pneumatic controllers and pneumatic intelligence transmission systems.

ISA-RP7.7 Recommended Practice for Producing Quality Instrument Air, 1984, 16 pp.

Establishes general equipment guidelines for producing instrument air of the quality defined in ANSI/ISA-S7.3-1975 (R1981). This document enumerates equipment characteristics to include types, range, and performance of the components necessary to meet air quality requirements of ANSL ISA-S7.3. This recommended practice lists tests of system, and components where applicable, to check performance of instrument air supply system to ANSI/ISA-S7.3 requirements.

S12.1 Definitions and Information Pertaining to Electrical Instruments in Hazardous (Classified) Locations, 1991, 12 pp.

Provides definitions and information pertaining to protection techniques, terminology, and the installation of electrical instruments in hazardous (classified) locations and provides an introduction and basic background to the ISA-SP12, Electrical Safety, series of publications and committee activities. It replaces the original ISA-RP12.1, Electrical Instruments in Hazardous Atmospheres, published in 1960. Provides a general review of applicable codes and standards, and it should not be used in lieu of those codes and standards for equipment design, manufacture, installation, and maintenance.

ISA-S12.4, Instrument Purging for Reduction of Hazardous Area Classification, 1970, 14 pp.

Covers a technique for reducing the hazard classification by the continuous addition of an air or inert gas within a general purpose enclosure. Refers only to hazards created by gases or vapors, and is concerned only with those system design criteria related to electrical ignition of a hazardous gas or vapor.

ISA-RP12.6 (ANSI/ISA-1977, Revised 1987), Installation of Intrinsically Safe Instrument Systems Hazardous (Classified) Locations, 1987, 10 pp.

Provides guidance for the design and installation of field installed wiring in non-hazardous locations and for the layout and wiring of panels which contain intrinsically safe wiring. Intended for use in conjunction with nationally recognized codes covering wiring practices, such as NEC Code NFPA 70 (ANSI C1) and Canadian Electrical Code, Part 1.

ISA-S12.10, (Revised ANSI/ISA-1988) Area Classification in Hazardous (Classified) Dust Locations, 1988, 24 pp.

Evaluates the degree of dust hazard in locations made hazardous by the pressure of a cloud or blanket of dust. Is in conformance with (and attempts to expand and clarify) the National Electrical Code and the Canadian Electrical Code.

ISA-S12.12 (ANSI/ISA-1984), Electrical Equipment for Use in Class I, Division 2 Hazardous (Classified) Locations, 1984, 24 pp.

Provides requirements for the design, construction, and marking of electrical equipment, or parts of such equipment used in Class I, Division 2 locations. This document establishes uniformity in test methods for determining the suitability of the equipment and associated circuits and components as they are related to their ability to ignite a specified flammable gas or vapor-in-air mixture. This standard applies only to equipment, circuits, or components designed and assessed specifically for use in Class I, Division 2, hazardous locations as defined by the National Electrical Code NFPA No. 70, Articles 500 and 501, or the Canadian Electrical Code (Part I), C22.1, Section 18.

ISA-S12.13, (ANSI/ISA-S12.13, Part I-1986), Part I, Performance Requirements, Combustible Gas Detectors, 1986, 24 pp.

Improves the level of electrical safety and safety-oriented performance of combustible gas detection instruments used in hazardous (classified) locations. Covers the details of construction, performance, and test for portable, mobile, and stationary electrical instruments for sensing the presence of combustible gas or vapor concentrations in ambient air; parts of these instruments may be installed or used in Class I hazardous locations and gaseous mines in accordance with codes specified by authorities having jurisdiction. This standard does not cover gas detection instruments of the laboratory- or scientific-type used for analysis or measurement, instruments used for process control and process monitoring purposes, or instruments used for residential purposes.

ISA-RP12.13, Part II, Installation, Operation, and Maintenance of Combustible Gas Detection Instruments, 1987, 152 pp.

Establishes user criteria for the installation, operation, and maintenance of combustible gas detection instruments, Covers storage, user recordkeeping, maintenance, checkout procedures, calibration, external power supply systems, etc. Provides a substantial list of references.

S12.15, Part I — Performance Requirements for Hydrogen Sulfide Detection Instruments (10–100 ppm), 1990, 28 pp.

Covers the details of construction, performance, and testing of portable, mobile and stationary electrical instruments used for continuous monitoring for the presence of hydrogen sulfide gas concentrations in air, parts of which may be installed or operated in hazardous (classified) locations.

RP12.15, Part II — Installation, Operation, and Maintenance of Hydrogen Sulfide Detection Instruments, 1990, 29 pp.

Establishes user criteria and applies to all hydrogen sulfide gas detection instruments that satisfy the performance requirements in ISA-S12.15, Part I.

ISA-RP16.1, 2, 3, Terminology, Dimensions, and Safety Practices for Indicating Variable Area Meters (Rotameters, Glass Tube, Metal Tube, Extension Type Glass Tube), 1959, 6 pp.

Combined RP16.1, 16.2, and 16.3 — intended to (a) establish uniformity of connection dimensions to permit interchangeability of one manufacturer's meters with another manufacturer's meters of the same size; (b) provide a common ground of understanding of the terminology, use, and component parts and accuracies of these meters, and (c) to provide a reference for the safe working pressures of these meters.

ISA-RP16.4, Nomenclature and Terminology for Extension Type Variable Area Meters (Rotameters), 1960, 3 pp.

Defines the nomenclature and terminology of various types of extensions applicable to 5 in. (125 mm) glass and metal tube variable area meters (rotameters) covered in ISA-RP16.1, 2, 3.

ISA-RP16.5, Installation, Operation, Maintenance Instructions for Glass Tube Variable Area Meters (Rotameters), 1961, 6 pp.

Covers the general considerations, important to the installation, operation and maintenance of meters to obtain the most reliable results.

ISA-RP16.6, Methods and Equipment for Calibration of Variable Area Meters (Rotameters), 1961, 7 pp.

Describes the methods and equipment used for calibrating the glass and metal metering tube area meters (rotameters) covered in RP16.1, 2, 3.

ISA-S18.1 (ANSI/ISA-1979, R 1985), Annunciator Sequences and Specifications, 1985, 36 pp.

Covers electrical annunciators that call attention to abnormal process conditions by the use of individual illuminated visual displays and audible devices. Sequence designations provided can be used to describe basic annunciator sequences and also many sequence variations.

ISA-S20, Specification Forms for Process Measurement and Control Instruments, Primary Elements and Control Valves, R 1981, 72 pp.

These forms are intended to assist the specification writer to present the basic information. In this sense they are "short-form" specifications or "check sheets" and may not include all necessary engineering data or definitions of application requirements. While the types of instruments described by these forms are more common to the process industries the forms should also prove useful in the other areas if special requirements are defined elsewhere.

ISA-S26, Dynamic Response Testing of Process Control Instrumentation, 1975, 25 pp.

Incorporating four revised ISA recommended practices, the standard establishes the basis for dynamic response testing of measurement and control equipment with pneumatic output and electric output, and for closed loop actuators for externally actuated control valves and other final control elements. Pulse testing techniques as well as methods for sine wave, step, and pulse-type signals are included.

ISA-RP31.3 (ANSI/ISA RP31.1-1977), Specification, Installation, and Calibration of Turbine Flowmeters, 1977, 21 pp.

Establishes minimum ordering information, recommended acceptance and qualification test methods including calibration techniques, uniform terminology and drawing symbols, and recommended installation techniques for volumetric turbine flow transducers having an electrical output.

ISA-S37.1 (ANSI/ISA-1975, R 1982), Electrical Transducer Nomenclature and Terminology, R 1982, 15 pp.

Establishes uniform nomenclature for transducers and uniform simplified terminology for transducer characteristics.

ISA-RP37.2, Guide for Specifications and Tests for Piezoelectric Acceleration Transducers for Aerospace Testing, R 1982, 19 pp.

Covers piezoelectric acceleration transducers, primarily those used in aerospace test instrumentation. Terminology used in this document follows ISAS37.1, "Electrical Transducer Nomenclature and Terminology," except that additional terms considered applicable to piezoelectric vibration transducers are defined.

ISA-S37.3 (ANSI/ISA-1975, R 1982), Specifications and Tests for Strain Gage Pressure Transducers, R 1982, 22 pp.

Establishes for strain gage pressure transducers; uniform minimum specifications for design and performance characteristics; uniform acceptance and qualification test methods, including calibration techniques; uniform presentation of minimum test data; and a drawing symbol for use in electrical schematics.

ISA-S37.5 (ANSI/ISA-1975, R 1982), Specifications and Tests for Strain Gage Linear Acceleration Transducers, R 1982, 18 pp.

Establishes uniform minimum specifications for design and performance characteristics, uniform acceptance and qualification test methods including calibration techniques, uniform presentation of minimum test data, and a drawing symbol for use in electrical schematics for strain gage linear acceleration transducers.

ISA-S37.6 (ANSI/ISA-1976, R 1982), Specifications and Tests of Potentiometric Pressure Transducers, R 1982, 27 pp.

Establishes for potentiometric pressure transducers; uniform minimum specifications for design and performance characteristics; uniform acceptance and qualification test methods, including calibration techniques; uniform presentation of minimum test data; and a drawing symbol for use in electrical schematics.

ISA-S37.8 (ANSI/ISA-1977, R 1982), Specifications and Tests for Strain Gage Force Transducers, R 1982, 16 pp.

Outlines uniform general specifications, acceptance and qualification methods, methods for data presentation, and includes a drawing symbol used in electrical schematics for tension, compression and combination tension/compression transducers.

ISA-S37.10 (ANSI/ISA-1975, R 1982), Specifications and Tests for Piezoelectric Pressure and Sound-Pressure Transducers, R 1982, 22 pp.

Establishes uniform specifications for describing design and performance characteristics, acceptance and qualification test methods and calibration techniques, and procedures for presenting test data for piezoelectric (including ferro-electric) pressure and sound-pressure transducers.

ISA-S37.12 (ANSI/ISA-1977, R 1982), Specification and Test for Potentiometric Displacement Transducers, R 1982, 21 pp.

Covers potentiometric displacement transducers, primarily those used in measuring systems. The specifications are not intended to cover transducers used in hazardous locations as specified in the National Electrical Code nor are all requirements covered for transducers used in nuclear power plants.

RP42.1 Nomenclature for Instrument Tube Fittings, 1992, 12 pp.

Defines nomenclature for tube fittings most commonly used in instrumentation. It is not intended as a substitute for manufactures' catalog numbers, nor dies it apply to special fittings. This standard is intended to apply to mechanical flared and flareless tube fittings as commonly used in instrument tubing systems.

ISA-S50.1 (ANSI/ISA-1975, R 1982), Compatibility of Analog Signals for Electronic Industrial Process Instruments, R 1982, 11 pp.

This standard applies to analog dc signals used in process control and monitoring systems to transmit information between subsystems or separated elements of systems. Its purpose is to provide for compatibility between the several subsystems or separated elements of given systems.

S50.02 Fieldbus Standard for use in Industrial Control Systems, Part 2: Physical Layer Specification and Service Definition, 1992, 94 pp.

Specifies the requirements for fieldbus physical layer component parts. It also specifies the media and network configuration requirements necessary to ensure agreed levels of data integrity before Data Link Layer error checking and interoperability between devices at the Physical Layer. The Fieldbus Physical Layer conforms to layer 1 of the OSI 7-layer model as defined by ISO 7498 with the exception that frame delimiters are in the Physical Layer.

ISA-51.1 (ANSI/ISA 1979), Process Instrumentation Terminology, 1979, 41 pp.

Intended to include all specialized terms used to describe the use and performance of the instrumentation and instrument systems used for measurement, control or both in the process industries.

ISA-RP52.1, Recommended Environments for Standard Laboratories, 1975, 18 pp.

Recommendations for three levels of standardization are presented—from the more general National Bureau of Standards, through commercial, industrial and government laboratories. Requirements for nine environmental factors are discussed.

ISA-RP55.1 (ANSI/ISA 1983), Hardware Testing of Digital Process Computers, R 1983, 54 pp.

Establishes a basis for evaluating functional hardware performance of digital process computers. Covers general recommendations applicable to all hardware performance testing, specific tests for pertinent subsystems and system parameters. Includes a brief glossary of terms used.

ISA-RP60.1, Control Center Facilities, 1991, 20 pp.

Covers the preparation of engineering designs and specifications for control center facilities. Because of the wide variety of industries using control centers, the information is general in coverage. References are made to applicable industry codes and standards and to national codes that are law under the Occupational Safety and Health Act (OSHA). The user is cautioned to consult local and state building and construction codes.

ISA-RP60.3, Human Engineering for Control Centers, 16 pp.

Assists the design engineer in establishing concepts which accommodate physical and mental capabilities of the operator while recognizing the operator's limitations. This recommended practice is limited to those aspects of human engineering that will affect the layout of and equipment selection that will affect the layout of and equipment selection for the control center. It is recognized that some of the human factors discussed in this document are also used in the design and manufacture of instruments.

ISA-RP60.4, Documentation for Control Centers, 1990, 24 pp.

Covers the type, content, and extent of documentation required as record data and information particular to a control center and control center facility design and fabrication. Provides guidelines covering various types of documentation and promotes uniformity of document terminology.

ISA-RP60.6, Nameplates, Labels and Tags for Control Centers, 1984, 24 pp.

Assists the designer or engineer in choosing and specifying the method of identifying items mounted on a control center or associated with a control center facility. This recommended practice summarizes identification methods and suggests the use of nameplates, labels, and tags. Examples are included for guidance in preparing drawings and specifications. This recommended practice also covers functional definitions associated with nameplates, labels, and tags.

ISA-RP60.8, Electrical Guide for Control Centers, 1978, 6 pp.

Assists the design engineer in establishing the electrical requirements of a control center; it is also intended to comply with the provisions of the NEC. Special considerations which may apply to particular devices or circuits are not taken into account in this recommended practice.

ISA-RP60.9, Piping Guide for Control Centers, 1981, 11 pp.

Assists the design engineer in defining the piping requirements for pneumatic signals and supplies in control centers.

ISA-RP60.11, Crating, Shipping and Handling for Control Centers, 1991, 37 pp.

Describes general crating methods available for protection against physical damage, vibration, pilferage, and climate and the various procedures and problems involved in handling, shipping, and storage. Presents a broad outline of the various practices so that due consideration may be given during the design and specification stages.

ISA-S61.1 (ANSI/ISA-S61.1-1977), Industrial Computer System FORTRAN Procedures for Executive Functions, Process Input–Output and Bit Manipulations, 1977, 11 pp.

Presents external procedure references for use in industrial computer control systems. These external procedure references permit interface with executive programs, process input and output functions and allow manipulation of bit strings. The FORTRAN statements described in this standard conform to the ANSI:X3.9-1966 Standard FORTRAN. No changes to standard FORTRAN syntax are intended.

ISA-S61.2 (ANSI/ISA-S61.2-1978), Industrial Computer System FORTRAN Procedures for File Access and the Control of File Contention, 1978, 7 pp.

Presents external procedure references for use in industrial computer control systems. These external procedure references provide means for accessing files, and also provide means for resolving problems of file access contention in a multiprogramming multiprocessing environment.

ISA-S67.01, (ANSI/ISA-S7.01-1981, R 1987), Transducer and Transmitter Installation for Nuclear Safety Applications, R 1987, 14 pp.

Covers the installation of transducers for nuclear-safety-related applications, excepting those for measurands of liquid metals. It establishes requirements and recommendations for the installation of transducers and auxiliary equipment for nuclear power plant applications outside of the main reactor vessel.

ISA-S67.02, (ANSI/ISA-1983) Nuclear-Safety-Related Instrument Sensing Line Piping and Tubing Standards for Use in Nuclear Power Plants, 1983, 14 pp.

Covers design, protection and installation of nuclear-safety-related instrument sensing lines for light water cooled nuclear power plants. The standard covers the pressure boundary requirements for piping, capillary tubing, and tubing lines up to and including one inch (25.4 mm) outside diameter or three-quarter inch normal pipe.

ISA-S67.03, (ANSI/ISA-1982), Standard for Light Water Reactor Coolant Pressure Boundary Leak Detection, 1982, 27 pp.

Defines design criteria that are intended to insure that adequate Reactor Coolant Pressure Boundary leak detection capabilities are provided to the nuclear plant operator and to meet the Code of Federal Regulations.

ISA-S67.04, (ANSI/ISA-1988) Setpoints for Nuclear Safety-Related Instrumentation Used in Nuclear Power Plants, 1988, 15 pp.

Develops a basis for establishing setpoints for actions determined by the design basis for protection systems and to account for instrument errors and drift in the channel from the sensor through and including the bistable trip device.

ISA-S67.06, (ANSI/ISA-1986) Response Time Testing of Nuclear-Safety-Related Instrument Channels in Nuclear Power Plants, 1984, 20 pp.

Delineates requirements and methods for determining the response time characteristics of nuclear-safety-related instrument channels. The standard applies only to those instrument channels whose primary sensors measure pressure, temperature, or neutron flux. This document provides the nuclear power industry with requirements and acceptable methods for response time testing nuclear-safety-related instrument channels.

ISA-S67.10, (ANSI/ISA-1986) Sample-Line Piping and Tubing Standard for Use in Nuclear Power Plants, 1986, 24 pp.

Covers design, protection, and installation of sample lines connecting nuclear-safety related power plant processes with sampling instrumentation. The standard applies to light-water-cooled nuclear power plants, covering the pressure boundary requirements for piping and tubing. It applies to the areas from the process tap to the upstream side of the sample panel, bulkhead fitting, or analyzer shut-off valve, and it includes in-line sample probes.

S67.10 Sample-Line Piping and Tubing Standard for Use in Nuclear Power Plants, 1994, 48 pp.

Covers design, protection, and installation of sample lines for light-water-cooled nuclear power plants and the pressure boundary requirements for piping and tubing. The boundaries of this standard span from the process tap to the upstream side of the sample panel, bulkhead fitting, or analyzer shutoff valve, and include in-line sample probes.

ISA-S67.14, (ANSI/ISA-1983), Qualifications and Certification of Instrumentation and Control Technicians in Nuclear Power Plants, 1983, 16 pp.

Identifies the criteria for certification of instrumentation and control technicians in nuclear power plants. These criteria address qualifications based on education, experience, training, and job performance.

S67.14 Qualifications and Certification of Instrumentation and Control Technicians in Nuclear Facilities, 1994, 32 pp.

Identifies the criteria for certification of instrumentation and control technicians at nuclear facilities. These criteria address qualifications based on education, experience, training, and job performance.

ISA-S71.01, (ANSI/ISA-1986), Environmental Conditions for Process Measurement and Control Systems: Temperature and Humidity, 1985, 18 pp.

Establishes uniform classifications of the environmental conditions of temperature and humidity as they relate to industrial process measurement and control equipment. The standard is compatible with IEC Publication 654-1, 1979, **Operating Conditions for Industrial-Process Measurement and Control Equipment, Part I: Temperature, Humidity and Barometric Pressure.**

S71.02 Environmental Conditions for Process Measurement and Control Systems: Power, 1991, 14 pp.

Classifies power parameters that affect industrial process measurement and control equipment. Specifications for other environmental conditions are beyond the scope of this standard. The classes of environmental conditions stated in this standard are suitable for use in activities related to process instrumentation, including design, manufacture, sales, installation, test, use and maintenance. These classifications pertain only to power as received by the equipment.

ISA-S71.04, (ANSI/ISA-1986), Environmental Conditions for Process Measurement and Control Systems: Airborne Contaminants, 1985, 16 pp.

Classifies airborne contaminants that may affect process measurement and control instruments. This classification system provides a means for specifying the type and concentration of airborne contaminants to which a specified instrument may be exposed. This standard is limited to airborne contaminants and biological influences only, covering contamination influences that affect industrial process measurement and control systems.

ISA-S72.01, (ANSI/ISA-1986), PROWAY-LAN Industrial Data Highway, 1985, 200 pp.

Specifies those elements which are required for compatible interconnection of stations by way of a Local Area Network (LAN) using the Token Bus access method in an industrial environment. The standard is compatible with (but more restrictive than) the IEEE 802.2 and 802.4 standards for general LANS.

ISA-RP74.01, Application and Installation of Continuous-Belt Weighbridge Scales, 1984, 28 pp.

Furnishes design criteria inducive to simplified specifications and provides recommendations for installation, calibration, and maintenance of continuous-belt, weigh-bridge type scales. This recommended practice provides an effective base of comparison of scale suppliers, establishes minimum values, and ensures that a scale specification and purchase incorporates the essentials to satisfy a particular weighing job. It permits early belt conveyor design, with the full knowledge of the weight scale configuration, regardless of the manufacturer.

ISA-S75.01, (ANSI/ISA-1986), Flow Equations for Sizing Control Valves, 1985, 34 pp.

Establishes equations for predicting the flow of compressible and incompressible fluids through control valves. The equations are not intended for use when mixed-phase fluids, dense slurries, dry solids, or non-Newtonian liquids are encountered. The prediction of cavitation, noise, or other effects is not a part of this standard.

The equations are not, however, intended for use with mixed phases.

ISA-S75.02 (ANSI/ISA 1988), Control Valve Capacity Test Procedure, 1988, 16 pp.

This standard provides a test procedure for obtaining the following factors for sizing control valves: valve flow coefficient (C); liquid pressure recovery factors (F) and (F); Reynolds Number factor (F); liquid critical pressure ratio factor (F); piping geometry factor (F); and pressure drop ratio factors (X and X). The standard is intended for control values used in flow control of process fluids and is not intended to apply to fluid power components as defined in the National Fluid Power Association Standard NFPA T.3.5.28-1977.

ISA-S75.03, (ANSI/ISA-1985), Face-to-Face Dimensions for Flanged Globe-Style Control Valve Bodies (Formerly ISA-S4.01.1), 1984, 12 pp.

Applies to flanged globe-style control valves, sizes 1/2 inch through 16 inches, having top, top and bottom, part, or cage guiding. This standard aids users in the piping design by providing ANSI Class 125, flat face, and ANSI Classes 150, 250, 300 and 600, raised face, flanged control valve dimensions, without giving special consideration to the equipment manufacturer to be used.

S75.04 Face-to-Face Dimensions for Flangeless Control Valves (ANSI Classes 150, 300, and 600), 1992, 10 pp.

Aids users in their piping designs for flangeless control values by providing face-to-face dimensions without giving special consideration to the equipment manufacturer to be used.

ISA-S75.05, (ANSI/ISA-1986), Control Valve Terminology, 1983, 33 pp.

Provides terminology for control valves of seven different types and also for common types of actuators used with these valves. This standard names individual valve parts, defines assemblies of parts, and provides terminology for part and assembly functions.

ISA-RP75.06, (Formerly ISA-RP4.2), Control Valve Manifold Designs, 1981, 20 pp.

Presents six control valve manifold types with space estimates for various sizes. Each of these six types consists of a straight through globe control valve, isolation upstream and downstream block valves and bypass piping with a manually activated valve.

ISA-S75.07, Laboratory measurement of Aerodynamic Noise Generated by Control Valves, 1987, 16 pp.

Defines equipment, methods, and procedures for the laboratory testing and measured of airborne sound radiated by a compressible fluid flowing through a control valve and its associated piping, including fixed-flow restrictions. The test may be conducted under any conditions agrees upon by the user and the manufacturer.

Although this standard is designed for measurement of noise radiated from the piping downstream of the valve, other test variations are optional, including the use of insulation and nonstandard piping. Applications of this standard to control valves discharging directly to atmosphere are excluded.

ISA-S75.08, (ANSI/ISA-1986), Installed Face-to-Face Dimensions for Flanged Clamp or Pinch Valves, 1985, 12 pp.

Applies to clamp or pinch valves sizes 1 inch through 8 inches. The purpose of this standard is to aid users in their piping design by providing installed face-to-face dimensions for control valves, incorporating clamp or pinch elements, which have flanges that mate with ANSI B16.1 Class 125 (PN20) and/or ANSI B16.5 Class 125 (PN20) flanges, without giving special consideration to the manufacturer of the equipment to be used.

ISA-S75.11, (ANSI/ISA-1985, R 1991), Inherent Flow Characteristic and Rangeability of Control Valves, 1985, 16 pp.

Defines the statement of typical control valve inherent flow characteristics and inherent rangeabilities and establishes criteria for adherence to manufacturer-specified flow characteristics. This standard uses the basic definitions from ISA-S75.05 and also defines specific terms related to flow characteristic and rangeability. A table listing inherent flow characteristic deviations and sample plots of relative flow coefficient versus relative travel are also given.

ISA-S75.12, (ANSI/ISA-1987), Face-to-Face Dimensions for Socket Weld-End and Screwed-End Globe-Style Control Valves, (ANSI classes 150, 300, 600, 900, 1500, and 2500), 1987, 12 pp.

Applies to socket weld-end globe-style control valves, sizes 1/2 inch through 4 inches, and screwed-end globe-style control valves, size 1/2 inch through 2-1/2 inches, having top, top and bottom, port, or cage guiding. This standard aids users in their piping designs by providing ANSI Classes 150 through 2500 socket weld-end control valve dimensions and ANSI Classes 150 through 600 screwed-end control valve dimensions, without giving special considerations to the equipment manufacturer to be used.

ISA-S75.13 (ANSI/ISA-1989), Method of Evaluating the Performance of Positioners with Analog Input Signals and Pneumatic Output, 1989, 31 pp.

This standard is intended for use by manufacturers, users or independent testing groups to determine or verify positioner performance. The standard specifies the use of an actuator of the user or manufacturer's choice and single or double-acting positioners.

ISA-S75.14, Face-to-Face Dimensions for Buttweld-End Globe-Style Control Valves, (ANSI/ISA-1984), 1984, 8 pp.

Applies to buttweld-end globe-style control valves, sizes 1/2 inch through 8 inches, having top and cage guiding. This standard aids users in their pipping designs by providing ANSI Class 4500 buttweld-end control valve dimensions, without giving special consideration to the equipment manufacturer to be used.

ISA-S75.15, (ANSI/ISA-S75.15-1987), Face-to-Face Dimensions for Buttweld-End Globe-Style Control Valves (ANSI/ISA Classes 150, 300, 600, 900, 1500, and 2500), 1986, 12 pp.

Applies to buttweld-end globe-style control valves, sizes 1/2 inch through 18 inches, for ANSI Classes 150 through 2500, having top, top and bottom, port, or cage guiding. This standard aids users in their piping designs by providing buttweld-end control valve dimensions, without giving special consideration to the equipment manufacturer to be used.

ISA-S75.16, (ANSI/ISA-S75.16-1987), Face-to-Face Dimensions for Flanged Globe-Style Control Valve Bodies (ANSI Classes 900, 1500, and 2500), 1986, 12 pp.

Applies to flanged globe-style control valves, sizes 1/2 inch through 18 inches, having top, top and bottom, port, or cage guiding. This standard aids users in their piping designs by providing ANSI Classes 900, 1500, and 2500 raised-face, flanged control valve dimensions, without giving special consideration to the equipment manufacturer to be used.

ISA-S75.17, Control Valve Aerodynamic Noise Prediction, 1989, 22 pp.

This standard establishes a method to predict the noise generated in a control valve of standard design by the flow of compressible single-phase gas or vapor and the resulting noise outside and downstream of the valve. This method was developed from fundamental principles of acoustics, fluid mechanics and mechanics and makes use of valve sizing factors defined in ANSI/ISA-S75.01 and S75.02. The standard addresses only aerodynamic noise and does not consider noise generated by mechanical vibrations, unstable flow patterns and other unpredictable behavior.

ISA-S75.18, Control Valve Stability, 1989, 14 pp.

The recommended practice defines control valve stem-position mechanical stability and establishes a measurement criterion for position instability of the valve. This document is intended to help the user recognize, measure, and diagnose the unstable motion of a valve. A bibliography with abstracts provides further reference.

ISA-S75.19 (ANSI/ISA-1989), Hydrostatic Testing of Control Valves, 1989, 28 pp.

This standard establishes requirements and definitions for standard hydrostatic shell testing of control valves to prove structural integrity and leak-tightness of the pressure retaining parts, including closure parts such as the bonnet-to-body joint, but excluding packings, bellows or other moving seals and packing lead-off connections. The standard applies to control valves having bodies, bonnets, cover plates and bottom flanges made of carbon steel, low and high allow stainless steel, nickel-base alloy, and cast or ductile iron.

S75.20 Face-to-Face Dimensions for Separable Flanged Globe-Style Control Valves (ANSI Classes 150, 300, and 600), 1991, 10 pp.

Applies to separable flanged-style control valves, sizes 1 inch through 4 inches. Aids users in their piping design by providing ANSI Classes 150, 300, and 600 raised face separable flanged control valve dimensions without giving special consideration to the equipment manufacturer to be used.

ISA-RP75.21, Process Data Presentation for Control Valves, 1989, 19 pp.

This document describes a technique for communication of process data and other requirements between process system designer or the user and the valve supplier to facilitate the selection of control valve actuators and accessories. The technique includes such features as the process data envelope, process schematic, piping configuration and process data worksheet.

S75.22 Face-to-Centerline Dimensions for Flanged Globe-Style Angle Control Valve Bodies (ANSI Classes 150, 300, and 600), 1992, 10 pp.

Applies to raised-face flanged globe-style angle control valves, 1 inch through 9 inches. Aids users in their piping design by providing ANSI Classes 150, 300 and 600 raised-face flanged globe-style angle control valve face-to-centerline dimensions without giving special consideration to the equipment manufacturer to be used.

S77.20 Fossil Fuel Power Plant Simulators-Functional Requirements, 1993, 10 pp.

Establishes the functional requirements for several types of fossil-fuel power plant control room simulators primarily used for operator training. It sets criteria for the degree of hardware replication and software modeling detail, performance, and functional capabilities of the simulated control room instrumentation. This standard does not completely address stand-alone DCS-based trainers/simulators, nor simulators used for engineering or test purposes such as part-task training devices intended for specialized training. This standard does not establish criteria for the use of simulators in training programs.

ISA-S77.42, (ANSI/ISA-1987) Fossil-Fuel Plant Feedwater Control System — Drum-Type, 1987, 32 pp.

Establishes minimum criteria for the control of levels, pressures, and flow for the safe and reliable operation of drum-type feedwater systems in fossil power plants. Aids in the development of design specifications covering the measurement and control of feedwater systems. The following requirements are defined for minimum system design: (1) process measurement requirements; (2) control and logic requirements; (3) final control device requirements; (4) system reliability and availability; (5) alarm requirements; and (6) operator interface. The safe physical containment of the feedwater shall be in accordance with applicable piping codes and standards and is beyond the scope of this standard.

S77.43 Fossil-Fuel Power Plant Unit/Plant Demand Development (Drum Type), 1993, 38 pp.

Establishes as the minimum requirements for the functional design specifications of unit/plant demand development for control systems for drum-type fossil-fueled power plant boilers. Addresses the unit/plant demand development subsystem for boilers with steaming capacities of 200,000 lbs/hr (25 kg/s) or greater. This subsystem includes firing rate demand development, throttle/header pressure control, and unit megawatt/steam flow control as applicable.

ISA-S82.01, (ANSI/ISA-1988) Safety Standard for Electrical and Electronic Test, Measurement, Controlling and Related Equipment — General Requirements, 1988, 65 pp.

This standard applies to electrical and electronic test, measuring, controlling and related equipment. This standard applies to equipment that is rated for connection to supply circuits which exceed extra-low voltage and which do not exceed 480 volts rms, between phases for three-phase supply circuits or 250 volts rms, single-phase or dc. This standard does not apply to: (1) medical and laboratory equipment; (2) watt-hour meters and associated equipment installed by electrical utility companies for measuring electrical energy and related quantities; and (3) general use battery charges, auxiliary supply sources, substitute power supplies, or laboratory-type power supplies not specifically rated for use with measuring or testing equipment.

S82.01 Safety Standard for Electrical and Electronic Test, Measuring, Controlling, and Related Equipment — General Requirements, 1993, 130 pp.

Specifies general safety requirements for electrical equipment intended for professional, industrial process, and educational use, including equipment and computing devices for measurement and test, control, laboratory use, and accessories intended for use with the above (e.g., sample handling equipment). This standard does not cover reliable function, performance, or other properties of the equipment, servicing (repair), or protection of servicing (repair) personnel.

ISA-S82.02, (ANSI/ISA-1988) Safety Standard for Electrical and Electronic Test, Measuring, Controlling, and Related Equipment — Electrical and Electronic Test and Measuring Equipment, 1988, 18 pp.

This standard applies to electrical and electronic and electromechanical measuring and testing equipment, and to the terminals, connectors, wiring and probes used in the interface between. This standard also applies to accessories and adaptors rated for use with measuring or testing probe assemblies, connectors or terminals. This standard applies to measuring or testing probe assemblies, connectors and terminals that are rated for measuring or testing branch circuits up to 1000 volts or ac or dc voltages up to 40 kilovolts incorporated within electrical end-product equipment circuits. This standard does not apply to equipment that is rated for use exclusively in extra-low voltage and power limited applications or equipment intended primarily for equipment-to-equipment interconnection (for example: IEEE interface bus, etc.)

ISA-S82.03, (ANSI/ISA-1988) Safety Standard for Electrical and Electronic Test, Measuring, Controlling, and Related Equipment — Electrical and Electronic Process Measurement and Control Equipment, 1988, 20 pp.

This standard applies to electrical, electronic (analog/digital) and electromechanical process measurement and control equipment which: (1) measures and controls directly or indirectly an industrial process through a final control device; (2) is intended to be connected to supply circuits which do not exceed 250 volts rms, single phase, or dc; and (3) is rated for use in either indoor, outdoor, or sheltered locations. This equipment includes but is not necessarily restricted to: (1) integrating, indicating, or recording equipment with or without a control function; (2) transmitters; (3) transducers; (4) analyzers; (5) supervisory or telemetry equipment; and (6) accessories used with any of the above equipment.

The following standard, identified by its ANSI number, was sponsored and published by ISA, approved by ANSI, and is available from either ISA or ANSI.

MC96.1, (ANSI/ISA-1975, R 1982) American National Standard for Temperature Measurement Thermocouples, 1982, 48 pp.

Covers coding of thermocouple and extension wire; coding of insulated duplex thermocouple extension wires; terminology, limits of error and wire sizes for thermocouples and thermocouple extension wires; temperature EMF tables for thermocouples; plus appendices that cover fabrication, checking procedures, selection, and installation.

ANSI C100.6-3, American National Standard for Voltage or Current Reference Devices; Solid State Devices, 1984, 12 pp.

Applies to physical devices used to maintain the unit of dc voltage or current having uncertainties of 100 ppm of output or less. This standard treats these devices from the standpoint of performance characteristics, but does not specify design or construction details or techniques. This part of the standard, C100.6-3, applies to solid state devices used to maintain the unit of dc voltage or current having uncertainties of 100 ppm of output or less.

APPENDIX C

Typical Job Titles and Descriptions

Job titles and descriptions are required in some organizations for the definition of responsibilities and/or organization charts when standards are created and approved. The following job descriptions are general in nature. They will vary depending on the company, on the complexity of the assignments and responsibilities, and on the individuals involved.

MANAGEMENT AND ENGINEERING FUNCTIONS:

- Manager, Control Systems and Instrumentation
- Chief Instrument Engineer
- Senior Control Engineer
- Control Engineer
- Control Engineering Technician

MAINTENANCE FUNCTIONS:

- Foreman, Control Systems and Instrumentation
- Instrument Inspector
- Instrument Service Specialist

Title: MANAGER, CONTROL SYSTEMS AND INSTRUMENTATION
Manager Control and Electrical Engineering
Chief Control Systems Engineer

Reports to: Division or Department Manager
Engineering Manager

Primary Functions:
Responsible for all departmental/sectional activities for control engineering, including:
- defining and reporting activities and needs to management;
- maintaining liaisons with other departments/sections to coordinate work assignments;
- providing administrative and technical support to other departments/sections;
- assigning of projects to personnel and manpower scheduling, recruitment, evaluation, and salary review;
- managing development of training program;
- making decisions on crucial or complex project activities;

- supervising all departmental/sectional personnel;
- evaluating employee performance;
- preparing departmental/sectional budgets, forecasts, and goals;
- promoting safety; and
- planning and approving budgets for allocation of financial and human resources.

Education/Experience:
Bachelor of Science in Engineering with 5–15 years experience in:
- operating with no technical guidance or control;
- process control and instrumentation, with a supervisory or managerial background;
- long-range and short-range planning and coordination;
- policy generation; and
- approval of standards.

Title: CHIEF INSTRUMENT ENGINEER
Instrument Engineer, Project Supervisor
Principal Control Systems Engineer
Systems Consultant

Reports to: Manager, Control systems

Primary Functions:
Leads project engineering and design for controls and instrumentation, usually supervising a task team of engineers and technicians, including:
- engineering administrative duties;
- participating in decisions concerning policies;
- maintaining budget restraints;
- forecasting manpower requirements;
- making decision concerning staff selection and remuneration;
- monitoring and controlling costs;
- scheduling estimation and observance;
- providing training and consulting services;
- assigning and checking the generation of standards;
- directing installations and follow-ups;
- making task assignments;
- reviewing technical work;
- troubleshooting as necessary;
- reporting progress to management; and
- assuring design adequacy.

Education/Experience:
Bachelor of Science in Engineering with 5–15 years experience including some administrative duties. Must be an authority in the field of control and instrumentation technology.

Title: SENIOR CONTROL ENGINEER
Senior Instrument Engineer
Control & Instrumentation Senior Engineer

Reports to: Manager, Control Systems and Instrumentation
Assigned Project Supervising Engineer

Primary Functions:
Under supervision, coordinates and participates in complete engineering and design
of instrument systems as required by the project assignment, including:

- implementing control requirements from functional guidelines;
- preparing design specifications;
- ensuring compliance with appropriate standards;
- monitoring and controlling costs;
- preparing and maintaining project schedules;
- selecting and procuring systems equipment;
- monitoring and training of engineers assigned to the project;
- reporting progress to management;
- participating in installation and start-ups; and
- providing technical support to other departments.

Education/Experience:
Bachelor of Science in Engineering with 5 or more years experience with some supervisory experience. Must be able to perform with little or no supervision.

Title: CONTROL ENGINEER
Instrument & Control Engineer Instrument Engineer

Reports to: Manager, Control Systems and Instrumentation
Assigned Project Supervising Engineer Senior Control Engineer

Primary Functions:
Under supervision, participates in the design and planning of control and instrument
systems as required by the project assignment, including:

- collecting background information;
- preparing drawings and calculations;
- designing or modifying systems;
- assisting in selection and procurement of equipment;
- ensuring compliance with applicable standards and codes;
- completing assigned tasks on schedule;
- assisting and supervising technicians and designers as needed; and
- possibly specializing in a specific control engineering activity.

Education/Experience:
Bachelor of Science in Engineering with 0 to 7 years experience depending on the job
level and responsibilities. Work is generally assigned in specific terms and is usually
reviewed.

Title: CONTROL ENGINEERING TECHNICIAN
Instrument Engineering Technician Instrument and Control Designer

Reports to: Senior Control Engineer
Assigned Project Supervising Engineer

Primary Function:

Helps engineers in the design of control and instrumentation systems by providing semiprofessional technical assistance, including:

- collecting background information;
- performing calculations;
- transmitting information to project team members;
- preparing design specifications;
- checking design documents to ensure compliance with applicable standards and codes;
- preparing diagrams;
- providing technical guidance to technicians with less knowledge;
- preparing requisitions;
- executing necessary tests and collecting data;
- maintaining engineering equipment;
- performing miscellaneous administrative work; and
- assisting in testing, field start-up, and training.

Education/Experience:

Depending on the job level and responsibilities, high school diploma with 1 to 10 years experience, or technical degree with 0 to 7 years experience. Work is assigned to solve specific problems and is usually checked at the detail level. Depending on the experience level, technical guidance is generally needed.

Title: FOREMAN, CONTROL SYSTEMS AND INSTRUMENTATION
Maintenance Manager, Instrumentation

Reports to: Maintenance Manager

Primary Functions:

Supervises all controls and instrument maintenance activities at the plant level, including:

- supervising all instrument maintenance personnel;
- planning manpower requirements and work assignments;
- maintaining budget allocations;
- evaluating shop and field maintenance procedures;
- ensuring maintenance of tools and test equipment;
- training maintenance personnel;
- evaluating employee performance;
- monitoring spare parts inventory; and
- assisting other departments' personnel as required.

Education/Experience:

High school diploma (trade or technical school preferred) and proven technical competence; 7 to 15 years experience.

Title: INSTRUMENT INSPECTOR
Instrument Coordinator

Reports to: Foreman, Control Systems and Instrumentation

Primary Functions:
Inspects instruments for malfunction, troubleshoots process control problems, and refers maintenance and repair problems to appropriate personnel, including:
- interpreting various instrumentation and engineering diagrams and specifications;
- performing inspections of instrument calibrations, installations, tests, and final checkouts;
- analyzing requirements for spare parts and procuring them;
- tuning instruments as required;
- supervising work of instrument service personnel as required; and
- verifying compliance with drawings and specifications.

Education/Experience:
High school diploma with a minimum of 10 years field experience, of which at least 3 years in an inspection or supervisory position.

Title: INSTRUMENT SERVICE SPECIALIST
Instrument Mechanic
Instrument Technician

Reports to: Foreman, Control Systems and Instrumentation

Primary Functions:
Maintains and troubleshoots control and instrumentation equipment and calibrates instrument hardware, including:
- maintaining thorough knowledge of equipment;
- possibly specializing in specific high technology or complex equipment;
- performing tests to ensure proper functioning of equipment;
- surveying available equipment;
- installing and repairing equipment; and
- supervising and assisting less knowledgeable technicians.

Education/Experience:
High school diploma and some technical training. For more responsible assignments, a technical degree is preferred with field responsibility experience. Depending on the level of experience and knowledge, work is generally assigned to solve specific problems and is usually checked (technical guidance may be required).

Engineering Contractor Scope of Work (Example)

CONTENTS

1.0 SCOPE OF WORK

1.1 This document provides the guidelines for the production of detail design by ABC (the Engineering Contractor). All detail design must conform to all statutory and code requirements in effect at the site. It is ABC's responsibility to meet such requirements. All electrically operated instruments must meet the electrical code in effect at the site and bear the UL approval label.

1.2 ABC must comply with the plant's requirements. If it becomes necessary to make any exceptions, these exceptions must be clearly identified and promptly brought to the attention of the plant Control Engineer and written approval must be obtained.

1.3 A NEMA enclosure 4X will be supplied and will incorporate a PLC rack I/O base (model #1234) complete with PLC card (model #5678) and communication interface module (model #7890). The rack will also include all necessary I/Os with 20% spare capacity. An external watchdog timer function is required. Fused disconnect terminals (model #AC123) will be provided between the I/O and field instruments. All components housed in this enclosure must be UL certified.

1.4 The PLC will be programmed in a structured and modular fashion using the QWE programming software. An example of PLC documentation requirements will be supplied by the plant control engineer to ABC prior to the start of programming. The interconnection between the PLC and the control room (at junction box JB-31) will be installed by a field contractor. The changes to the operator interface in the control room will also be done by that same field contractor.

1.5 ABC will provide all control and instrumentation engineering and field support during construction, commissioning, and start-up.

1.6 The design and drafting requirements shall include the preparation of all the required documentation such as:

P&ID (including instrument identification)

Control scope definition

Logic diagrams

Instrument process data sheets

Instrument index

Definitive cost estimates

Drawing and document registration

Programming of PLC

Instrument specification sheets

Vendor requisition/evaluation/selection

Loop diagrams

Electrical schematics

Cable conduit schedule

Conduit routing and junction box drawings

Panel Specifications including layout

Alarm and trip testing schedule and procedures

Calculations (valves, orifice plates, etc.)

Equipment operating and maintenance manuals

Manuals for PLCs

Spare parts lists

Instrument location drawings

Instrument installation specfications

The format of all these drawings and documents must comply with the examples to be submitted by the plant control engineer. Any deviation from such a format must be first approved by the plant's control engineer.

In addition to the above, the following activities are in the Engineering Contractor's scope of work:

- Participate in hazard and operability reviews.
- Check vendors' drawings and inspect panels at shop.
- Liaison with the plants, site visits, answering field inquiries, etc.
- Assist in construction, commissioning, and start-up and be available immediately when needed.
- Finalize as-built drawings and submit on disk in CAD format.

1.7 Piping isometrics produced by piping engineering shall show all field instruments (complete with elevations and tag numbers) and the equipment or process line upon which they are mounted or to which they are connected.

1.8 Conduit layout drawings produced by electrical engineering shall show all field run conduits and cables with details on the identification and number of wires as well as the elevation and size of cable trays. Junction boxes and control/interlock panels shall also be shown on these drawings.

2.0 ENGINEERING DESIGN

2.1 All drawings shall be generated on CAD and shall be coordinated with the plant control engineer to ensure compatibility of software revisions. Any deviations from these requirements must first be approved by the plant's control engineer.

2.2 The design and drafting work by ABC shall be carried out under the supervision of a registered engineer. Prior to the start of design, ABC will be required to produce evidence of such registration and experience as well as the name of the proposed supervisor. The proposed supervisor and the assigned design team must be experienced in the field of control engineering as required under this contract. Thereafter, the named supervisor and the assigned design team shall not be changed without the prior approval of the plant's control engineer.

2.3 Unless otherwise specifically called for on the drawings or specifications, uniformity of manufacture shall be maintained for any particular item throughout the project.

2.4 Manufacturer's instructions shall be carefully read and rigidly adhered to in installation, supplemented by details given herein by these specifications and on plans. Any damage resulting from failure to observe the manufacturer's instructions or the result of proceeding with the work without complete knowledge of how a particular job is to be done will be ABC's responsibility, and ABC shall make good any resulting loss or damage.

3.0 RECOMMENDED SUPPLIERS

To maintain similarity of equipment with the existing plant, the following suppliers are recommended. If other suppliers are perceived as more appropriate for this job, plant approval is required.

DEF Inc. for control valves
JKL Inc. for transmitters
PQR Inc. for pressure and temperature switches
ERT Inc. for gages
PKR Inc. for tube fittings

The supplier of the PLC will be selected by the plant's control engineer, at which time ABC will be advised.

4.0 DESIGN CHECK

4.1 A set of sample drawings shall be submitted to the plant for review and comment prior to the start of the detail design.

4.2 To ensure product quality, a complete system check of all documentation produced for a project will be performed following the completion of all design and drafting by ABC. This system check shall be performed by representatives of ABC and of the plant prior to the start of construction on site.

Date; Aug 18/93

Packaged Equipment Supplier Scope of Work (Example)

CONTENTS

1.0 SCOPE
2.0 PRE-CONTRACT AWARD
3.0 DESIGN REQUIREMENTS
4.0 RECOMMENDED SUPPLIERS
5.0 CODE REQUIREMENTS
6.0 DESIGN CHECK

1.0 SCOPE

This standard provides a guideline of the plant's requirements for the supply of control equipment and the production of detailed design for control engineering for packaged equipment.

All control equipment and design shall comply with all statutory, code, and plant requirements in effect at the site.

2.0 PRE-CONTRACT AWARD

2.1 General Requirements

Bidders must familiarize themselves with this specification and ensure that proposals reflect plant's standards and requirements. Where a Bidder cannot or is unwilling to comply, such reservations must be noted at the time of bid.

2.2 Major Control Equipment Requirements

2.2.1 Bidders shall generally submit for evaluation, conceptual P&I Diagrams, a process control description, and a list of instruments. This information shall convey clearly where vendor design and instrument supply responsibilities lie and interface occurs between vendor and the owner's instrument design and supply.

2.2.2 The list of instruments to be supplied shall show:

- all control equipment cross referenced to the conceptual P&I Diagrams and to the general process description,

223

- a description of the instrument function (e.g., differential pressure measurement across filter), and
- supplier name and model number for all control equipment proposed.

2.2.3 Bidders shall submit the name of the Control Engineer assigned to the Project to enable direct communication with the owner's Control Engineering personnel.

2.3 Minor Control Equipment Requirements

Where it is agreed that an item of process equipment is minor, it will be sufficient for the Bidder to forward the information called for under 2.2.2 only.

3.0 DESIGN REQUIREMENTS

3.1 Where a Vendor is required to supply detailed design for Control Engineering, the electrical code in effect at the site, as well as the plant's Standards, must be closely followed unless written approval of noncompliance has been obtained from the plant.

3.2 The following is a list of documents required from the vendor. Guidelines on their preparation is shown in the plant standards.

Instrument Index

Electrical Control Schematics

Loop Diagrams

Instrument Specification Sheets

Documentation for Programmable Electronic Systems

Control Panel drawings

All drawings shall be generated on CAD, shall conform to the plant's Standards, and shall be coordinated with the plant to ensure compatibility of software revisions. Any deviations from these requirements must first be approved by the plant control engineer.

3.3 Complete detailed design shall be forwarded to the owner as soon as possible and in any case not later than six (6) weeks after contract award. All detailed design and purchase orders shall be submitted to the plant Control Engineering personnel for review prior to ordering.

3.4 All in-line instruments, including but not limited to control valves, relief valves, rupture discs, thermowells, orifice plates, flow and pressure switches, pressure taps, etc., installed in or connected to process vessels, piping, and rotating or other machinery shall comply with the mechanical codes in effect at the site and with the corporate standards related to this contract.

3.5 As part of the design activities, the Vendor shall provide a schedule that shows milestones for the key activities. This schedule shall be provided within two weeks of purchase order receipt.

4.0 RECOMMENDED SUPPLIERS

In general, the plant requires that on a given project, all hardware be of a specific make and model. Plant Standard No.:C1230 shows a list of recommended suppliers for panel hardware and installation material, respectively. Items not shown on these Standards must be brought to the attention of the plant and then agreed upon.

5.0 CODE REQUIREMENTS

5.1 All design and drafting shall comply with the codes and legal requirements in effect at the site. It is the responsibility of the Engineering Contractor to ensure and meet compliance. In addition, all engineering work must conform to the National Electrical Code and to the ISA standards and practices for instrumentation.

5.2 Wherever the drawings or specifications call for material, workmanship, arrangement, or construction of a superior quality than is required by any applicable codes, the drawings and specifications shall prevail. Otherwise, should there be a conflict between any codes and the drawings/specifications, the applicable codes shall prevail.

5.3 All electrically operated instruments, or the electrical components incorporated in an instrument, shall be UL or FM approved and bear the approval label.

6.0 DESIGN CHECK

6.1 A complete system check of all documentation produced for a project will be performed following the completion of all design and drafting by the Vendor. This system check shall be performed by representatives of the Vendor and the Owner prior to the start of construction on site.

6.2 Following the completion of the system check, the Vendor shall supply to the Owner six sets of all documents. These sets would include all drawings, specifications, manuals for all control equipment, etc.

Date; Aug.18/93

APPENDIX F

Change Forms for Hardware/Software Modifications

Form 1—INDEX OF SYSTEM CHANGES

	DATE	DESCRIPTION OF CHANGE	BY
1.			
2.			
3.			
4.			
5.			

Form 2A—SYSTEM CHANGE

Project:

Originated by: Date:

Completion Required by:

Approved by: Date:

DESCRIPTION OF REQUIRED SYSTEM CHANGE

Form 2B—HARDWARE MODIFICATIONS

Prepared by: Date:

Approved by: Date:

1. Processor:

2. Memory:

3. Communication Modules:

4. Power Supplies:

5. Cables:

6. Racks:

7. Inputs/Outputs:

    Digital input:

    Digital output:

    Analog input:

    Analog output:

Form 2C—IMPLEMENTATION OF SOFTWARE MODIFICATION

ACTION	BY	DATE	COMMENTS
1. Ensure existing program is on removable disk.			
2. Modify existing program.			
3. Backup modified program on another removable disk.			
4. Test Program.			
5. File copy disk of latest update. Disk location:			
6. File copy disk of previous update. Disk location:			
7. Operator advised of completion.			

Form 2D—UPDATE OF MANUALS AND DRAWINGS

MANUAL	SECTION	BY	DATE
1. Operator's Manual			
2. Control Scope Definition			
3. Logic Diagrams			
4. PES Manual			
System Start-up			
Communications			
Input/output			
Operator interface			
Reference Documents			
5. Maintenance Manual			
6. P&IDs			

APPENDIX G

Programmable Electronic Systems Specification Checklist

This checklist should be used in conjunction with the section on PESs in Chapter 6.

1. Purpose and Overview:
   - Centralized or distributed controls (line of demarcation; PC for interface, PLC for controls)
   - Interface with other control systems and/or instrumentation (existing and/or new)
   - Operators
     number
     location
     computer skills (familiarity/interest)
     range of authority/responsibility
     authorized access to control and/or trip system levels
   - Expected future expansion and needs
2. Architecture:
   - Distribution of functions
   - Number of SCADA nodes
   - Distance, cable length
   - Redundancy (communication, power, I/Os, processors, etc.)
   - Cabinets type, rating
   - Forced ventilation
   - Number and locations of terminals/printers,
   - Maintenance on-line or off-line for I/Os, processors, etc.
   - Control room location, space, environment, lighting
   - UPS
   - Memory types, size
3. Security and Access Requirements:
   - Lockable
   - Password
4. Environmental Considerations:
   - Temperature, humidity
   - Corrosion
   - Static electricity, electromagnetic noise
   - Vibration, dust
   - Area classification

- Grounding
- Lightning arrestors
5. Analog Inputs:
   - Distribution
   - Types
   - Quantity
   - Resolution (12 bits)
6. Analog outputs:
   - Distribution
   - Types
   - Quantity
   - Resolution (12 bits)
7. Discrete inputs:
   - Distribution
   - Types
   - Quantity
   - High speed inputs (pulses)
   - Bar code readers
8. Discrete outputs:
   - Distribution,
   - Types,
   - Quantity,
   - Bar code printers.
9. Control functions:
   - Number of PIDs (fixed/variable settings)
   - PID redundancy
   - Math
   - Logic
   - Ramps, tracking
   - Special functions
   - Sampling and execution time
   - List of critical modulating/discrete loops
   - Bar code readers/printers
   - Critical (safety) type trips/alarms requirements:
     hardwired
     PESs (hot backup or triple redundancy fault tolerant)
10. Interface functions:
    - Number of graphics
    - Alarms (priority levels, audible location, historical storage of info, etc.)
    - Trends
    - Reports (number, on-request and/or automatic, inclusion of manual data, etc.)
    - Calculations
    - SPC
    - CRT display retrieval time
    - CRT display update time
    - Disk size
    - Similar functionality at all CRTs (with full redundancy)
    - Located only in control room or in plant
    - Hardware:
      enclosure rating (e.g., Nema1)

     colored CRTs

     on desks or on consoles

     arrangement in control room

     touch screen/ membrane keyboards/trackball

     separate annunciator

     control room communication (FM antenna on roof)

     CRT size

- Paper chart recorders/historical data storage; what is the smallest time increment to be trended at the operator interface (> 1 sec)?

11. Communication:
    - On-line or off-line maintenance
    - Update speed
    - Link to other networks

12. Electrical Power:
    - Quality
    - Amount required
    - Distribution
    - Effect of power failure (hardware/software/data retention/data recovery)
    - Effect of re-established power (auto start/operator reset command/ uncontrolled action)
    - UPS, UPS type.

13. Study of effect of Failures (System/Components):

14. Manpower requirements:
    - Engineering
    - Maintenance
    - Training schedule

15. Start-up/Shutdown Requirements from Control System:

16. Emergency Shutdown Philosophy:
    - Separate push buttons
    - Effect on master safety relay
    - Interaction with nonprocess alarms/systems (fire, gas emissions, lab results)
    - Emergency shutdown or sequential shutdown

APPENDIX H

Control Panel Specification (Example)

ABC, Inc., ENGINEERING Dept.
North American Division

PAGE 1 OF XX

CONTROL PANEL SPECIFICATION

STANDARD No.: 12A
Effective: Nov. 1993

CONTENTS:

1.0 SCOPE
2.0 DOCUMENTATION
3.0 CUSTOM PANELS
4.0 STANDARD PANELS
5.0 PANELS IN HAZARDOUS AREAS
6.0 NAMEPLATES
7.0 ELECTRICAL
8.0 PURGING
9.0 PNEUMATICS
10.0 CERTIFICATION
11.0 INSPECTION AND TESTING
12.0 SHIPPING

1.0 SCOPE

1.1 This Specification provides the guidelines for the design, construction, assembly, testing, and shipping of control panels.

1.2 The manufacturer shall furnish the panels completely fabricated and finished, with all components mounted, piped, wired, and tested in accordance with this Standard. The panel shall be built in compliance with all code requirements in effect at the site.

1.3 All instruments and equipment not specified as being supplied to the panel manufacturer are the responsibility of the panel manufacturer and should be in accordance with all the Specifications of this Project.

1.4 The latest edition of the following codes and standards form part of this Standard:

235

- The National Electrical Code
- ISA standards and practices for instrumentation

1.5 All electrically operated instruments, or the electrical components incorporated in an instrument, shall comply with the requirements of the current edition of the electrical code in effect at the site and shall be approved and bear the UL or FM approval label. Materials supplied and installed by the Panel Manufacturer shall be new.

1.6 Unless otherwise specifically called for on the drawings or specifications, uniformity of manufacture shall be maintained for any particular item throughout the panel.

1.7 The Panel Manufacturer shall be responsible for the correct installation and assembly of all items or equipment. Manufacturer's instructions shall be carefully read and rigidly adhered to in installation supplemented by details given herein by these specifications and on plans. Any damage that results (1) from failure to observe the Manufacturer's instructions or (2) from proceeding with the work without complete knowledge of how a particular job is to be done will be the Panel Manufacturer's responsibility, and he shall make good any resulting loss or damage.

1.8 The work under this specification shall be carried out by certified and trained tradesmen with adequate supervision and equipment necessary to complete the work, in accordance with good trade practice, shown on the drawings and specifications. The Panel Manufacturer may be required to produce evidence of such certification and training.

1.9 All instruments shall be installed and connected in such a way that the instrument can be maintained and removed for servicing without having to break fittings, cut wires, or pull hot wires. The Panel Manufacturer shall provide necessary unions and tubing connections to all instruments to allow removal.

2.0 DOCUMENTATION

2.1 The panel fabricator will be supplied with all documentation required for complete and correct fabrication and assembly of the panels. This documentation includes the following:

- Instrument Index
- Loop Diagrams
- Electrical Control Schematic
- Instrument Specifications
- Front of Panel General Layout
- Nameplate Drawing (where applicable)
- Certified Vendor Drawings (where applicable)

2.2 The Front of Panel General Layout shall show the physical size of the control panel and approximate positions of front-of-panel instruments, lights, switches, push buttons, and displays. The panel layout shall give approximate locations of tube and cable entries and pneumatic/electric supplies. Exact cutout dimensions are the responsibility of the Panel Manufacturer.

2.3 The Manufacturer shall furnish either one reproducible or three copies of the following drawings for approval by the plant Control Engineering (prior to commencement of construction):

Steel Fabrication Drawings (for custom panels)

Detailed Front of Panel Layout

Detailed Back of Panel Layout

Wiring Diagram and Terminal Layout

Tubing, Air Header, and Bulkhead Layout

2.4 The Manufacturer shall furnish either one reproducible or three copies of the above drawings in an "as built" condition after completion of the panel. In addition, a set of "as built" drawings shall be placed in the drawing pocket prior to shipment.

2.5 All drawings shall be generated on CAD, shall conform to the plant's Engineering Standards, and shall be coordinated with the plant to ensure compatibility of software revisions. Any deviation from these requirements must be approved by the plant Control Engineer.

3.0 CUSTOM PANELS

Custom-built panels are not required. Panels will be constructed using standard off-the-shelf components as described in section 4.0.

4.0 STANDARD PANELS

4.1 Free-standing interlock and terminal panels will be supplied. They will contain wall or surface mounting devices. The Panel Manufacturer shall use HIJK series 1234 (or plant-approved equal). Panel enclosures shall comply with NEMA 4 class requirements.

4.2 Special consideration should be given to the use of doors with 0.1 in. (3 mm) acrylic panels to allow viewing of the panel content.

5.0 PANELS IN HAZARDOUS AREAS

The panels will not be located in a hazardous area.

6.0 NAMEPLATES

6.1 All nameplates shall be engraved, 3-ply, laminated plastic nameplate, white on black core. These nameplates shall bear the instrument tag number and description. Edges shall be bevelled, and minimum size of characters shall be 3/16 in. high.

6.2 Nameplates for all panel devices shall be attached with adhesives only in clean room environments. They shall be mechanically attached (rivets or screws) in all other areas.

7.0 ELECTRICAL

7.1 General

7.1.1 No wire splicing is permitted in cable ducts or anywhere in panel except on identified terminal blocks.

7.1.2 Wiring is to be arranged so that all wires coming into the panel go to individual terminals, marked as shown on drawings. For internal wiring, not more than two (2) wires shall go to one terminal point.

7.1.3 All wires shall be identified at each end with a permanent marker indicating the wire number shown on the drawings, using slip-on, or sleeve, or wraparound laminated-type markers.

7.1.4 All terminals shall be suitably protected so as to make accidental touching of live parts unlikely. The exception is locations in which access to the live parts is through an enclosure not normally open except for electrical maintenance.

7.1.5 Terminal strips shall be Model BB4508. At least 25% or 10 spare terminal points, whichever is greater, should be provided on each strip, unless otherwise specified.

7.1.6 A grounding lug to accept a 2/0 ground wire shall be mounted in close proximity to the power distribution panel.

7.1.7 The Panel Manufacturer shall supply and install a dual power supply system protected by diodes in case one of the two should fail. Each power supply units shall be sufficient to power all loops in the panel and have at least 25% spare capacity. Each of the two power supplies shall have an output contact to alarm in case of failure.

7.1.8 All wiring shall have the following color coding:

1. For 120 V AC power and 120 V AC discrete control signals
   Phase or hot conductor (H) — black
   Neutral conductor (N) — white
   Intermediate conductors — brown
2. For 24 V DC power and 24 V DC discrete control signals
   Positive conductor — black
   Negative conductor — white
   Intermediate conductors — brown
   (Exceptions to these requirements may be dictated by the plant current guidelines).
3. For 4–20 mA (24 V DC) analog signals
   Positive conductor — black
   Negative conductor — white
   (Exceptions to these requirements may be dictated by the plant current guidelines).
4. For thermocouple extension wires, use ANSI color code. For other specialized wiring, either follow the manufacturers' color on the lead wires or refer to the plant Control Engineer.
5. For earth ground (if insulated) — green
6. Intrinsically safe wiring shall be identified by the use of bright blue color. This color will not be used on any other circuits. This color shall be non-removable and may be in the form of a blue stripe on wires whose colors follow the general scheme described above. Raceways, wireways, terminal blocks, and field junction boxes shall also be identified with a bright blue label bearing the legend INTRINSICALLY SAFE.
7. Temporary jumpers shall be of orange color with a minimum length of 2 feet (70 cm). The orange color will only be used for temporary jumpers.

7.2 120 V AC Power and Discrete Control Signal Wiring

7.2.1 All power wiring shall be #12 gage; all discrete control signal wiring shall be #14 gage. All such wiring shall be stranded copper, cross-linked polyethylene-insulated, 600-V minimum insulation, 90°C minimum temperature rating.

7.2.2 All 120 V AC wiring shall be run in cable ducts separate from low voltage wiring.

7.2.3 There shall be no 220 V AC (or higher voltage) power wiring in the panel unless to an approved double voltage relay, clearly marked with a sign reading "DANGER" and the appropriate voltage.

7.2.4 The Panel Manufacturer shall furnish and install multiple circuit power distribution panels as required, with circuit breakers. Circuit breakers shall be BB Inc. Type NGB (or plant-approved equivalent). At least two (2) tool receptacles (with ground fault protection) and two (2) overhead lights, with switches, shall be provided for each eight (8) feet of panel length. Power for panel-mounted instruments and for back-of-panel instruments shall be by three-prong grounded plug and flexible cord to conveniently located receptacles. All other wiring shall be hard wired to terminals unless otherwise specified on drawings.

7.3 24 V DC Power and Signal Wiring

Exceptions to the following requirements (i.e., 7.3.1 and 7.3.2) may be dictated by the plant existing guidelines.

7.3.1 All 24 V DC power and discrete control wiring shall be #16 gage copper unless otherwise specified.

7.3.2 All 4–20 mA wiring shall be #16 or #18 gage stranded copper, shielded, twisted pair unless otherwise specified.

7.3.3 Thermocouple, 24 V DC, and 120 V AC wiring shall be run in three separate cable ducts with a minimum of 1 ft (30 cm) separation.

7.4 Special Wiring

All special wiring not covered above shall be selected and installed according to the recommendations of the electrical code and the manufacturer of the instruments.

7.5 Intrinsically Safe Wiring

7.5.1 Cables carrying intrinsically safe circuits shall not be run alongside other cables.

7.5.2 No intrinsically safe circuit cable shall be terminated in the same enclosure or terminal block housing as the nonintrinsically safe wiring. Field wiring terminals for intrinsically safe circuits in control room areas, panels, etc., shall be segregated from other nonintrinsically safe field wiring terminals. They shall be located in separate enclosures.

7.5.3 The safety of equipment used in hazardous areas can be seriously jeopardized if the wiring requirements in the control panel are not strictly followed. The Panel Manufacturer has this responsibility.

Where a conduit, raceway, cable, or other conductor system crosses a boundary between hazardous areas of different classification or between a hazardous area and a nonhazardous area, vents or seals or both shall be provided to ensure that no flammable atmospheres or substances can be transmitted through the conduct or cable across such a boundary. Areas of high fire risk shall be avoided when locating panels.

7.5.4 Intrinsically safe redundant, or temporarily redundant, circuit cables shall be disconnected and removed from equipment at both ends. At the control panel, they shall be bonded together and to ground.

Spare cores in a multicore cable shall be connected to IS ground in the control panel only, which is normally the safe area, and elsewhere shall be fully insulated.

All intrinsically safe cables, wiring, and other equipment shall be positively identified.

7.5.5 Only certified equipment shall be installed in hazardous areas. In cases where certified apparatus is not available, this shall be first discussed with the plant control engineer.

8.0 PURGING

8.1 Purging is required for panel P-17. The panel shall be purged with clean, dry, oil-free instrument air.

8.2 Purging shall conform to the pressure sensing and interlocking requirements of the electrical code in effect at the site and of ISA-S12.4.

8.3 The air purge shall ensure that there will be at least three changes of air per hour in the enclosure.

8.4 The purge meter shall be visible and adjustable from the front of the closed panel.

9.0 PNEUMATICS

9.1 The materials to be used for the tubing and piping of panels are described in detail in Specification S45.

9.2 The tubing shall be installed in a neat and orderly manner, free from kinks and flats. Tubing shall be arranged to provide easy removal and maintenance of instruments and accessories. All piping requirements and color coding for a control panel shall be in accordance with ISA-RP60.9.

9.3 No single tubing shall be run without adequate support. All valves shall have rigid support.

9.4 All of the external connections shall terminate at a bulkhead plate. Each bulkhead termination shall be permanently identified according to the Instrument Loop Diagrams. Both ends of tubing shall be identified by permanent markers according to the Instrument Loop Diagrams. At least 20% or six (6) spare bulkhead connections, whichever is greater, complete with bulkhead union fittings, shall be provided on the bulkhead plate.

9.5 For panels that require purging, one bulkhead termination is to be provided for connection of the purge meter.

9.6 The Panel Manufacturer shall supply and install a NOPQ Inc. Model 94 (or plant-approved equal) duplex air filter regulator complete with 2 in. input pressure gage and two 2 in. output pressure gages in each panel. These units shall have an output of 20 psig (or 140 kPag) and shall be capable of handling inputs over the range of 40 to 100 psig (275 to 700 kPag). The capacity of each filter regulator shall be at least 25% greater than required by the instruments installed in the panel.

9.7 A pressure relief valve that is capable of handling the combined maximum capacity of the two filter regulators shall be installed on the downstream side of the filter regulators, before the take-off points. The relief valve shall be set to relieve at 25 psig (175 kPag).

9.8 A 2 in. instrument air supply header shall be required. It shall have 1/4 in. take-offs equipped with shutoff valves for each instrument and a 1/4 in. drain valve at its lowest point. At least 20% extra take-offs with shutoff valves shall be installed.

9.9 For field panels in which pneumatic instruments are employed, the Panel Manufacturer shall supply and install an identical air supply system to the control room panel whenever three or more air users are installed in or on the panel.

9.10 The Panel Manufacturer shall ensure that all lines installed shall be clean, both internally and externally, and that all joints are free from leaks by performing pressure tests in accordance with ISA-RP7.1.

9.11 Teflon tape shall be the only jointing material used on pipe threads of fittings, valves, etc., in the panels. Teflon (tape or paste) or any pipe sealant should not be used in tube fittings to avoid plugging pneumatic components.

9.12 All tubing shall be identified by a stainless steel tag at all instrument termination and at all fittings. All such tags shall be supplied by the Panel Manufacturer. The tag shall bear the tubing identification shown on the documentation. In the absence of this identification number, the tag shall bear the identification number of the instrument to which it connects and the function (i.e., input, output, air supply, etc.).

9.13 All tubing shall have the following ISA-based color coding:

Air supply to instrument — red

Transmitted measurement — orange

Controller output to valve — yellow

All other signals — natural

Any deviations from these requirements must first be approved by the plant Control Engineer.

10.0 CERTIFICATION

10.1 The Panel Manufacturer shall obtain from the appropriate authorities all necessary inspections for the approval of the wiring and equipment supplied and/or installed by him. The Panel Manufacturer shall bear the cost of all such inspections and approvals. All deficiencies noted by such inspections shall be corrected by the Panel Manufacturer at no cost to the plant. After all approvals have been obtained, the Panel Manufacturer shall affix to the panel his union labels covering electrical and pipefitting, along with any other labels deemed necessary. Such labels shall all be affixed prior to panel checkout by the plant Control Engineer.

11.0 INSPECTION & TESTING

11.1 Prior to the arrival of the plant Control Engineer, the Panel Manufacturer should thoroughly check the panel mechanically and functionally. High voltage testing equipment shall not be used.

11.2 The Panel Manufacturer will, as a minimum, perform the following:

1. Check all alarm circuits for correct operation.
2. Check all electrical power circuits for correct operation.
3. Check all air supply lines for correct operation.
4. Check all electrical and pneumatic circuits for correct functional operation, loop by loop.
5. Check all nameplates for correct location, spelling, wording, and size of letters.
6. Check the physical appearance and mechanical construction of the panel, inside and outside.
7. Check for any signs of physical damage or negligence.
8. Check for leaks in pneumatic lines.

11.3 It should be noted that the plant Control Engineer may visit the Manufacturer's shop at any time during the panel fabrication in order to check progress and/or inspect the panel and its internal components.

11.4 The Panel Manufacturer shall correct any errors and omissions at no cost to the plant. Modifications and/or changes to the panel at the request of the plant Control Engineer shall be charged or credited as the case may be, to the plant, for the amount of labor and/or material involved only.

12.0 SHIPPING

12.1 The Panel Manufacturer will ship the panel by air-ride truck, suitably protected for shipping. Any and all damages to the panel, complete with instruments and/or instruments shipped separately, caused by inadequate protection for shipping are to be made good by the Panel Manufacturer at no cost to the plant.

12.2 To avoid damage during shipping, all tray-mounted and plug-in instruments shall be removed, reboxed, and shipped separately in tagged boxes.

APPENDIX I

Instrument Installation Specification (Example)

CONTENTS

1.0 SCOPE

This Specification provides the requirements for the installation of instruments, control systems, and their accessories.

All equipment and installation must comply with all code, statutory, and plant requirements in effect at the site. It is the responsibility of the Contractor to ensure and meet compliance.

2.0 GENERAL

2.1 The Contractor shall visit the site prior to tendering to familiarize himself with all conditions and requirements to be met in carrying out his work under this contract. This includes the review and understanding of the safety requirements in effect at the plant.

2.2 The Contractor's scope of work includes all items of instrumentation and control systems shown in the following documentation, which forms part of this specification: Scope of Work, Instrument Index, Specification Sheets, Loop Drawing, Electrical Schematics, and, for some instruments, Installation Details and Vendors' Data.

Any exceptions to the scope of work shall be separately identified by the plant. All instrumentation devices, as listed in the Instrument Index, including those supplied by the plant, shall be mounted and connected by the Contractor. A manufacturer, such as a panel fabricator, may for shipping purposes ship pieces of the equipment and instrumentation separately. These pieces shall be installed and connected by the Contractor to form an operating unit.

2.3 The Contractor shall familiarize himself with all furnished data before commencing the installation work. Should there be inconsistencies between any of the documents, the Contractor shall immediately notify the plant. The plant will then determine which portions of specifications are applicable.

2.4 The Contractor shall be responsible for the correct installation and assembly of all items or equipment. Manufacturer's instructions shall be carefully read and rigidly adhered to in installation supplemented by details given herein by these specifications and on plans. Any damage that results from failure to observe the manufacturer's instructions or failure to understand how a particular job is to be done will be the Contractor's responsibility, and he shall make good any resulting loss or damage.

2.5 The work under this contract shall be carried out by certified and trained tradesmen with adequate supervision and equipment necessary to complete the work, in accordance with good trade practice, shown on the drawings and specifications. The Contractor may be required to produce evidence of such certification and training.

3.0 REFERENCE CODES AND STANDARDS

3.1 The latest edition of the following codes and standards form part of this Standard and must be adhered to:

- The latest edition of the National Electrical Code
- The latest edition of ISA's Standards and Recommended Practices for Instrumentation and Control

3.2 Wherever the drawings or specifications call for material, workmanship, arrangement, or construction of quality that is superior to that required by any applicable Codes and Standards, the drawings and specifications shall prevail. Otherwise, should there be a conflict between any Codes and Standards and the drawings and specifications, the applicable Codes and Standards shall prevail.

4.0 PERMITS AND INSPECTIONS

4.1 The Contractor shall furnish to the plant a certificate of final inspection and approval certifying unconditional approval from the local Electrical Inspection Department. The Contractor shall pay all fees required to furnish such certificate.

4.2 Where the local authorities require additional certificates of compliance for the installation work, the Contractor shall pay all fees required to furnish such certificates.

4.3 If testing is done by a third party, then the contractor shall obtain approval of the third party by ICI prior to starting the testing.

5.0 INSTALLATION DETAILS

5.1 All electrically operated instruments, or the electrical components incorporated in an instrument, shall be approved and bear the UL or FM approval label. All material supplied and installed by the Contractor shall be new.

5.2 Unless otherwise specifically called for on the drawings or specifications, uniformity of manufacture shall be maintained for any particular item throughout the project.

5.3 The Contractor shall inspect and note apparent damage or defect at time of receipt and during storage, handling, or installation. Any discrepancies shall be immediately reported to the plant.

5.4 All field-mounted instruments shall be installed and connected in such a way that the instrument can be maintained and removed for servicing without having to break fittings, cut wires, or pull hot wires through metal conduit (rigid or flexible). The Contractor shall provide necessary unions and tubing connections to all instruments to allow removal. Sufficient clearance shall be provided above, below, or in front of instruments to permit removal without disturbing other equipment.

5.5 The Contractor shall not adjust or tamper with the calibration or settings of any instrument or instrument accessory until checkout time (refer to 14.0 of this Standard). In most cases, instruments have been factory calibrated or factory set before shipping to site.

5.6 The Contractor shall ensure that wherever dry air purging and/or heating may be specified for an outdoor instrument enclosure, these shall be activated as early as possible for the protection of instruments mounted therein.

5.7 The Contractor shall ensure that after installation, care shall be taken to protect any instruments, conduits, tubing, and control valves from dirt, water, insulation, debris, and paint. All field-mounted instruments such as transmitters, controllers, transducers, and recorders shall be protected by heavy plastic bags until final acceptance by the plant Control Engineer.

5.8 No cutting of concrete or structural members by the Contractor shall be done without the written approval of the plant.

6.0 EQUIPMENT IDENTIFICATION

6.1 The Contractor shall ensure that all instruments and control equipment, including junction boxes, shall be identified with stainless steel tags embossed or stamped with the equipment identification number. The identification number shall be complete and read the same in all respects as the number given on the Instrument Index. Any missing tags shall be supplied and installed by the Contractor.

6.2 The tag shall be affixed to the instrument body or housing wherever possible and to the instrument support or adjacent tubing only when unavoidable. The Contractor shall avoid placing the tag where routine maintenance would require the tag's removal. Stainless steel wire is to be used for tag attachment.

6.3 All wiring shall be identified with suitable nonconductive, abrasion- and solvent-resistant markers. The markers shall bear the wire numbers as shown on the documentation.

6.4 All wiring shall have the following color coding:

6.4.1 For 120 V AC power and 120 V AC discrete control signals:

Phase or hot conductor (L1 or H) — black

Neutral conductor (L2 or N) — white

Intermediate conductors — brown

6.4.2   For 24 V DC power and 24 V DC discrete control signals:

Positive conductor — black

Negative conductor — white

Intermediate conductors — brown

6.4.3   For 4–20 mA (24 V DC) analog signals:

Positive conductor — black

Negative conductor — white

6.4.4   For thermocouple extension wires, use ANSI color code. For other specialized wiring, either follow the manufacturer's color on the lead wires or refer to the plant Control Engineer.

6.4.5   For earth ground (if insulated) — green

6.4.6   Instrinsically safe (IS) wiring shall be identified by the use of bright blue color. This color will not be used on any other circuits. This color may be in the form of a blue stripe on wires whose colors follow the general scheme described above. Raceways, wireways, terminal blocks, and field junction boxes shall also be identified with a bright blue label bearing the legend INTRINSICALLY SAFE.

6.4.7   All temporary jumpers will be of orange color with a minimum length of 2 feet (70 cm). The orange color will be used only for temporary jumpers.

6.5   All tubing shall be identified by a stainless steel tag at all instrument terminations and at all fittings. The tag shall bear the tubing identification shown on the documentation. In the absence of this identification number, the tag shall bear the identification number of the instrument to which it connects and the function (i.e., input, output, air supply, etc.).

6.6   All tubing shall have the following ISA-based color coding:

Air supply to instrument — red

Transmitted measurement — orange

Controller output to valve — yellow

All other signals — natural

Any deviations from these requirements must first be approved by the plant Control Engineer.

7.0 DRAWINGS

7.1   Prior to final inspection, the Contractor shall supply six copies of wiring diagrams, operating and maintenance instructions, and renewal parts lists for each piece of equipment purchased and installed by him as part of the work.

7.2 All authorized changes and deviations from the drawings made by the Contractor shall be recorded by him on a set of drawings that shall be handed over to the plant before final inspection of the work.

8.0 EQUIPMENT STORAGE

8.1 Unless otherwise specified, the Contractor will be responsible for receiving, unloading, safekeeping, and storage of all materials and equipment supplied by the plant or by the Contractor. When accepting deliveries, the Contractor will inspect the equipment and materials against the plant's Instrument Index, Specifications, and purchase orders to ensure quantity, type, ranges, etc., are as specified. By certification of the Supplier's packing list, the Contractor will be deemed to have acknowledged that all equipment and materials are complete and satisfactory in every respect.

8.2 The Contractor shall provide a separate adequate storage space, indoors, secure, protected from unauthorized tampering, free from fire hazard, clean, and dry. This facility shall be heated. All instruments, wherever possible, shall be kept in their original shipping cartons until they are installed. This separate storage space shall be maintained apart from areas where piping items and equipment are stored.

8.3 The Contractor shall be responsible for issue of all stored instruments whether installed by Contractor or other disciplines, and maintenance of accurate records showing equipment and material received, stored, issued, and installed.

8.4 The Contractor shall be responsible for reasonable protection of all installed instruments from damage by inclement conditions or physical damage. The Contractor shall bear all costs of repair or replacement of such damaged instruments prior to acceptance by the plant.

9.0 WORK SPECIFICALLY EXCLUDED

9.1 Installation of all in-line devices, namely, control valves, orifice flanges, orifice plates, in-line flowmeters, process shutoff valves, safety relief valves, rupture discs, venturis, air header supply piping, and thermowells, shall be the responsibility of the Mechanical Contractor. The connections of tubing or wiring to the in-line instrumentation is the responsibility of this Contractor.

9.2 The installation of all impulse piping from the process up to and including the first block valve is part of the process/utility piping contract and is detailed on the piping drawings.

9.3 All in-line devices, except thermowells, must be removed when the piping is being flushed, cleaned, or pressure tested. All inline devices shall be reinstalled after the flushing, cleaning, or pressure testing is completed.

10. APPROVED PRODUCTS

10.1 Power and Control Cabling, 120 V AC

All wire shall be THWN for 600-volt service. Minimum wire size shall be #12 AWG for power supplies and #14 AWG for discrete control signals. Wire in close proximity to heating devices shall be UL approved. For additional details, refer to the plant's Electrical Construction Specifications.

10.2 Power and Control Cabling, 24 V DC

10.2.1 For 24 V DC power and 24 V DC discrete control signals
10.2.1.1 Single Pair 16 gage cables in conduits:

- DXWKW Electronic Instrument Wire, part number: 1245–146
- Plant-approved equal

10.2.1.2 Multipair Cables:

- DXWKW Steel Armored Electronic Instrument Cable, 20 gage, part number: 154673–327356 (for 24 pair cables)
- Plant-approved equal

All multipair cables should be of the same construction and each should terminate in an individual junction box. Each cable should contain a minimum of 20% spare pairs.

10.2.2 For 4–20 mA (24 V DC) analog signals
Similar to 10.2.1 above except that 18-gage may also be used.

10.3 Special Cabling

Where instruments require special cables (e.g., pH electrode cable and data highway cables), the instrument manufacturer's requirements shall be followed. Load cell cables, another example of special cabling, are factor-matched for resistance and must not be cut. The designer will ensure that sufficient length is available, and the installer must coil and tie neatly in a well protected area. In some cases, some special cabling may be supplied by the plant; see attached documentation for details.

10.4 Conduits and Flexible Conduits

Plant-approved equal products may be used instead of the following.

10.4.1 Conduit Fittings
Condulets — ABC, Type ZX
Conduit Hubs — MFTY, Type ST
Lock Nuts, Bushing, and Straps — TDTR

10.4.2 Flexible Conduits
XYZ — Type UA

10.4.3 Flexible Conduit Fittings
TDTR — Type SX

10.5 Terminal Strips

For all field locations, the Contractor shall use WSXZ Type AKB (or plant-approved equal), DIN rail-mounted. At least 20% or six (6) spare terminal points, whichever is greater, should be provided on each strip, unless otherwise specified.

10.6 Electrical and Pneumatic Junction Boxes

These boxes shall be NEMA 4X construction, fabricated from fiberglass, and provided with corrosion-proof hardware and a hinged scratch-resistant window, HBCD Type A45 or plant-approved equal. All main cable entries shall be through resilient seals in the bottom of the box, with a drip loop. Any conduit entries should also be in the bottom or side of the box and be provided with a drip loop and a bug-proof drain.

10.7 Tubing

10.7.1 Individual instrument air supply and pneumatic field transmission lines to individual instruments from air supply header, field junction boxes, or control panels shall be seamless type 316 SS tubing, 1/4 in. O.D., 0.030 in. min. wall thickness unless otherwise specified.

10.7.2 Panel instrument air supply and field air supply subheader shall be seamless type 316 SS tubing, 1/2 in. O.D., 0.030 in. min. wall thickness unless otherwise specified.

10.7.3 Process tubing connecting the process to the instrument shall be 316 SS, 3/4 in. O.D., and shall meet the plant piping requirements of the process to which it connects.

10.8 Multitube Bundles

Multitube bundles must have the mechanical protection needed to prevent damage from occuring. The Contractor will submit to the plant Control Engineer a sample of the proposed multitube bundle for approval prior to installation. Multitube bundles shall terminate in individual junction boxes or bulkhead. Each bundle should contain a minimum 20% spare tubes. All spares must be terminated.

10.9 Tube Fittings

10.9.1 All tubing fittings for instrument air supply and pneumatic field transmission shall be APKR 316 SS flareless compression type (or plant-approved equal).

10.9.2 Fittings shall not be used at temperatures and pressures exceeding the manufacturer's recommendations. Service conditions such as vibration and thermal cycling shall be considered in the application.

10.9.3 All tube fittings for process tubing must meet the plant piping requirements on the process to which it connects.

11. EXECUTION

11.1 General

11.1.1 It should be noted that this Instrument Installation Specification and its Reference Documents do not cover each and every detail. The Contractor is expected to be familiar with current good practice for the installation of the instruments and hardware indicated, and shall provide and install all items such as clips, supports, clamps, brackets, stands, etc., as well as all necessary welding, paiting, wiring, junction boxes, tubing, fittings, etc., that are required to complete the installation and connection of instruments as they are required from suppliers.

11.1.2 Items listed on the Instrument Index that are noted as "Supplied by Contractor" shall be the responsibility of the Contractor to purchase and install.

11.1.3 All items supplied by the Contractor shall be suitable for the process area concerned.

11.2 Mounting

11.2.1 In the absence of detailed installation/mounting drawings and instructions, items of instrumentation shall be mounted according to good instrument installation practice with reference to maintenance, freedom from vibration, and damage by process fluids. They shall not obstruct or present personnel hazard in an access passage or aisle or create an unsafe condition such as sharp edges or protrusions. Where any doubt may exist as to these requirements, the Contractor shall contact the plant Control Engineer for a decision.

11.2.2 Instruments and junction boxes shall be accessible so that personnel may service or remove any instrument or instrument auxiliary without danger of falls, burns, or hazards beyond that which the job normally entails. Accessibility requirements are based on having each instrument installed so that it may be serviced by one person. Instrument equipment and associated installations shall be acceptable where they are 4.5 feet (1.4 meters) ±10% above grade, flor, or walkway. Headroom clearance for all instrumentation items shall be maintained at no less than 7.5 feet (2.3 meters) from grade in all areas of normal personnel access unless specified otherwise.

11.2.3 Instruments and junction boxes shall be mounted level and plumb, and in such a manner so as to provide accessibility, protection from mechanical damage, heat, shock, and vibration, and shall not interfere with or be interfered by any structure, other equipment, piping, or electrical work, and shall not obstruct walkways or other means of access provided for maintenance or process use such as forklift truck access and access for cranes. Instruments shall not be installed until all heavy mechanical work adjacent to their installation has been completed.

11.2.4 Field-mounted items of instrumentation and junction boxes shall be mounted on building columns and walls where such building columns or walls are accessible. Support stands are to be provided when the mounting of instruments on columns and walls is not practical and shall not be fixed to floor grating. The support stands shall be fabricated from 2 in. mild steel pipe and painted in accordance with the painting specifications used on this Project. Instruments shall be mounted using brackets supplied with the instruments wherever possible.

11.2.5 Supports and stands shall be attached to the building structure, beams, columns, or other permanent structural members. Supports and stands shall NOT b e attached to handrails, process equipment, piping, vessels, conduit, or instruments. All supports and stands shall be mounted perpendicular to their supporting structure and shall be finished so as to present no sharp edges, points, or irregular angles.

11.2.6 Unless otherwise specified by the Plant, the Contractor shall not mount or support items of instrumentation by welding or drilling any structural steel, piping, equipment, or vessel. The Contractor shall, wherever necessary, mount or attach instrumentation items to structural steel by a suitable clamping method. All supports and stands shall be fabricated so they will not become a trough or trap for spilled liquids. All supports and stands shall be painted to match supporting structures. Where welds are allowed by the plant control engineer, they shall be ground smooth, preprimed, and painted in accordance with the painting specifications used on this Project to match support or stand, prior to installation of tubing tray or instrument. All welds shall be in accordance with the standards and codes from AWS.

11.2.7 Unless approved by the plant control engineer, instruments, impulse lines, tubing, or wiring shall not be attached to process lines or process equipment apart from the following exceptions:

- Equipment designed specifically for pipe or flange mounting such as pressure and temperature gages
- Control valve mounted items such as limit switches and positioners

Instrument items connected to piping or equipment shall not be installed in such a way so as to place damaging or undesirable stress on the piping, equipment, or instruments. Piping and equipment shall not be supported on or from items of instrumentation or their accessories.

11.2.8 Where no other suitable means of support exists, the Contractor shall supply and install 3/4-inch channel, angle, or tubing trays to provide support for individual tubing runs. Such support shall be of a material and finish that is suitable for the process area concerned. These supports shall be so installed so as to minimize any catch place for rainwater, snow, process drippings, or dust accumulation.

11.2.9 All tubing shall be installed in continuous length from:

- the instrument to the instrument air supply valve,
- the instrument to a pneumatic junction box fitting or bulk head fitting, and
- the instrument to another instrument.

In no case shall union fittings or splices be permitted in tubing runs. All splices and connections shall be made accessible in junction boxes or at the instruments.

11.2.10 Indicating gages shall be positioned so as to be easily read from a normal operating area. "Plainly visible" is defined as line of sight not to exceed 14 feet (4.25 meters).

11.2.11 All tubing and/or conduit penetrations through walls or floors shall be properly sealed, watertight, and dusttight. The holes or slots in walls, floors, or ceilings where cables or tubing pass through between hazardous and non-hazardous areas shall be sealed after installation of the cables or tubing in accordance with the electrical code in effect at the site.

11.3 Panels

11.3.1 Unless otherwise specified, control panels for control room and field installation, as well as interlock panels, will be supplied piped and wired, ready for installation, with plug-in or slide-in instruments packaged separately. The Contractor shall install plug-in and slide-in instruments correctly in their respective panels.

11.3.2 It is the responsibility of the Contractor to move the panel from the delivery vehicle when it reaches the plant boundaries to the control room.

11.3.3 The Contractor shall be responsible for the installation of all panels, as specified in the Reference Documents. Control panels shall not be installed in the control room until the room is enclosed and finished and all structural and painting work is completed.

12. WIRING

12.1 General

12.1.1 All such wiring must be done in accordance to the latest edition of the National Electrical Code.

12.1.2 Armored multiconductor cables and single wires in conduit shall be run from the control room to local junction boxes. Twenty percent spare wires shall be provided in either case, and the choice between conduit and multiconductor shall depend on the economics of each situation. Signal wiring may be run only in conduit or in armored cable, and, in the larger installations with a central control room, armored cables will be preferred. Hence, field signal wiring should be in armored cables run in cable trays, unless otherwise agreed with the plant Control Engineer.

12.2 Termination

12.2.1 All final connections to field-mounted instruments shall be made with flexible conduit. Single pair will be provided from the junction boxes to the individual instruments; refer to 10.2.2.

12.2.2 Wire shall not be spliced in conduit runs or anywhere in the field except on identified terminal blocks in approved junction boxes.

12.2.3 The termination of cable cores and single conductors shall be by either crimped (normally preferred) or soldered pins. Makeup of all crimped connections shall be carried out with connector manufacturer's approved tools. The wire to spade connector junctions and also the screened pairs in the area where the individual foil screens are cut back shall be protected with an adhesive-lined heat shrink tubing or sleeve of suitable diameter. This tubing shall be AKXS Corp. Type 750 or plant-approved equal. Performed sleeves or caps of the same material may be used.

12.3 Grounding

12.3.1 It is essential that the individual shields in a multiconductor cable be connected to the shields of the individual pair of cable to which they connect. At the same time, it is important that the shields are not otherwise grounded to the structure or to each other at the junction box. At the instrument end, no connection is to be made to any shield, foil, or drain wire. The contractor must follow the grounding requirements as shown on the loop drawings.

12.3.2 The ground continuity of electrical equipment housed in nonmetallic enclosures shall be maintained by bonding together the armour or metallic sheath of all incoming and outgoing cables. The bonding connections shall be suitably protected against weather and corrosion. Refer to the plant standards 2/3–601–1 for further details on grounding requirements.

12.4 Cable Routing

12.4.1 Cable entry in equipment should, wherever practical, be located on the underside of equipment to reduce the risk of water or other liquids entering the equipment. Where side entry is unavoidable, cables should incline downwards away from the equipment to ensure that water does not flow towards the cable entry.

12.4.2 Cables shall be routed neatly to run either vertically or horizontally but not diagonally across walls, ceilings, or floors.

Cable runs shall be accessible for maintenance and shall not be positioned directly over or under large plant items, in close proximity to moving machinery, immediately above or adjacent to steam or other hot pipes, or directly below pipes carrying corrosive liquids. There should be a minimum distance of 16 in. (400 mm) between any cable and the lagging of steam or hot process lines. Cables shall be positioned clear of process pipes, service pipes, ventilation ducts, hoist blocks, overhead cranes, and other similar services.

12.4.3 Main cable routes will normally be defined in the Scope of Work. When the routing of the cables is not indicated on a drawing or described on the Scope of Work, the Contractor shall submit details of his proposed routing to the plant control engineer for approval prior to commencing the installation.

12.4.4 Armored multiconductor cables and conduits shall not be bent to a radius less than those stated below:

Armored multiconduit cables — 12 times overall diameter of cable

Conduit — 4.5 times overall diameter of conduit

12.4.5 Unless otherwise specified, armored multiconductor cables rising from the ground shall be protected to a height of at least 6 ft (2 m) by galvanized steel casing or other plant-approved means to suit the particular situation.

12.4.6 To avoid interferences arising between cables that carry instrument signals and electric power, these cables shall cross only at right angles and shall be kept physically separate on cable trays.

12.4.7 There are four types of instrumentation and control wiring:

1. Very low level DC analog signals such as thermocouples, strain gages, pH sensing, etc.
2. Low level DC analog signals (4–20 mA at 24 V DC)
3. Low voltage discrete signals and low voltage power wiring (24 V DC)
4. High voltage discrete signals and high voltage power wiring (120 V AC)

The contractor shall run each type in a dedicated multiconductor or conduit. Shielded wiring must be used for types 1, 2, and 3. A minimum parallel separation of 1-1/2 ft (0.45 m) between the types of multiconductors or conduits shall be maintained unless otherwise requested by the plant Control Engineer. When the separation is vertical, the signal wiring should be in the top tray and the high voltage in the bottom tray; with this arrangement, the signal wires are not in the electric field that exists between the high voltage lines and ground.

The contractor shall keep low voltage cabling (types 1, 2, and 3) at a minimum distance of 5 ft (1.5 m) from power transformers and switchgear.

In addition, special wiring (see 10.3) shall be installed according to equipment vendor recommendations.

12.5 Wiring In Hazardous Areas

12.5.1   Unarmored PVC cables that carry intrinsically safe circuits shall not be run alongside other unarmored cables. They shall be run either in separate conduits or separate armored cables.

12.5.2   No intrinsically safe circuit cable shall be terminated in a junction box housing nonintrinsically safe wiring. Field wiring terminals for intrinsically safe circuits in control room areas, panels, etc., shall be segregated from other nonintrinsically safe field wiring terminals. They shall be located in separate enclosures.

12.5.3   The safety of equipment used in hazardous areas can be seriously jeopardized if the wiring requirements are not strictly followed. The Contractor has this responsibility. Should the Contractor be in doubt of the requirements, he shall obtain clarification from the plant Control Engineer.

Where a conduit, raceway, cable, or other conductor system crosses a boundary between hazardous areas of different classification or between a hazardous area and a nonhazardous area, vents or seals or both shall be provided to ensure that no flammable atmospheres or substances can be transmitted through the conduit or cable across such a boundary. Areas of high fire risk shall be avoided, particularly for junction boxes and cable runs.

12.5.4   Intrinsically safe redundant, or temporarily redundant, circuit cables shall be disconnected and removed from equipment at both ends, at the supply end bonded together and to ground, and at the plant end bonded between cores and insulated from ground.

Spare cores in a multicore cable shall be connected to IS ground in the safe area only, and elsewhere shall be fully insulated.

All intrinsically safe cables, wiring, junction boxes, and other equipment shall be positively identified in accordance with 6.4.6 of this Specification. Junction boxes shall be identified inside and outside.

12.5.5   Only certified equipment shall be installed in hazardous areas. In cases in which certified apparatus is not available, this shall be discussed with the plant Control Engineer.

12.5.6   To minimize the total number of electrical enclosures in hazardous areas, the Contractor shall NOT provide and install extra junction boxes or other equipment, except with the specific approval of the plant Control Engineer.

12.5.7   The cabling connections and other work carried out by the Contractor on equipment for use in hazardous areas shall be such as not to invalidate the equipment certification.

13. TUBING

13.1 General

13.1.1   Multitube bundles of plastic instrument tubing shall be installed between control panels and field-mounted junction boxes. Bundles shall have 20% spare tubes. Multitube bundles shall not be bent to a radius less than that recommended by their manufacturer.

13.1.2 Field instruments that require an air supply as well as a signal line could be connected to the junction box by two-tube bundles. An air supply shutoff valve shall be supplied inside the box. When more than one instrument is supplied from a single takeoff, an individual shutoff valve shall be supplied for each user in a manner that allows independent shutoff of each user.

13.1.3 The air supply takeoff from the major supply header shall be made from the top or side of the header or branch. The takeoff shall terminate within 1-1/2 feet (0.4 meters) of the user instrument with a quarter-turn ball valve consistent with the piping specifications.

13.2 Termination

13.2.1 The termination of pneumatic tubing shall be by bulkhead connectors suitably mounted within the junction box.

13.2.2 Teflon (tape or paste) or any pipe sealant should not be used in tube fittings to avoid plugging pneumatic components.

13.3 Installation

13.3.1 All tubing shall be clean and free of oil, grease, dirt, and other foreign materials, and must be blown out with clean instrument air before being connected to other tubing or devices.

13.3.2 All tube ends shall be cut square and deburred so that they remain perfectly round. Tubing shall be routed and formed so that it may be removed or disconnected without dismounting the instrument (using bends, loops, offsets, etc.). Fittings shall not be installed excessively close to a bend. Tubing sections shall be fitted properly to prevent springing or side stresses on fittings. Metal tubing shall be bent using a suitable bending tool and with a bend radius that prevents crimping, cracking, or collapsing of the tube.

13.3.3 Tubing trays shall be used to support three or more tube lines. Tube clips could be used to support single or double tube lines. Tube clips whether used on horizontal or vertical runs, shall be every 2 feet (0.7 meter), at changes in direction, and where leaving supports for connection to instruments.

13.3.4 Supports shall be provided to protect tubing from its own weight, vibration, wind, external mechanical injury, and exposure to unusual service conditions, e.g., operator handholds and footholds. Supports shall allow tubing movement as a result of device motion and thermal expansion where applicable.

13.3.5 All tubing shall be installed with loops or bends so as not to transmit stress or vibration to the instrument it is serving and so it may be disconnected without bending, twisting, or distortion. A tubing loop shall consist of one coil turn of 4 to 6 inches (100 to 150 mm) diameter.

13.3.6 The Contractor shall install all tubing in such a way as to allow for thermal expansion over runs and strain relief at all fittings or connections.

13.4 Routing

13.4.1 Tubing and tubing bundles shall be run above ground and shall be adequately supported on racking or trays.

13.4.2 Unless otherwise specified, multitube bundles rising from the ground shall be protected to a height of at least 3 feet (1 meter) by galvanized steel casing or other plant-approved means to suit the particular situation.

13.4.2 Multitube bundle routes will normally be defined in the Scope of Work. When the routing is not indicated on a drawing or described on the Scope of Work, the Contractor shall submit details of his proposed routing to the Owner for approval prior to commencing the installation.

13.4.4 All tubing shall be routed neatly to run either vertically or horizontally but not diagonally across walls, ceilings, or floors.

13.4.5 Multimode bundle runs shall be accessible for maintenance and shall not be positioned directly over or under large plant items, in close proximity to moving machinery, immediately above or adjacent to steam or other hot pipes, or directly below pipes that carry corrosive liquids. There should be a minimum distance of 16 inches (400 mm) between any multitube bundles and the lagging of insulated hot process lines on hot surfaces. Multitube bundles shall be positoned clear of process pipes, service pipes, ventilation ducts, hoist blocks, overhead cranes, and other similar services.

13.5 Process Tubing

13.5.1 All process tubing shall not be less than 3/4 in. and shall originate at the shut-off valve supplied and installed by the process/utility piping Contractor. On gas and liquid lines, the tubing shall be sloped continuously with an appropriate grade of one in ten or greater. Sloping ensures the gas and liquid go to predictable locations in the tubing. On steam lines, the tubing must remain horizontal to ensure a steady liquid head.

Field instruments shall be located as close as possible to their process connection, while allowing for convenient access for operation and maintenance.

All process tubing shall conform to, or exceed, the process/utility piping code specification with respect to design temperature and pressure and materials of construction.

13.5.2 For process tubing for a typical gas installation, with no condensable fluids, the measuring device should be located above the process line. All horizontal lines should be sloped 1 : 10 to allow any trapped liquids to flow back to the process.

13.5.3 For process tubing for a typical liquid or condensable fluid, such as steam, the measuring device should be located below the process line. All horizontal lines should be sloped 1 : 10 to allow trapped gases to flow back to the process. On condensable fluids, filling tees shall be required to allow for the creation of a stable static head.

13.5.4 Process tubing subject to plugging shall be provided with suitable connections for cleaning. Also, process tubing that handles gases containing moisture or other extraneous matter or hazardous liquids shall be provided with suitable drains, settling chambers, or traps.

13.5.5 Tubing that contains liquids subject to freezing shall be protected by electric heat tracing. The supply and installation of heat tracing cables and their required power supply is the Contractor's responsibility.

13.5.6 Impulse tubing shall be tested as part of and under the same conditions as the process/utility piping system. Before and after testing, impulse lines shall be flushed and blown down with water or air to remove all contamination. Prior to testing and cleaning, all impulse lines shall be disconnected from the instrument and blanked off. In no case shall any instrument, other than control valves and thermowells, be subject to test pressures.

13.5.7 A test device such as a tee shall be located between the instrument isolating valve (the shutoff valve) and the instrument so that calibration and occasional checks on the instrument's output may be made without disconnecting the instrument. This test device shall have a threaded plug on the vent side.

14.0 CHECKOUT

14.1 The Contractor shall ensure that every instrument and control component bears its tag with identifying tag number. If any of these tags have been removed or lost during installation or not supplied, the Contractor shall replace the missing tags with others similar to those originally supplied.

14.2 The Contractor shall perform the following work after completion of the installation:

1. Check the entire instrument installation, including the instrumentation of packaged systems, to confirm that all instruments and associated equipment and accessories have been correctly installed and connected.
2. Clean the control tubing by blowing out with clean dry air.
3. Perform tubing pressure tests as per ISA-RP7.1 and ensure that all connections have been made correctly.
4. Ring out all wiring to ensure that all connections have been made correctly. High voltage devices are not to be used for such checks. No circuits may be energized without the prior approval of the plant Control Engineer.

14.3 All post-installation calibration, if required by the plant, shall be done by the Contractor in the presence of the plant Control Engineer. The Contractor shall assure his equipment installation is complete, correct, and ready for calibration.

1. The Contractor shall calibrate all field instruments at five points (0, 25, 50, 75, 100%) and ensure that each individual instrument is in good working order. All test equipment necessary to properly calibrate instruments to within manufacturer's specified accuracy, or 0.25% if unspecified, shall be provided by the Contractor and be certified by the test equipment manufacturer within 6 months prior to use. All equipment and procedures used for calibration shall meet the approval of the plant Control Engineer two months prior to checkout.
2. The Contractor shall calibrate filled thermal systems at two points and ensure that the instrument is in good working order. Two temperature baths shall be used for calibration.
3. The Contractor shall calibrate direct-operated alarms and shutdown switches at their set value (as per attached documents).
4. The Contractor shall check that all control valves are in good working order, are lubricated where required, and that the control valve input signal matches the corresponding valve section. Control valves shall be stroked at five points (0, 25, 50, 75, 100%) with a simulated input signal.

14.4 The Contractor shall maintain complete and accurate records of final calibrations and adjustments to instruments and control systems. These records shall be in the form of individual instrument component data cards or signed-off spec sheets. The plant and the Contractor's representatives both will sign off on this record. If, for any reason, the final calibration differs from that shown in the reference documents, the plant should be advised of the deviation and the reason for such deviations prior to final acceptance of the installation.

14.5 Final acceptance of the instrument loops will be based on the plant Control Engineer's checking the functionality of each individual completed loop by simulating process and events, as specified by the plant Control Engineer. Upon receipt of the final calibration records and signatures of both the plant representative and the Contractor's representative on the loop check sheet, acceptance log book, or other plant specified document, acceptance will be completed signifying transfer of jurisdiction.

Date; Aug.18.93

APPENDIX J

Specification Sheet List

The following list may be used as a starting point for an index of custom developed forms.

Blank Form

Pressure Gauges
Pressure Switches
Pressure Transmitter

Temperature Gauges
Temperature Switches
Temperature Elements — T/C & RTD
Temperature Transmitter — T/C & RTD
Temperature Instrument — Filled System

Flow Switches
Flowmeter — Differential Pressure
Flowmeter — Positive Displacement
Flowmeter — Turbine
Flowmeter — Magnetic
Flowmeter — Rotameter (Variable area)
Flowmeter — Target
Flowmeter — vortex
Flowmeter — Misc.

Level Gauges
Level Switches
Level Measurement — Capacitance
Level Measurement — Ultrasonic
Level Measurement — Misc.

pH Measurement
Conductivity Measurement
Humidity measurement
Opacity measurement
Vibration switch

Valve — Globe/Angle
Valve — Butterfly
Valve — Ball & Plug
Valve — Solenoid
Valve — Pilot
Self-Actuated Regulator — Pressure

Self-Actuated Regulator — Temperature
Rupture Disk
Safety and Relief Valve

Actuator
I/P Transducer
Signal Converter
Receiver/indicator
Controller
Pushbutton station
Recorder
Limit Switch
Three-valve manifold

Annunciator
Annunciator Nameplate Schedule
Programmable Controller
Process Stream Analyzer

Bibliography

STANDARDS AND RECOMMENDED PRACTICES

Standards and Recommended Practices for Instrumentation and Control, 11th edition (Instrument Society of America, 1991).
ISO Standard 8402, 9000 series, and 10000 series.
Manual on Installation of Refinery Instruments and Control Systems, (American Petroleum Institute), Part I — Process Instrumentation and Control

Section 1, Flow — 3rd edition, 1977
Section 2, Level — 4th edition, 1980
Section 3, Temperature — 3rd edition, 1976
Section 4, Pressure — 4th edition, 1980
Section 6, Control Valves and Accessories — 3rd edition, 1976
Section 7, Transmission Systems — 3rd edition, 1974
Section 8, Seals Purges, and Winterizing — 3rd edition, 1974
Section 9, Air Supply Systems — 4th edition, 1980
Section 11, Electrical Power Supply — 2nd edition, 1965
Section 13, Alarms and Protective Devices — 3rd edition, 1976

Part II — Process Stream Analyzers, 3rd edition, 1977
Safety Guidelines for the Application, Installation, and Maintenance of Solid-State Controls, NEMA Standards Publication No. ICS 1.1-1987.

TEXTBOOKS

Bacon, J. M., *Instrumentation Installation Project Management* (Instrument Society of America, 1989).
Ball, P., *The Guide to Reducing Human Error in Process Operations* (The Human Factors in Reliability Group of The SRD Association, 1991).
Battikha, N. E., *The Management of Control Systems — Justification and Auditing* (Instrument Society of America, 1991).
Gunkler, A. A., and Bernard, J. W., *Computer Control Strategies for the Fluid Process Industries* (Instrument Society of America, 1990).
Liptak, B., *INSTRUMENT ENGINEERS' HANDBOOK* (Chilton Book Company, 1982).
Magison, E. C., *Electrical Instruments in Hazardous Locations*, Third Edition (Instrument Society of America, 1972).
Russell, J. P., *Quality Management Benchmark Assessment* (ASQC Quality Press, Quality Resources, 1991).

ARTICLES

Bhasin, V. C., "Sixteen Considerations for Valve Selection You Can't Afford to Ignore," *Chemical Processing*, December 1990.

Gill, A., "Analyzer Installation and Maintenance," *INTECH*, February 1994.

Pacques, J.-J., "Basic Safety Rules for Using Programmable Controllers," *Proceedings of the 1989 International Conference*, ISA, 1989.

Rusnak, J., "The Fundamentals of Flowmeter Selection," *INTECH*, April 1989.

Scott, A. B., "Control Valve Actuators: Types and Application," *INTECH*, January 1988.

Wade, H. L., "High-Capability Single-Station Controllers: A Survey," *INTECH*, September 1988.

VENDOR INFORMATION

Considerations for the Selection of Transmitters (Application Data Sheet 3015, Rosemount, 1973).

Control Valve Hanbook (Fisher Controls Company, 1977).

Index